Preliminary Edition Notice

You have been selected to receive a copy of this book in the form of a preliminary edition. A preliminary edition is used in a classroom setting to test the overall value of a book's content and its effectiveness in a practical course prior to its formal publication on the national market.

As you use this text in your course, please share any and all feedback regarding the volume with your professor. Your comments on this text will allow the author to further develop the content of the book, so we can ensure it will be a useful and informative classroom tool for students in universities across the nation and around the globe. If you find the material is challenging to understand, or could be expanded to improve the usefulness of the text, it is important for us to know. If you have any suggestions for improving the material contained in the book or the way it is presented, we encourage you to share your thoughts.

Please note, preliminary editions are similar to review copies, which publishers distribute to select readers prior to publication in order to test a book's audience and elicit early feedback; therefore, you may find inconsistencies in formatting or design, or small textual errors within this volume. Design elements and the written text will undergo changes before this book goes to print and is distributed on the national market.

This text is not available in wide release on the market, as it is actively being prepared for formal publication. This may mean that new content is still being added to the author's manuscript, or that the content appears in a draft format.

If you would like to provide notes directly to the publisher, you may contact us by e-mailing studentreviews@cognella.com. Please include the book's title, author, and 7-digit SKU reference number (found below the barcode on the back cover of the book) in the body of your message.

D1108912

The Human
Experiment

Origins and Evolution of Humanity

2nd Revised Preliminary Edition

Written and edited by David Carmichael
University of Texas, El Paso

cognella®
SAN DIEGO

Bassim Hamadeh, CEO and Publisher
John Remington, Executive Editor
Gem Rabanera, Project Editor
Alia Bales, Production Editor
Jess Estrella, Senior Graphic Designer
Kylie Bartolome, Licensing Associate
Natalie Piccotti, Director of Marketing
Kassie Graves, Vice President of Editorial
Jamie Giganti, Director of Academic Publishing

3970 Sorrento Valley Blvd., Ste. 500, San Diego, CA 92121

Contents

Acknowledgments

Many people have assisted in the preparation of this textbook, but none have been more central or important to the process than my undergraduate students at the University of Texas at El Paso (UTEP). For the past several years, my students have been using portions of this book in the form of supplementary essays in the online version of my course, Introduction to Physical Anthropology and Archaeology, and they have been comparing those excerpts to some of the standard traditional textbooks used for that class. The students appreciated the approach used in those earlier essays, including a style that is more accessible and less jargon-laden than many introductory texts, and it was their urging and encouragement that led to the development of this book. I would like to specifically thank a small, dedicated group of students who created an informal focus group and did a thorough reading of an earlier version of this work, compared it to other textbooks, and then provided insightful and valuable suggestions for its improvement. They are Nathan Eby, Michel Edmonston, Chandler Franklin, Kimberly Garcia, Annelle Mena, and Julius Tano. Julius Tano and Michel Edmonston also assisted in identifying and obtaining illustrations for the book, and Michel graciously allowed me to use some of the primate photographs he has taken during overseas trips. Unless otherwise noted in the credits, the other photographs were taken by the author.

I would like to thank the editors and production staff at Cognella, especially Gem Rabanera, John Remington, and Abbey Hastings, and the outside reviewers who were instrumental in helping me negotiate the many steps involved in the development and production of the book.

Chapter 1: Introduction

Perspectives and Approaches

Is warfare a uniquely human behavior? Is it an inevitable or innate human behavior? Do you know how many human races there are? What do IQ tests measure? Have you ever wondered how evolution can be both a fact and a theory? Are humans really descended from monkeys? Are you related to the Neanderthals? Do you know what the most important human invention of all time was? (Hint: it's not the cell phone.) What makes the New World new? How did we become who we are as a species, and what does that mean for other species and the rest of the planet? How are modern warfare and environmental degradation related to ancient patterns of human behavior? How does intensive production agriculture affect public health? The contents of this book touch on all these questions, and in the process, students are provided with an introduction to what anthropologists know about the origins of the human condition, or the human experiment. Brief answers to each of these and other questions are provided at the beginning of the relevant chapters, and the evidence or reasons for those answers may be found in greater detail in the remainder of each chapter.

Humans are a remarkable species with a fascinating and sometimes surprising history. The story of our development spans some 5 or 6 million years of prehistory and stretches across nearly every land mass on the planet. It begins in tropical African rainforests and grassland savannas before moving into neighboring continents. Humans adapted to life along sea coasts, in arid deserts, and in the shadows of massive continental glaciers; we adapted to the rigors of the Arctic and the thin air of high altitude mountain ranges. The story of humanity is also a story of change: of biological evolution and cultural evolution, through which our species has adapted to changing local and regional environments (Cohen and Kurland 2008). At each step along the way, our adaptation has involved biological and/or cultural changes, the consequences of which are still being felt today. We are a product of our prehistory, and by understanding the patterns of past change, it is possible to gain insight into our current circumstances and challenges.

Figure 1.1: The faces of human diversity

We live in what is arguably the most technologically advanced society to have ever existed on the earth. We also suffer from a remarkably high degree of scientific illiteracy. The National Science Board's (NSB) report entitled *Science and Engineering Indicators 2016* summarizes a series of recent polls about Americans' knowledge of and attitudes toward science and technology. Americans as a whole (84%) express a high level of interest in science and technology (42% very interested, with another 42% interested). This level of expressed interest is higher than that reported for other topics, such as agriculture (21%), economics and business (39%), and the military and defense policy (34%; NSB 2016, Table 7-3). Nevertheless, many Americans remain poorly informed about science. Depending on which poll results are consulted, the data indicate that between 70 and 94 percent of Americans do not understand the scientific process, and many do not apply critical reasoning skills to the consideration of scientific topics. Fewer than half of American adults know the earth moves around the sun and takes a year to do so (Sagan 1996, 324). Only slightly more than half of Americans know that antibiotics do not kill viruses (NSB 2016, Table 7-3). Fewer than half of Americans know that electrons are smaller than atoms, and only 22 percent know what molecules are. Fewer than half know that the earliest humans did not live at the same time as dinosaurs. Only slightly more than half of the men in the United States know that it is the father's gene that determines whether their baby is a boy or girl. Only 49% of Americans agree that humans evolved from earlier species of animals (NSB 2016, Table 7-3), a lower percentage than almost all the other developed countries in the world.

It has been said that *pseudoscience* is embraced in proportion to the extent that real science is misunderstood or misrepresented. Pseudoscience involves claims presented such that they appear to be scientific even though they lack supporting evidence, do not follow the scientific method, and therefore lack plausibility. Belief in various pseudoscientific claims is relatively widespread and growing. Twenty-five percent of Americans and 55% of teenagers believe in astrology. Forty-nine percent of Americans believe in extrasensory perception (ESP), 25% believe in ghosts, 46% believe in psychic or spiritual healing, and 45% believe the earth has been visited by extraterrestrial beings in the past. About 47% of Americans believe God created humans in their present form in the past 10,000 years, and two-thirds of those surveyed favor teaching this view (creationism) in public school science classes. Nearly half of those surveyed believe in the lost continent of Atlantis. Belief in these and other pseudoscientific claims have increased in recent decades (Feder 2006). Yet none of these beliefs are supported by evidence or scientific reasoning.

As Carl Sagan has noted, "we live in a society exquisitely dependent on science and technology, in which hardly anyone knows anything about science and technology. This is a clear prescription for disaster" (1993, 52). We elect our politicians from amongst our midst, so it should come as no surprise that our leaders share our relative lack of understanding of science. Sagan estimates that out of the 535 members of Congress, rarely in the twentieth century have as many as 1 percent had any significant background in science. It has been revealed that Nancy and Ronald Reagan relied on an astrologer for help in making decisions on private and government matters while they occupied the White House (Sagan 1996, 19). Thomas Jefferson may have been the last scientifically literate President, although cases could be made for Theodore Roosevelt and Jimmy Carter (Sagan 1996, 7).

Over the years, when I have polled students in my introductory anthropology classes, I usually find about one out of every 100 students who can actually build an automobile engine. For the rest of us, taking our vehicle to the mechanic for repairs is an act of trust, but one with which we are often uncomfortable. Most of us would be highly skeptical if our mechanic said, "Your car had a big problem, but I fixed it; trust me! That will be $1,000!" We would want a better explanation as well as some proof of the work done, such as the worn parts. Shouldn't we be equally skeptical of our leaders' views and intentions regarding issues such as global warming, the risks of food additives, airport safety, radioactive waste disposal, the effectiveness of medical treatments, or the justification for starting a war? Why should we believe a United States senator who studied economics but not environmental science when he says global warming is a hoax? Or a talk radio host who says there would be no rise in sea level even if the polar ice caps melted, because it's like ice cubes melting in a glass of water? Why are so many people satisfied with the emotional appeal of such statements rather than demanding evidence and sound reasoning? How can citizens help decide government policy if we don't understand the science underlying the issues?

Clearly, there are a number of factors that contribute to scientific illiteracy in America, leading to what Isaac Asimov has referred to as a cult of ignorance (1980). Although many people value higher education as a way to achieve social mobility or a more comfortable way of life, there are also many Americans who embrace the anti-intellectual belief that being knowledgeable is elitist. Some Americans doubt that the effort involved in earning a college education is worthwhile. Others may resent that college has become too expensive for many citizens. Many people have a desire for simple solutions to complex problems and are generally intolerant of the uncertainty or complexity that comes with the scientific method. Other factors include the generally poor coverage given to science topics in the news media, the glamorization of pseudoscience claims, political agendas and government funding priorities, among others. Even our school systems are not without blame.

In an effort to determine how students are formulating their pseudoscience beliefs, researchers at the University of Texas at Arlington surveyed a national sample of high school science teachers (Eve and Harrold 1986; Eve and Dunn 1990). Forty-three percent of the teachers think the story of Noah's ark is true; 19% believe that dinosaurs and humans lived at the same time; 30% want to teach creation science; 26% feel that some races are more intelligent than others (wrong in two ways, as we will see in Chapter 5); 22% believe in ghosts; and 16% believe in Atlantis (the lost continent, not the space shuttle). Students in one of my classes conducted a similar survey of local middle school teachers, and they learned that students' beliefs about claims such as Atlantis, ancient astronauts, pyramid power, creation science, dowsing and ESP are very similar to those held by local school teachers. It's really no wonder students are misinformed about science when some of their science teachers are misinformed about science. Most American adults identify the internet and television as their primary sources of information on science and technology, and more than two-thirds believe that the quality of science and math education in US schools is inadequate.

So, this textbook is part of an effort to fight back against anti-intellectualism and scientific illiteracy. I will attempt to stimulate students to think about thinking. I hope students will ask, "How do we know what we think we know?" Given the introductory scope of the text, it will be possible to touch on only the major high points regarding human antiquity. Nevertheless, it is reasonable and desirable to expect students to be able to recognize warranted arguments and distinguish them from spurious claims and nonscientific arguments.

Major Themes

The materials typically included in an introductory textbook on biological anthropology and archaeology are, for the purposes of this book, organized according to four broad, overarching issues or themes that are of interest not just to anthropologists, but to the general public as well. Thus, the detailed data and the arguments presented throughout the textbook all relate in some way to one or more of these four major themes or perspectives:

1. Evolution Is a Fact and a Theory

People who doubt this statement often either don't have a clear idea of what evolution really is or have been exposed to an inaccurate caricature of the concept, so let's deal with that right up front. Evolution does NOT mean that we are descended from chimpanzees or monkeys. No living species can be descended from another contemporary species. Nor does it mean that we can choose to evolve as individuals during our lifetimes.

Rather, *biological evolution* is change in populations of organisms. Darwin referred to it as *descent with modification*; a more contemporary definition would be *change in gene frequency over time*. The fact of biological change in species is not in dispute. Evolution can be observed in the laboratory, and in the wild, even within a single human lifetime. The reason we have not yet cured AIDS is that the virus has evolved and continues to change as we develop new drugs. Some antibiotics that were once effective in treating bacterial infections no longer work because the bacteria have changed. These bacteria have developed drug resistance; in other words, they have evolved. Change in gene frequency over time does not necessarily lead to new species, but it can if the processes involved act over a sufficiently long period of time. The fossil record provides the evidence of speciation, or long-term changes in gene frequency.

Evolution is also a theory—or, more precisely, there are several theories of evolution, processes that explain the fact of species change. How can evolution be both a fact and a theory? Good question. The answer has to do with the differences in the way terminology is used in science versus the popular vernacular of society at large (National Academy of Sciences [NAS] 2008, 11). In science, the term theory means *a well- supported explanation*. It does NOT mean a guess, hunch, or hypothesis, as is often the case in popular use (or misuse) of the term. So, there are several well-supported explanations for changes in populations of organisms, and they will be discussed in Chapter 4.

2. Humans Share a Common Ancestry with Apes

Many people are uncomfortable with the idea that we humans are part of the animal kingdom. Yet many cultures around the world recognize the similarities between humans and nonhuman primates; this relationship is even alluded to in some creation stories, including the Mayan account mentioned in Chapter 2. Such observations of similarity are correct; Darwin correctly predicted our close biological relationship with the apes more than a century ago. In fact, Morris Goodman (1999), researcher at Wayne State University, reports that humans and chimpanzees have 95% of their DNA sequence and 99% of coding DNA sequences in common. Now, this doesn't mean that humans descended from chimpanzees. But it does mean that both humans and modern chimps evolved from a common prehistoric ancestor, probably about 6 to 10 million years ago. There are a number of human and prehuman ancestors revealed by the fossil record, and there are transitional forms—that is, fossils that exhibit both humanlike and apelike characteristics. Although new fossils are being discovered all the time, at present it is thought that our common ancestor with the apes is one of the species predating *Ardipithecus*. Fossil evidence that supports this conclusion will be presented and discussed in chapters 6 through 9.

3. There Is Only One Human Race: Le Tour de France

One of my colleagues in sociology likes to say the only human race is the Boston Marathon. I refer to the Tour de France because I'm a serious cyclist and cycling fan. But the point is the same—there are NO biological races within the human species. Why would we make such a claim? After all, everybody *knows* there are people of different races, right? I mean, we've grown up learning to judge people and treat people differently based on their race, so those groupings must be biologically real, right? Wrong. Certainly, there are groupings that most people refer to as *races*, but they are not valid biological groupings. Rather, they are sociopolitical constructs that we use to classify (and sometimes mistreat) one another. However, the racial classifications most people use do not reflect the actual distribution of genetic variability within our species. In fact, the more we learn about genetics and the human genome, the clearer it is that our racial classification fails to reflect the real patterns of genetic variation. There is so much more to individuals than their skin color, and the other traits vary independently of skin color.

Figure 1.2: There is only one human race: Le Tour de France

My brother is married to a Chinese woman, and they have three fine sons. My nephews have grown up in Hong Kong, Beijing, Tokyo, and California, and they've had the dubious honor of being discriminated against on two continents because they are "Amerasian." My brother has sometimes expressed his anger at the way his sons have been treated, and when he learned that anthropologists generally don't accept the validity of biological races, he wondered why anthropologists "aren't telling anyone about this." I responded that some anthropologists have been making the case against race for more than 70 years, at least since Ashley Montague's book *Man's Most Dangerous Myth: The Fallacy of Race* (1942), but apparently most people don't want to hear it. Perhaps skin color is too convenient a way to discriminate against others. . . .

The bad news is we have used race as an excuse to mistreat each other. The good news is there is no valid biological basis for continuing to do so. In Chapter 5, we will consider several kinds of evidence that suggest race is not a valid biological concept for humans, as well as why race is not useful for understanding human variability. I hope readers will understand why most anthropologists conclude that there is no biological basis for discrimination against any group of humans as defined by our misguided racial classification. There are no biological races, just many culturally defined ethnicities that have evolved in the context of our human experiment.

4. The Neolithic Revolution Was the Most Important Development in Human Prehistory

The Neolithic period is the prehistoric era during which human populations invented food production. That is, they switched from being hunter-gatherers dependent on wild plant and animal foods to producing their own food through plant and animal domestication. This shift is considered by many researchers to be the most important change humans ever made, because it seems to be the only time that a species has changed to adapt to a completely new ecological niche without undergoing speciation. Instead, humans altered the natural environment to suit the needs of their growing populations. The ability to produce food and store the surplus was the basis for the development of nearly all of the complex societies in the world and the basis for cultural developments such as market economies, political hierarchies, craft specialization, trade, warfare, and most other aspects of recent historical and modern society. In fact, the demographic and ecological consequences of the Neolithic Revolution in food production are still being felt by our world today. Contemporary challenges such as population growth, poverty, war, and global warming will be discussed in this context in Chapter 14.

The Discipline of Anthropology

> I know of no department of natural science more likely to reward a [person] who goes into it more thoroughly than anthropology. There is an immense deal to be done in the science pure and simple, and it is one of those branches of inquiry which brings one into contact with the great problems of humanity in every direction (Thomas H. Huxley).

Anthropology is the scientific study of humanity. It is arguably the broadest and most comprehensive of the human sciences, encompassing all aspects of human biology and culture. Although individual researchers focus on one or a couple of areas of specialization as is the case in other disciplines, anthropologists as a group study every aspect of human existence, in all geographical regions and at all time periods past and present (Ashmore and Sharer 2010, 16; Kelly and Thomas 2014, 18). In fact, all anthropologists would agree that one of the key defining traits of anthropology that distinguishes it from other disciplines is our commitment to a global, comparative holistic approach (Peters-Golden 2008, 15; Kelly and Thomas 2014, 18). If we hope to understand the human condition in the broad sense, it is necessary to look beyond our own personal experiences, beyond our community or ethnic group, and even beyond our own culture and nation. Therefore, anthropology draws upon cross-cultural comparisons of groups from all over the world when making observations about or proposing explanations for the human condition (Figure 1.3). All cultures have intrinsic value in teaching us about the range of behaviors that are human and the various conditions under which those behaviors developed. This idea that one culture is not better than another is called *cultural relativism*. Our interest is not in judging other peoples, but in understanding them, and thereby adding to an ever more comprehensive picture of what it means to be human.

Yet, the human experience is vast and complex. No one can be an expert in every aspect of humanity or every region or period of interest to researchers. Thus, anthropological training and research today involves the development and use of specialized knowledge and skill sets focused on one or a few areas of technical and geographical specialization. The field of anthropology is commonly divided into four subdisciplines (see Figure 1.3), each of which contains a number of areas of specialization.

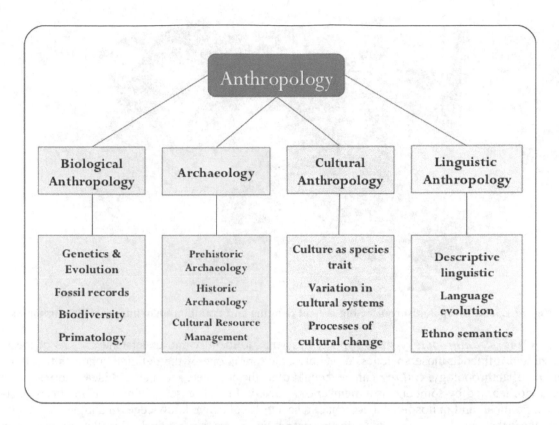

Figure 1.3: The four subfields of anthropology

Biological anthropology deals with the biological aspects of human behavior and the biological evolution of humans and related species. Biological anthropologists work on a variety of topics that will be discussed in this book, including primatology, primate and human anatomy, paleoanthropology, genetics, and modern human variation.

Figure 1.4: Jane Goodall conducting research among chimpanzees at the Gombe Reserve, Tanzania

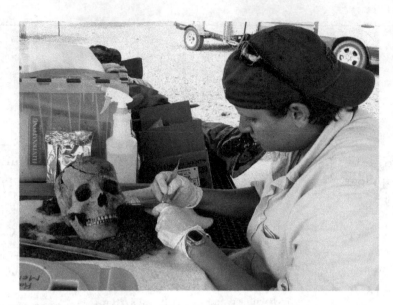

Figure 1.5: Anthropologist conducting in-field cleaning and examination of human skeletal remains

Cultural anthropology studies modern societies to identify and understand the sets of ideas that organize and influence those societies, or cultures. Culture is one of the defining concepts that unite the discipline of anthropology. *Culture* can be thought of as the complete set of shared ideas, norms, and rules for behavior learned by someone as a member of a society. In this sense, culture is the intellectual, social, spiritual, political, and philosophical content of a society's collective knowledge. In another sense, cultural knowledge is the way that humans adapt to our surroundings. It is the set of behaviors that allow a society or culture to interact with the environment and the other groups of people with whom we share our part of the world. Cultural anthropologists live with and study living peoples in an effort to understand the details of human cultural behavior both within and between groups.

Figure 1.6: Cultural anthropology research; documenting the Apache Girls' coming-of-age ceremony, Mescalero Apache Reservation, New Mexico

Figure 1.7: Visitation and documentation of significant cultural heritage sites with members of the Ysleta del Sur Pueblo (Tigua Pueblo) at the tribally owned Chilicote Ranch in West Texas

Archaeology as it is practiced by many researchers today can be considered to be the cultural anthropology of past human groups. Archaeologists cannot observe historic or prehistoric human behavior directly, so they rely on making inferences about the past from the material remains of human behavior, such as artifacts, features (such as campfires, houses, roadways, etc.), and the spatial and temporal relationships among them. Using these material traces, archaeologists attempt to reconstruct and explain past cultural behavior using methods and reasoning similar to those used by forensic scientists. Indeed, forensic science is an outgrowth of archaeology.

Figure 1.8: The author instructing a student in surveying and mapping at the Three Rivers Site (LA 4921) in New Mexico

Figure 1.9: Students in the University of Texas at El Paso archaeological field school excavating the floor of a prehistoric pithouse at the Three Rivers Site (LA 4921), New Mexico

Figure 1.10: Archaeologists on a ledge in front of Sierra Diablo Cave in West Texas screening sediments from excavations in the cave

Linguistic anthropology involves the study of human language, including its origin, the historical relationships among different languages, language structure, symbolism, and the ways that language influence human perceptions and communication about the world around us.

Anthropology is holistic in another way. Not only do we need to examine all sorts of societies in all kinds of settings, but we also need to study all aspects of the societies we encounter. We accept the view that all aspects of human behavior are connected and that traits or behaviors that we might categorize as anatomical, biological, linguistic, economic, dietary, religious, or political, for example, are all interconnected. Each aspect of human behavior is connected to and influenced by the other parts; the past is connected to the present, and our present-day condition is a product of that connection (Peters-Golden 2008, 16). Changes in one aspect of human biology or cultural behavior have implications for other parts of our behavior because everything is connected. The perspective that humanity is a product of the interaction between our biological or genetic inheritance and our cultural heritage is called the *biocultural approach*. Thus, it might be argued that biological evolution explains human origins, but biocultural evolution explains our development as a species.

Learning Objectives

In a recent national survey of university professors, 96% of the respondents identified critical thinking skills as the single most important thing that students should learn during their undergraduate education. The survey results are pretty remarkable, especially when one knows that professors disagree about many things and that getting all or most of them on the same page can be as challenging as herding cats. Yet, professors largely agree that it is more important for students to learn *how to think*, rather than focusing on the details of *what* to think. Facts as we know them today will be revised as future research yields new discoveries; new analytical techniques will be developed in the future; new technologies will lead to new areas of research that have not yet been developed. To a large extent, we are preparing students to address questions that haven't yet been asked, fill job openings that don't yet exist, and generate policy solutions for problems that haven't yet been defined. How can students hope to do this if they spend all their time memorizing the details of things as we presently know them? Well, they can't. However, by using critical thinking skills, students should be able to examine and evaluate any data, claims, and arguments they encounter in the future.

In the current anti-intellectual climate of fake news and so-called alternate facts, it is often challenging to identify what is really known and what is not. Unfortunately, many students do not understand or use critical thinking skills, not even those who believe they do. A few semesters ago I asked students in an introductory anthropology class to discuss their ideas about critical thinking. The results were cause for some concern. Many students thought they and their fellow students were using critical thinking all the time, but they didn't really know what critical thinking means.

Some thought it simply means thinking, apparently as opposed to not thinking at all. Others said it was thinking about a topic rather than taking notes. Some believed that it refers to making decisions quickly in critical situations, such as in a medical emergency. Many students believe critical thinking is having an open mind or thinking outside the box. In other words, many students conceive of critical thinking as a sort of postmodern openness to various ideas. Very few mentioned anything about data evaluation, logic, reasoning, decision-making, or problem solving, all of which are components of critical thinking. At the most basic level, *critical thinking* is the knowledge and use of methods of logical inquiry and reasoning applied to the problems we encounter in life (Glaser 1941). The methods allow one to evaluate claims and make warranted decisions about whether or not to accept them. Critical thinking is all about decision-making: about rejecting false claims and incorrect explanations.

I recognize that many students are challenged by some of the ideas presented in this book, especially those ideas that may seem to conflict with firmly held political views or religious beliefs. In fact, students who encounter scientific findings that challenge their views sometimes allege that scientists are politically motivated or anti-religious. Such is generally not the case (Berra 1990, 142; NAS 2008, 12). For one thing, the scientific method is purposely intended to weed out explanations that are ineffective because they are biased. Second, religious beliefs are beyond the purview of science. Third, and perhaps most importantly, scientists are generally not driven by a desire for "fortune and glory," such as one might attribute to Indiana Jones. Instead, most scientists really do what they do simply because they are curious about the world. The attraction of science is what physicist Richard Feynman has called "the pleasure of finding things out" (Gribbin 2004, 30). I hope students will embrace the spirit of discovery and accompany researchers as we try to find out some things about the human condition.

If students are not regularly challenged by the content of their courses, they are probably not getting their money's worth from college. Nevertheless, it is certainly not the intent of this book to suggest what anyone's religious beliefs or political views should or should not be. The scientific knowledge about our past is presented as it is currently understood. I do not expect students to "believe" the textbook, but I do hope that you will develop an understanding of the interpretations and explanations presented. I hope you to will be able to express why scientists hold the views they do and that you will come to respect the intellectual process that led to their conclusions.

This book is an introduction to the evidence for biological and cultural changes in humans and our ancestors, as well as changes in the environments to which they have adapted. There are so many lines of inquiry, and so many details of evidence that bear on these general issues, that some textbooks on human evolution seem to get bogged down in presenting an overwhelming number of details, challenging students to succeed at memorization. I chose not to structure this book in that way, for two main reasons. First, new fossils and archaeological and finds are being discovered so often that some of the specific facts one might memorize today will be superseded by new discoveries in a few years. Second, I don't want students to merely remember a list of facts from the textbook; I hope readers will understand why scientists have drawn the conclusions they have. In other words, I want you to understand the connection between the scientific evidence and the warranted explanations for that evidence. Vocabulary, names, dates, and other such details are important only to the extent that they relate to an understanding of the larger issues: how we know things about the human past and the broad patterns of change leading to modern humanity.

It is my hope that students will gain enough understanding of biological anthropology and archaeology to answer the questions posed in the first paragraph of this chapter. In other words, you should be able to discuss the broad outlines of human development, from our separation from other primates, to our expansion across the globe, the nature of our hunter-gatherer roots, and the invention of agriculture and civilizations. There are some features of the book that will hopefully help students meet these learning objectives. Throughout the textbook, you will encounter color-coded words and phrases. Statements that are printed in green are understood to be true, while those highlighted in red are considered to be incorrect. Words highlighted in blue are important concepts or vocabulary terms, the latter of which may be found in the glossary. Quick link codes are provided at various places throughout the book to provide access to videos and websites containing supplementary materials that help illustrate important concepts.

Throughout the book, examples will be used that illustrate how earlier discoveries were superseded by later ones and how previous explanations or understandings were replaced by more recent ones as our understanding of the past has improved. We will explore many of the highlights of human evolutionary change, and I hope you learn some interesting and surprising things. I also hope that the overall approach to the information about our human experiment will help the reader become a more discerning consumer of ideas and claims in other areas of life. Even a book on human evolution, with its necessary focus on the prehistoric past, is more relevant to our present circumstances than one might first imagine. We will all benefit if more people develop some understanding about the scientific knowledge that could help inform public policy relating to evolution, education, race, global warming, public health, sustainable development, food safety, and other contemporary issues.

About the Title

I'm sure that some of you are wondering why the evolution of humanity is referred to as "the human experiment." The textbook title is intended to emphasize the scientific understanding that the appearance of our species on the planet was not inevitable. Humans have no inherent right to exist, and we have no guarantee of our long-term survival. Although scientists would not say that evolution is random, the appearance and disappearance of particular species has not occurred in a way that would seem to indicate the existence of a grand plan that would necessarily lead to and explain the existence of humans. We are just one of thousands of species that have benefitted by being able to respond to an opportunity provided by nature. Most of the species that have existed on earth are already extinct. All of today's modern humans are descended from a very small ancestral population numbering perhaps as few as 600 breeding individuals. That population nearly became extinct about 140,000 years ago, due to the demands of severe climate change.

We don't know what the future will hold, in terms of climate change, large-scale migrations, the spread of diseases, and other conditions to which we will need to adapt. Each adaptive response humans have made during our existence, whether by biological evolution or culture change, have essentially been experiments in adaptation, and this will continue to be the case in the future. We have been fortunate so far, but we have also had help. Although it may not seem like it today, humans have always been dependent on nature, on natural resources and other organisms. The earliest hominins who became human did so by discovering fire and inventing tools while inheriting and then influencing key aspects of human biology, such as enhanced cognition and bipedal locomotion, which permitted cultural change. Throughout the process of becoming human, we have always interacted with aspects of nature that are nonhuman: food, medicinal resources, stone, clay, etc. (Smart and Smart 2017, 3). Some Native American cultures, such as the Mescalero Apaches, go so far as to explicitly identify humans as the weakest of the beings that inhabit the earth who are therefore reliant on their more capable animal relatives (Farrer 1994, 23).

Thus, when discussing human development, we are speaking of biocultural evolution, a process by which biological and cultural changes are triggered, conditioned, and redirected by the interplay of biological change and human agency. In the earliest parts of our ancestry, change was dominated by biological processes and was very much dependent on nonhuman influences. One might say that early humanity was an experiment that grew out of the operation of the processes of nature. In more recent times, change has involved greater human agency but also working in concert with nature in complex ways. So the invention of plant domestication or the hierarchical sociopolitical systems that characterize complex societies are biological or social experiments devised by us. To the extent that human actions have effects on other species (such as food crops, insect pests, and animals that thrive in human-altered habitats), we are also conducting experiments in co-evolution. We cannot predict the future, so we don't know what changes we will encounter or what the outcome of these experiments will be. We can get some ideas by looking at the overall trajectory of human existence and by examining the successes and failures of earlier species and societies, but we are really living in an ongoing experiment.

References and Further Reading

Ashmore, Wendy, and Robert Sharer. 2010. *Discovering Our Past: A Brief Introduction to Archaeology.* Boston: McGraw Hill.

Asimov, Isaac. 1980. "A Cult of Ignorance." *Newsweek,* January 21, 1980.

Berra, Tim M. 1990. *Evolution and the Myth of Creationism: A Basic Guide to the Facts in the Evolution Debate.* Stanford, CA: Stanford University Press.

Cohen, Jeffrey H., and Jeffrey A. Kurland. 2008. "Thinking About Change: Biological Evolution, Culture Change, and the Importance of Scale." In *Thinking Anthropologically: A Practical Guide for Students,* edited by Philip Carl Salzman and Patricia C. Rice, 45–54. Upper Saddle River, NJ: Pearson Prentice Hall.

Eve, Raymond A., and Francis B. Harrold. 1986. "Creationism, Cult Archaeology, and Other Pseudoscientific Beliefs: A Study of College Students." *Youth & Society* 17, no. 4 (June): 396–421.

Eve, Raymond A., and Dana Dunn. 1990. "Psychic Powers, Astrology & Creationism in the Classroom?: Evidence of Pseudoscientific Beliefs among High School Biology & Life Science Teachers." *American Biology Teacher* 52, no. 1 (January): 10–21.

Farrer, Claire R. 1994. *Living Life's Circle: Mescalero Apache Cosmovision.* Albuquerque: University of New Mexico Press.

Feder, Kenneth. 2006. *Frauds, Myths and Mysteries: Science and Pseudoscience in Archaeology.* 5th ed. New York: McGraw-Hill.

Feder, Kenneth. 2005. "Skeptics, Fence-Sitters, and True Believers: Student Acceptance of an Improbable Prehistory." In *Archaeological Fantasies: How Pseudoarchaeology Misrepresents the Past and Misleads the Public,* edited by G. Fagan. Abingdon-on-Thames: Routledge Press.

Glaser, Edward M. 1941. *An Experiment in the Development of Critical Thinking.* New York: Teacher's College, Columbia University.

Goodman, Morris. 1999. "Molecular Evolution '99: The Genomic Record of Humankind's Evolutionary Roots." *American Journal of Human Genetics* 64, no. 1 (January): 31–9.

Gribbin, John. 2004. "The Pleasure of Finding Things Out: Why Scientists Do Science." *SKEPTIC* 10, no. 4: 28–30.

Kelly, Robert L., and David Hurst Thomas. 2014. *Archaeology: Down to Earth.* Belmont, CA: Wadsworth Cengage Learning.

Montague, Ashley. 1942; 1998. *Man's Most Dangerous Myth: The Fallacy of Race.* 6th ed. Lanham, MD: AltaMira Press.

National Academy of Sciences. 2008. *Science, Evolution and Creationism.* Washington, DC: National Academies Press.

National Science Board. 2016. *Science and Engineering Indicators 2016* (NSB-2016-1). Arlington, VA: National Science Foundation.

Peters-Golden, Holly. 2008. "Thinking Holistically." In *Thinking Anthropologically: A Practical Guide for Students,* edited by Philip Carl Salzman and Patricia C. Rice, 15–25. Upper Saddle River, NJ: Pearson Prentice Hall.

Sagan, Carl. 1993. "Why We Need to Understand Science." *Mercury* 22, no. 2 (March/April): 52. Astronomical Society of the Pacific.

Sagan, Carl. 1996. *The Demon-Haunted World: Science as a Candle in the Dark. New York:* Ballantine Books.

Schick, Theodore Jr., and Lewis Vaughan. 2005. *How to Think About Weird Things: Critical Thinking for a New Age.* 4th ed. New York: McGraw-Hill.

Smart, Alan, and Josephine Smart. 2017. *Posthumanism: Anthropological Insight.* Toronto: University of Toronto.

Chapter 2: Different Ways of Knowing

Science, Myth, Religion, and Pseudoscience

There are different ways of knowing about the past, and it is important to understand how mythology and science differ in their approaches to acquiring and presenting knowledge. It is appropriate to discuss these differences at the outset of the book in order to clear up some common misconceptions about the nature of science and its relationship to religion. To this end, let's consider three examples of creation stories, comparing them to one another and to the scientific framework that will be used throughout the rest of the book.

I spent several years studying with the late Bernard Second, former head holy man of the Mescalero Apache tribe. In order for me to understand traditional Apache land use patterns, he thought it important that I be taught the Mescalero creation story. Some of the information he provided is esoteric and private, but some of it is appropriate to share with students. However, Bernard specifically asked that when I discuss Mescalero tribal origins, I should refer to their creation story and not call it a creation myth. Why would he make this particular distinction? Well, because he understood the connotation of the term myth as used in mainstream US society. The meaning or implication of calling something a myth is to suggest that it is untrue, fictional, or just a story. And, of course, Bernard would want you to know that the creation story of his people is not a myth in that sense, because their story is true, at least to them.

Now may be a good time to point out that some of the terms used in science have different meanings from when they are used in every day speech. Myth is one of these words. In anthropology, a *myth* is simply a story, usually involving the supernatural, generated to explain some aspect of the world. In this definition there is no judgment made of whether or not the myth is objectively true; it just is. But Bernard knew that this is not the way most of you would understand the word myth. He wanted to be sure I would call your attention to this difference so that you wouldn't dismiss his creation story as a fiction or a fairy tale. Why would he care? Perhaps because we and other societies have fought wars over disagreements about whose creation story is the correct one. Perhaps because he hoped that students will respect the Mescalero Apaches for being an intellectual people. In either case, the point here is that anthropology and anthropologists take myths seriously; they are part of the cultural knowledge of the people we study.

Creation stories, a specific kind of myth, often embody and reveal interesting details about a people's perception of the world, and the parts of their environment they conceive as being the most important. Let's consider some examples of creation stories summarized by Feder and Park (2007) to see how they are constructed. The myths are derived from three different cultures: the Yanomamo, Hebrews, and Mayans. We could have included others as well, because all cultures have their own creation story and there are literally thousands from which to choose. But three examples are enough to make the basic point that there are other creation stories besides the ones you and I were raised to accept as being true.

The Yanomamo cosmos consists of four layers, even though one layer is empty (Chagnon 1997, 99–100). Having an empty layer might seem strange to us, but the number four is sacred in Native American cultures. Anything that involves the sacred (such as knowledge of the past) is properly structured according to the number four. (It can be argued that the number three has similar significance in mainstream US culture.) The Yanomamo were created when one of the First Beings was shot with arrows by two other First

Beings. Upon being hit, Periboriwa bled from his thighs, and each drop of blood that hit the earth became a Yanomamo man. Therefore, all the men descended from those first Yanomamo are fierce, born of blood. In fact, the Yanomamo's name for themselves translates as "the fierce people" (Chagnon 1977, 102–106). One of the men created in this way got pregnant in his legs and gave birth to women and another kind of men, who were timid and docile. This "explains" the existence of women, as well as men who may resemble women (i.e., homosexuals, bisexuals, etc.). It may seem odd to us that such a detail is included early in the Yanomamo creation story, but it makes sense when one becomes aware that the most powerful of the holy people in Native American cultures are people of ambiguous gender. These Two Spirit people are important because they transcend the boundaries that confine the rest of us and are therefore authorized to control more ritual knowledge and, therefore, power. Thus, this creation story explains the origin of an important class of tribal leaders.

Well, one might say that the Yanomamo story isn't true, because it is not written down; it's just oral tradition. (Or one might admit that it's simply not the story we were taught to believe as true.) So, let's consider another creation story that *was* written down, the Mayan creation story from the *Popol Vuh* (Tedlock 1996). Before creation there were no people, animals, birds, fish, crabs, trees, or stones. (Note that birds, fish,

Figure 2.1: The Mayan Hero Twins from the *Popol Vuh*, the sacred book of the Maya

and crabs are all animals; their being identified specifically might indicate that they are of special importance to the Mayas.) The creators first made the earth and the animals and ordered the animals to speak, but they could not. So, the creators made people; the first people could speak, but they had no minds and were made of mud, so they dissolved in water. Next, the creators made people out of wood, but they lacked blood and minds and couldn't remember their creators in order to praise them. So, birds and jaguars (also of special importance) were enlisted to destroy the wood people. However, some wood people escaped and become the monkeys, thereby explaining their obvious resemblance to actual human beings (Tedlock 1996, 63–73). Finally, the gods created the first true people from yellow and white corn meal. Even if one knows little about Mayan beliefs, this scenario strongly suggests that corn and cornmeal are of great importance in Mayan culture.

Finally, let's consider the Hebrew myth, which I'm sure most of you know as the Christian creation myth as well (Feder and Park 2007, 4–6). Here we have two different stories, from Genesis 1 and 2. Order is created from chaos in six days, and humans are given favored status and instructed to be fruitful, multiply, and replenish and subdue the earth. Hmm; could this story have had any influence on the way Western societies have settled and harvested the landscape? In the second story, God creates man and later creates the first woman from the man's rib. He punishes the first man and woman for eating from the forbidden tree of knowledge. As we know, it was a snake that spoke to the woman and convinced her to eat the forbidden fruit.

Figure 2.2: Adam and Eve in the Garden of Eden

So which one of these creation stories is correct? Most of us were probably trained to identify the Hebrew myth as being correct and any others as being untrue. This is perhaps expected but not logically defensible. Although the Hebrew myth was written down, the Mayan myth was also written down, so shouldn't it be just as believable? All of the stories are more or less equally supernatural. Isn't a woman being created from a man's rib and conversing with a snake just as supernatural as women being born from a man's thighs or people being made of corn meal? Clearly the answer is yes. In fact, because each of the myths appeals to a supernatural explanation of the past, they all have equal intellectual standing in one important way: they are all equally nonscientific. It is impossible to test empirically for the existence of Jehovah, Periboriwa, or K'ucumatz. One must accept the existence of any one of them on the basis of faith. And what is faith? It is the acceptance of a proposition in the absence of evidence. There is no objective independent evidence for any of the stories that would disprove the others. So, depending on one's perspective, all the myths are either equally true or equally false, or they just are (to use the anthropological sense of the meaning of myth); in short, they have equal intellectual standing. There is no physical, scientific evidence for choosing one over the other, so we make such choices based on our ethnocentric notions of what is right or wrong. *Ethnocentrism* is the concept that members of a society believe their own culture is good and correct and others' cultures and beliefs are not as good or correct—a good thing in small doses, but dangerous when taken to extremes.

If we are honest with ourselves, we must admit that there is no strictly logical way to determine whether one myth is correct or better than another. Yet, in the scientific framework of knowledge, being able to identify the correct, or better, or more useful explanation is precisely what we are trying to do. The scientific method is designed to help researchers formulate and evaluate explanations, discarding those that are incorrect and confirming those that are best supported by the evidence.

There are specific rules that must be followed if one intends to generate a scientific explanation. We will examine some of these rules in more detail in a later section, but for now it is useful to compare the basic characteristics of scientific and religious explanations (Table 2.1).

It is important to recognize that scientific arguments, statements, or explanations are not beliefs. Although one often hears people say they believe or don't believe in evolution, for scientists, it is not really a matter of belief. Rather, scientists accept the warranted argument that evolution actually happens; they accept the warranted (justified) argument that the evidence supports natural selection. It is simply not a matter of faith. I don't expect you to *believe* that evolution is a fact. Instead, I want you to understand the *warranted argument* that shows evolution is supported by empirical evidence. By extension, the nature of your faith is your own concern. Science is not in the business of judging, promoting, or attacking any particular belief system. Science can't and doesn't weigh in on the question of the existence of the supernatural. The supernatural is, by definition, beyond nature and is therefore outside the purview of scientific understanding.

Table 2.1: Comparison of Major Aspects of Scientific and Religious or Mythological Ways of Knowing

Science	Religion/myth
Warranted argument	Statement of belief, opinion
Commit to naturalistic explanations	Invoke supernatural powers
Testable, falsifiable	Not testable; acceptance by faith
All premises open to question	Doctrine not subject to question
Observation of empirical data	Revealed knowledge
Bounded explanations	Unbounded; anything can happen
Some explanations better than others	Explanations intellectually equal

In order for an explanation to be scientific, it must be naturalistic or, in Darwin's terms, materialistic. Explanations that involve supernatural beings or forces are automatically disqualified from being scientific. This fact is not because of some particular scientific animosity toward religion; it is simply that the basic rules of science must be followed if one's explanation is to be certified as being scientifically justified or warranted by the evidence. Scientific propositions must be naturalistic, because it is this characteristic that makes them testable, and scientific explanations must be testable. In contrast, religious doctrines are not testable in this way. How would one design an independent, empirical test of the existence of a god? There is no way to prove or disprove the existence of God; one must accept His existence as a matter of faith. Scientific explanations are not faith-based; they are the result of logical arguments generated to account for empirical evidence observed in nature.

A scientific explanation must also be bounded, meaning that the scope of the explanation, or the conditions under which it applies, are specified. An explanation invoking the supernatural is not bounded because anything is possible in a supernatural world. A supreme, all-powerful supernatural being can decide at any moment to suspend the laws of nature and create a woman from a man's rib, cause women to be born out of a man's thighs, or allow living people to travel to the stars or converse with the dead. If anything is possible, then appeal to the supernatural explains everything, and no further inquiry is necessary or possible.

Scientific explanations must be justified by reference to empirical evidence. This means that an important part of science is making observations of nature, gathering data. In contrast, religious arguments are based upon revealed knowledge. Support for a particular theological interpretation may be sought through careful study of the doctrinal texts, but this does not constitute observation of natural phenomena, data collection, or independent empirical testing in the scientific sense. Moreover, in myth and religion there is generally little concern for making repeated empirical observations of nature, because empirical observations of nature do not provide evidence of supernatural processes. (At least it is not possible to demonstrate that natural occurrences are indicative of supernatural processes.) In fact, it might be argued that if one feels compelled to search for empirical evidence to support a religious belief, it could indicate a lack of faith, which is the real basis of accepting the revealed knowledge. Some of my Hopi Indian friends used to tease me about being a scientist, about always asking so many questions about everything. In contrast, they just accept that the world is the way it is without asking why. They accept it on faith.

Given that scientific explanations are evaluated against empirical evidence, it is possible (and desirable) to accept or reject various competing explanations. In fact, science proceeds by discarding the incorrect explanations. This is not possible in the same way when one is comparing competing religious explanations. As we saw above, all the religious or mythological explanations that are equally supernatural have equal intellectual standing. While there are certainly emotional or cultural reasons to choose one over another, there is no logical or empirical way to identify one religious view as being true and reject the others as being false.

All parts of a scientific explanation, and all of the underlying assumptions and related corollaries, must be subject to testing and potential falsification. Testing information and explanations is antithetical to the ways of knowing in religion and myth because certain basic religious tenants or doctrines are not subject to testing. They are accepted on faith, as a condition of one's membership among the believers. For example, members of the Creation Research Society (CRS), who purport to conduct "creation science," must subscribe to a statement of belief. Among other things, members must agree that "the Bible is historically and scientifically true and the account of origins in Genesis is a factual presentation of simple historical truths" (CRS 2018). Therefore, any tests, observations, or data that would conflict with this belief are simply not considered. This is not a scientific way of handling evidence and testing knowledge (Berra 1990, 134–135).

It is readily apparent that science and religion are quite different ways of knowing, operating by different philosophical rules for obtaining and evaluating information. Yet, this doesn't mean the philosophies are inevitably in conflict. They function differently and some scientists, such as Stephen Jay Gould (2002), would say they complement each other. Depending on which poll one reads, somewhere between 45 and 60 percent of scientists in the United States claim to hold Christian beliefs. Accepting the warranted argument for evolution is not problematical for most Christians, as it does not pose a threat to their belief system. In 1996 Pope John Paul II issued a papal edict in which he said new knowledge has confirmed that Darwin's theory of evolution is more than a hypothesis. Nevertheless, the minority of Christians who view the Bible as a literally true, complete history of humanity will be challenged by some of the findings of evolutionary science. If you find yourself in that situation, please know that I don't intend to suggest what you should believe in your spiritual life. I do hope that you will follow the warranted arguments made by scientists and understand how their arguments are supported by the evidence.

Creationism and Intelligent Design

How many people in this country actually doubt the former existence of dinosaurs? Dinosaurs, evidence for whose existence comes only from the fossil record, are prominent in popular science literature and museum exhibits. Both more or less realistic models and fuzzy stuffed dinosaurs are even sold in children's toy stores. How many fossils of *Tyrannosaurus rex* (T-rex) have been recovered? According to the Black Hills Institute of Geological Research (2005), the remains of only 36 T-Rex individuals have been found, and most specimens are less than 50 percent complete. Yet, how many people argue that the evolution of T-Rex never happened? There are many more than 36 specimens of fossilized human ancestors that demonstrate the fact of evolution in the human line, but nearly half of adult Americans continue to prefer a creationist view of human origins. Although the scientific community is in agreement that evolution happened, the general public of the United States is divided on the issue (Shermer 2006, xvii–xviii). Why? What is it about *human* evolution that people find so challenging?

Creationism has a long history in the United States, and there are at least eight different versions or schools of creationist thought with contemporary adherents in this country (Scott 2004, 57–64). According to a 2005 poll by the Pew Research Center, when these different versions are taken together, 42 percent of Americans believe in creationist views. Sixty-four percent are in favor of teaching creationism in public school science classrooms, either alongside or instead of evolution (Shermer 2006, xviii). Interestingly, this preoccupation with challenging evolution and promoting creationism is almost entirely confined to the United States. It is simply not a compelling issue anywhere else in the developed world. But here in the United States, we even have presidential candidates devoting valuable time during television debates to declare their disbelief of evolution. This is rather remarkable; "to maintain a belief in a 6,000-year-old earth requires a denial of essentially all the results of modern physics, chemistry, astronomy, biology, and geology" (Krauss 2006). To this list we can also add the findings of biological anthropology, primatology, paleoanthropology, archaeology, and forensic science. So what, specifically, are these creationist views?

Although there are a variety of specific creationist ideas, some basic views held by many creationists are elaborated in the works of Henry Morris (1974), Duane Gish (1978), and Scott Huse (1992). Morris is widely considered to be the father of the twentieth-century creation science movement; he helped organize the Creation Research Society (CRS) in 1963 and was one of the founders of the Institute for Creation Research. He also helped found Creation-Life Publishers, which carries many antievolution book titles. Books, papers, and official statements of these groups claim that evolution is scientifically and historically false, as well as being harmful sociologically. They argue that real understanding of humankind and their world can come only from a creationist frame of reference. Yet, they claim to deal with the creation-evolution controversy from a strictly scientific viewpoint, even though CRS members are required to sign a statement of belief (CRS 2018). Finally, one of the main goals of creation science is to restore confidence in special creation as the true explanation of the origin of the world. Duane Gish, who has made his reputation on the lecture circuit by debating scientists who support evolution, provides a definition of special creation:

> By creation we mean the bringing into being by a supernatural Creator of the basic kinds of plants and animals by the process of sudden, or fiat, creation.
>
> We do not know how the Creator created, what processes He used, for He used processes which are not now operating anywhere in the natural universe. This is why we refer to creation as special creation. We cannot discover by scientific investigations anything about the creative processes used by the Creator (1978).

Morris elaborates on the details of the special creation model which is 1) super-naturalistic, 2) externally directed, 3) purposive, and 4) completed. (As we will see in the next chapter, these traits are the opposite of the basic premises of evolutionary thought.) The model also proposes a period of time during which creative processes were at work; after the creation was completed, these processes are believed to have been replaced by processes of conservation, put into place by the Creator to maintain the basic systems he created (Morris 1974, 11–12). Corollaries to the basic creation model include the assumption of a young earth, the claim that there has been no appearance of new kinds (i.e., species) of organisms, the claim that there are no intermediate forms between apes and humans, acceptance of the literal truth of the worldwide Noachian flood, and the appearance of civilization at the same time as the creation of humans. Any evidence that would contradict these beliefs is considered to be irrelevant. Morris states "no geological difficulties, real or imagined, can be allowed to take precedence over the clear statements and necessary inference of Scripture" (1970, 33). With science and the scientific method so clearly excluded from "scientific creationism," one wonders why Morris and his colleagues would even pretend to deserve the label of science, unless it is only to gain access to the public schools.

It is beyond the scope of this book to provide a detailed analysis of the history of creationism and its contemporary variations. Students who want to pursue those topics on their own are invited to consult Scott (2001, 2004) and Numbers (1992). What is of concern here is how creationist efforts to undermine the teaching of evolution have changed over the years. The US courts recently ruled on the tenth major legal case involving the teaching of creationism in public school science classes (National Center for Science Education 2018). The legal cases go as far back as the famous 1925 Scopes "Monkey Trial" in which John Scopes was prosecuted for violating an outright ban on teaching evolution in Tennessee. The prosecution actually won the case and Scopes was fined, but testimony presented during the trial made the antievolution law seem silly. So although Scopes was a creationist victory in the short term, it ushered in a period during which laws and policies banning the teaching of evolution were ignored or replaced. In 1968, in *Epperson v. Arkansas*, the Supreme Court declared such laws banning the teaching of evolution to be unconstitutional (Berra 1990, 133).

After the public rejection of laws expressly forbidding the teaching of evolution, creationists devised another tactic in an attempt to keep their views in public school science classrooms. State laws were passed requiring equal time be devoted to teaching creationism in the form of "creation science," or "scientific creationism," alongside evolution in the public schools. In 1981, the Arkansas Act of 1981, or the Balanced Treatment Act, was declared unconstitutional in Federal District Court because it was found to be "simply and purely an effort to introduce the Biblical version of creation into the public school curricula," in violation of the first and fourteenth amendments to the Constitution (Berra 1990, 136). Similarly, in 1987, the US Supreme Court struck down the Louisiana Creationism Act of 1981 as unconstitutional because the purpose of the law "was to restructure the science curriculum to conform with a particular religious viewpoint." The court further noted that forbidding the teaching of evolution when creation science is not taught undermines the provision of a comprehensive science education (Berra 1990, 137).

With the defeat of these two equal-time laws on constitutional grounds, it became clear that any other similar state laws would also be overturned, so advocates of creationism changed tactics again and focused attention on local and state school boards. Efforts were made to place as many creationists as possible on school boards, paving the way for board members to make changes in school science curricula at the local and state levels. One result has been the well-publicized and somewhat embarrassing changes to the science curriculum in Kansas when creationists held the majority on the state school board. More recently, concerned parents challenged a similar move by a local school district in Dover, Pennsylvania, and that high-profile case was decided in US District Court in 2005. A summary of that case is presented below, but first, let's consider the pattern here. More than ten important legal cases spanning the past 85 years have been tried in an effort to undermine the teaching of evolution and promote creationism as an alternative. In all that time and in all those cases, no evidence has been presented in support of creationism.

Instead, the proponents of creationism have resorted to legal maneuvering. Michael Shermer considers this pattern of behavior in contrast to the way science operates. His own research has involved an attempt to apply chaos theory to human history, in an effort to explain phenomena such as the Nazi holocaust. Shermer would have been pleased if historians had found his theoretical model useful and taught it to their students, but they have not.

> Maybe I did not communicate my theory clearly. Possibly historians do not use such theoretical models. Worse, perhaps my theory is wrong or useless. Should I appear before Congress to demand that legislation be passed to give my theory equal time with other theories of history? Should I lobby school board members to force history teachers to teach my theory of history (Shermer 2006, 90)?

Clearly, the answer is no. This is not the way the advancement of scientific knowledge proceeds. But this approach is exactly what the proponents of creationism have done. In the case of *Kitzmiller v. Dover Area School District*, the "theory" in question is intelligent design (ID). ID has failed to earn certification as a scientific alternative to evolution. In fact, it is not even seriously considered by scientists, so ID proponents on the school board, at the urging and with the assistance of the Discovery Institute (a think tank in Seattle), resolved to promote their views by making procedural changes to the curriculum. They were sued by parents who were concerned about the quality of their children's science education. It is worth reviewing the arguments and findings of the case to clarify what is really at stake: the integrity of public science education in the United States.

Kitzmiller v. Dover

ID is based on the belief that the world is too complicated and nature is too interconnected for it to have appeared as the result of the operation of natural principles. Instead, ID proponents claim that there must be a designer, just as a watch must have a watchmaker. And because the world and all its parts are so complex and marvelous, that designer must be infinitely intelligent—thus, intelligent design. This argument is the essence of natural theology, a philosophical position dating back to the seventeenth century. The watchmaker analogy is borrowed from William Paley's 1802 work, *Natural Theology or Evidences of the Existence and Attributes of the Deity*. Natural theology fell out of favor among naturalists and most other scientists during Darwin's day, but it has undergone something of a revival among members of the general public as part of the creationist movement. Modern proponents of this view generally refuse to identify the designer, in an effort to make ID appear to be a scientific theory or at least to avoid admitting it is a religious doctrine. Nevertheless, it is clear that the designer is understood to be God.

More specifically, ID proponents believe the existence of a designer is proven by the "fact" that some structures are "irreducibly complex" (Behe 2006).For example, they argue that an eye that is not fully formed (i.e., unlike ours) would be of no use, therefore there can be no earlier, less well-formed eyes that are transitional to a "fully formed" eye. They simply deny the possibility of transitional forms that would support the idea of evolution. Unfortunately for ID proponents, scientists have discovered many examples of transitional forms in the animal kingdom, including in the human lineage. In the case of eyes, similar light-sensing organs have evolved separately in several different animal lineages. Moreover, it can be argued that even eyes that don't function exactly like ours could still be useful to an organism. Wouldn't an eye capable of sensing light and dark be better than no eye at all? Are the eyes of deer and elk useful and effective? Ever wonder why we have camouflage hunting clothing in patterns of black and orange? Orange camouflage is readily visible to us (good thing; its purpose is to prevent one hunter from shooting another), but not to deer. Does that mean deer eyes don't work because they are not "fully formed" with color vision like we and the other primates have? No, it doesn't mean any such thing. Scientists have been debunking ID arguments like these for years (see Scott 2004; Shermer 2006).

The ID notion fails in at least four ways. First, it provides no new evidence about nature or new insights or explanations that account more effectively for what we already know about nature. Instead, ID represents a throw-up-one's-hands approach to knowing: something like, "if I don't know how it could happen, then I guess a supernatural entity is the cause!" (See comments by Gish quoted above for a version of this sentiment.) Second, appeal to the supernatural automatically disqualifies ID from being scientific. Even if ID proponents refuse to admit that God is the intelligent designer, an appeal to any supernatural entity as an explanatory device violates the rules of science. The leading ID expert witnesses admitted as much in *Kitzmiller v. Dover*. Third, the criticisms leveled against evolution by ID proponents have been answered by science, a fact also revealed in the court case. Finally, if one chooses to argue that the nature and benevolence of the Creator is reflected in nature, it would seem to be necessary to deny the many details of nature that are cruel or messy in human terms.

One example of cruelty in nature is illustrated by the life cycle of the wasp *Cotesia congregata*. The mother wasp injects her eggs into the body of a caterpillar along with a virus that disables the caterpillar's immune system to prevent it from attacking the eggs. When the eggs hatch, the larvae eat the caterpillar alive from the inside out, saving the nerves and circulatory system for last so that the host doesn't rot. Other examples involve what might be considered "bad mothering." Such behavior is common in nature and often an important part of the reproductive cycle (Angier 2006). Disturbing a rabbit's nest may result in the mother consuming all her bunnies. Pandas often produce an heir and a spare, and when the firstborn does well, the mother will simply walk away and abandon the second infant. Many hawks and owls have a similar approach, with the exception that they will eat the younger offspring or encourage the older chick to peck it to death. A mother nurse shark has two uteri in which her babies develop, but she lacks a placenta with which to feed them. So, she incubates up to 20 eggs, and when the babies' jaws are developed, they feed on each other. Eventually, only one baby shark emerges from each uterus.

Then there are all the vestigial structures observed in nature; they would make for poor or awkward designs if created from scratch, but they are readily understandable as a record of evolution from earlier forms. Why else would moles, bats, whales, dogs, and humans share the same forelimb bones, if not for their being inherited from an ancient common ancestor? Awkward designs and cruel behaviors should be of little comfort to those who hope to see the nature of the Creator revealed in His creations.

There were *three main legal questions before the judge in Kitzmiller v. Dover*: whether ID is scientific or creationist in nature, whether teaching ID is intended to improve science education or promote religious belief, and whether or not it is constitutional to teach ID in public school science classrooms. Judge John E. Jones found that ID is not science, but rather a religious doctrine, which both students and adults would recognize as such. Additionally, he concluded that the ID doctrine is clearly an outgrowth of earlier creationist arguments. The purpose of introducing such a doctrine into the public schools is not to enhance science education, but to seek government authority in promoting one religious doctrine at the expense of other beliefs. Furthermore, the judge recognized another ID agenda that was revealed in the Wedge Document submitted as evidence during the trial. The Wedge Document is an internal policy paper prepared by the Discovery Institute in which the goals of the ID movement are laid out.

> Dramatic evidence of ID's religious nature and aspirations is found in what is referred to as the "Wedge Document." . . . The Wedge Document states in its "Five Year Strategic Plan Summary" that the intelligent design movement's goal is to replace science as currently practiced with "theistic and Christian science." . . . ID aspires to change the ground rules of science to make room for religion, specifically, beliefs consonant with a particular version of Christianity (Jones 2005, 28–29).

Expert witnesses for the ID position confirmed in their testimony that the existence of a supernatural designer is a central tenant of ID and that in order for ID to be considered science, the ground rules of science have to be changed so that supernatural forces can be included as causal agents. It is this explicitly religious nature of ID that led the judge to conclude that the Dover school district's policy requiring the teaching of ID is unconstitutional because it is a violation of the Establishment Clause. One of the more remarkable aspects of Judge Jones's decision was the vehemence with which it was expressed. Rather than simply presenting his findings, he admonished the Dover school board and other proponents of ID in the hope that the same arguments would not be revisited in another court in the future. Students may follow the link provided in the references and read the entire court decision, but here are the main points from the strongly worded conclusion:

> The proper application of both the endorsement and Lemon tests to the facts of this case makes it abundantly clear that the Board's ID policy violates the Establishment Clause. In making this determination, we have addressed the seminal question of whether ID is science. We have concluded that it is not, and moreover that ID cannot uncouple itself from its creationist, and thus religious, antecedents.

> Both Defendants and many of the leading proponents of ID make a bedrock assumption which is utterly false. Their presupposition is that evolutionary theory is antithetical to a belief in the existence of a supreme being and to religion in general. Repeatedly in this trial, Plaintiff's scientific experts testified that the theory of evolution represents good science, is overwhelmingly accepted by the scientific community, and that it in no way conflicts with, nor does it deny, the existence of a divine creator.

> To be sure, Darwin's theory of evolution is imperfect. However, the fact that a scientific theory cannot yet render an explanation on every point should not be used as a pretext to thrust an untestable alternative hypothesis grounded in religion into the science classroom or to misrepresent well-established scientific propositions.

The citizens of the Dover area were poorly served by the members of the Board who voted for the ID policy. It is ironic that several of these individuals, who so staunchly and proudly touted their religious convictions in public, would time and again lie to cover their tracks and disguise the real purpose behind the ID Policy.

. . . Those who disagree with our holding will likely mark it as the product of an activist judge. If so, they will have erred as this is manifestly not an activist Court. Rather, this case came to us as the result of the activism of an ill-informed faction on a school board, aided by a national public interest law firm eager to find a constitutional test case on ID, who in combination drove the Board to adopt an imprudent and ultimately unconstitutional policy. The breathtaking inanity of the Board's decision is evident when considered against the factual backdrop which has now been fully revealed through this trial. The students, parents, and teachers of the Dover Area School District deserved better than to be dragged into this legal maelstrom, with its resulting utter waste of monetary and personal resources (Jones 2005, 136–138).

It is remarkable that key members of the Dover school board repeatedly lied under oath, and made some pretty outrageous statements in court. For example, board member Buckingham said:

"Nowhere in the Constitution does it call for a separation of church and state." He explained that this country was founded on Christianity. Buckingham concedes that he said, 'I challenge you (the audience) to trace your roots back to the monkey you came from'" (Jones 2005, 105).

This entire statement is egregiously incorrect; we will consider the third part of it in our discussion of evolution in the following chapters, but I'd like to address the first two statements here because they reflect a fairly common misconception, one often included in creationist critiques of government policy regarding the teaching of evolution. The claim is that because there is no separation of church and state in the Constitution, it should be legal to teach religious doctrines in public schools. Furthermore, it is alleged that the United States was founded as a Christian nation, and therefore Christian doctrines should be taught in public schools to the exclusion of all other beliefs.

The first claim involves the Establishment Clause, the legal basis upon which the *Kitzmiller v. Dover* case was decided. Christian fundamentalists often claim there is no constitutional basis for the separation of church and state, but such a statement is either misinformed or disingenuous. It is true that the original Constitution did not create a separation of church and state. However, such a separation was created in the First Amendment and included in the Bill of Rights. By definition, amendments to the Constitution become part of the Constitution, so the Establishment Clause of the first amendment is indeed part of the Constitution. If one wishes to argue that freedom of religion is not part of the Constitution (as amended) then one would have to admit that other rights recognized in later amendments (such as the right to keep and bear arms, right to a speedy trial, protection of private property, abolition of slavery, women's suffrage, etc.) are not constitutional either. Clearly, the argument is untenable.

It is also commonly alleged that the United States was intended to be a Christian nation. This claim is also false. The founding fathers certainly considered this as a possibility, but many of them were personally familiar with the dangers of investing the government with religious authority. So, after debating the issue, the delegates to the Constitutional Convention wrote an entirely secular document. The Constitution contains no mention of Christ or Christianity. It refers to religion only twice, in the First Amendment, which prevents the government from making laws respecting an establishment of religion, and in Article VI, which prohibits religious tests for public office. Thomas Jefferson observed that through ratification of the First Amendment, the American people built a wall of separation between church and state (Americans United 2005, 2).

Further evidence of the founders' intention to create a secular government comes from other early official documents. Jefferson and James Madison helped pass the Virginia Statute for Religious Freedom, a 1786 law guaranteeing religious freedom to all. President George Washington wrote a famous letter to a Jewish community in Rhode Island celebrating the fact that Jews had full freedom of worship in America. James Madison (1785) wrote an eloquent statement in opposition to a bill introduced in Virginia that would have levied a tax to pay teachers of religion. In 1797 President Adams signed the Treaty of Tripoli, in which Article 11 assures the subjects of Tripoli that "the Government of the United States of America is not in any sense founded on the Christian religion" (Walker 1997, 6).

When confronted with statements by creationists who are willing to lie under oath and misrepresent the Constitution, students may justifiably wonder why anyone would do such things. Why would people, especially self-described Christians who supposedly adhere to high standards of moral behavior, lie about such matters? This is a good question, and various writers have attempted to find an answer. Shermer may be correct when he proposes that fear is the real reason people are so resistant to accepting the fact of evolution (2006, 29–32). Some creationists recognize that Darwin's strictly materialistic take on nature leaves no room for miracles like those described in the Bible. They are afraid that readers of the Bible will pick and choose which portions to believe as literally true and which portions to treat as allegorical. Ultimately, they fear that people's faith in the Bible will diminish (Scott 2004, 228). Others seem to fear the idea that the existence of the universe and our appearance as a species are without purpose. They would like to see humans as the culmination of a grand, externally directed design in which the rest of the world was created expressly for our use. Scientific evidence to the contrary suggests that we are just another species among many and that we cannot find the meaning of our existence merely by observing nature.

But perhaps the most persistent fear is that relating to contemporary social conditions. Darwinian evolution is often blamed for the moral degeneration of modern society. It is even alleged that the mere exposure of the public to Darwin's ideas is sufficient to cause a whole range of social ills:

> The fruit of evolution has been all sorts of anti-Christian systems of beliefs and practice. It has served as an intellectual basis for Hitler's Nazism and Marx's communism. It has promoted apostasy, atheism, secular humanism, and libertinism as well as establishing a basis for ethical relativism, which has spread through our society like a cancer. The mind and general welfare of mankind has suffered greatly as a result of this naturalistic philosophy.
>
> . . . It is no mere coincidence that the modern deterioration of morality has occurred contemporaneously with the advance of the evolutionary philosophy. The moral collapse of today can indeed be largely attributed to the very system that wipes out all moral standards (Huse 1992 124–125).

Darwin would have probably been shocked by the notion that his theory of adaptation to changing local environments could be construed as the cause of modern society's perceived social problems. Modern social scientists know that the causes of social problems are various and much more complicated than the mere exposure of our students to the idea of evolution. Surely if that were indeed the cause of all our social problems, we would have stopped teaching evolution long ago, thereby creating a perfect society. It is remarkable and disturbing that such a simplistic world view can be embraced by so many people in this day and age.

A False Dilemma

The claim that scientific and religious ways of knowing are inevitably in conflict is false. The claim that you must choose one or the other is a claim that in philosophy is referred to as a *false dilemma*. Not all Christians feel threatened by evolution. In fact, more than 17,000 ministers from around the United States have signed the letter written by the Clergy Letter Project (2005), an initiative started by ministers and academics in Wisconsin in as a response to efforts, like those in Dover, to discredit evolution. The letter notes that evolution is "a foundational scientific truth," and to reject it "is to deliberately embrace scientific ignorance and transmit such ignorance to our children." According to the Gordon-Conwell Theological Seminary, there are approximately 38,000 different Christian denominations in the world. It should go without saying that these various groups don't agree on all points of doctrine; otherwise they wouldn't have established separate denominations. The positions espoused by Morris, Gish, the Discovery Institute, etc., have been politically influential in recent decades, but they don't necessarily represent the majority of Christians in the United States or elsewhere in the world. It is certainly possible to embrace science and still maintain a spiritual belief.

Something like half of the scientists in the United States claim to hold Christian beliefs. And even for those who do not, there can still be a spiritual element to the scientific endeavor. Albert Einstein did not believe in a personal God, but he did have what he considered religious experiences:

> What I see in nature is a magnificent structure that we can comprehend only very imperfectly, and that must fill a thinking person with a feeling of humility. This is a genuinely religious feeling that has nothing to do with mysticism (1946).

Carl Sagan (2006, 31) phrased it differently when he suggested that science is, at least in part, informed worship. Perhaps American psychologist William James expressed the same feeling when he defined religion as a "feeling of being at home in the Universe" (Sagan 2006, xv).

Long before I knew of James's remark, I knew and appreciated that feeling: the sense of awe and wonder at the enormity of the cosmos, as well as the place of humanity within its fabric. Some years ago, I drove out into a remote section of the desert in the middle of the night to escape the glare of city lights and watch the Leonid meteor shower. It was cold, so I took a thermos of hot tea and a Pendleton blanket. Wrapped in the blanket and sitting on the warm hood of my jeep, I let the night envelop me. The meteor shower was awesome; I saw several meteors per minute, ranging from short bursts of green to long, white streaks arching across the sky. How amazing it was to know that I was seeing pieces of space debris traveling 30,000 miles per hour, heated to 300°F by the compression of the air ahead of them. From a distance of 60 miles they were silent, but I wondered how loud their flight and burnup would be if it were possible to observe them up close. Could they really contain the chemical precursors to life on earth?

As the darkness deepened, I became more aware of the surroundings, the smaller-scale aspects of nature in the quiet desert night. The air was calm, but there was just the slightest stirring—not so much that one would call it a breeze, but not still either. It was as if the movement was so gentle that I could feel it with only a single cell at the base of a single hair follicle on my arm. And that not-quite-a-breeze carried on it the subtle scent of moisture coming off the sage and the soft sounds of kangaroo rats scurrying across the dunes. My senses were heightened by the breathtaking spectacle of nature, and I marveled at how interconnected the cosmos is, from the distant fireballs to the rodents on the sand. To feel at home and at peace on my portion of the cosmic fabric was at once humbling and exhilarating. Surely this is what Sagan and James were talking about.

References and Further Reading

Americans United for Separation of Church and State. 2005. "Is America a Christian Nation?" https://www.au.org/resources/publications/is-america-a-christian-nation.

Angier, Natalie. 2006. "One Thing They Aren't: Maternal." *New York Times*, May 9, 2006. https://www.nytimes.com/2006/05/09/science/09mama.html.

Behe, Michael J. 2006. *Darwin's Black Box: The Biochemical Challenge to Evolution.* Free Press, 2nd edition.

Berra, Tim M. 1990. *Evolution and the Myth of Creationism.* Stanford, CA: Stanford University Press.

Black Hills Institute of Geological Research. 2005. Specimen Catalog for *Tyrannosaurus rex.* www.bhigr.com/pages/info/rex_chart.htm.

Chagnon, Napoleon A. 1997. *Yanomamo. Case Studies in Cultural Anthropology.* Fort Worth, TX: Harcourt Brace College Publishers.

Clergy Letter Project. 2005. www.theclergyletterproject.org

Creation Research Society. 2018. "Statement of Belief." https://creationresearch.org/statement-of-belief/.

Einstein, Albert. 1979. *Albert Einstein, the Human Side: New Glimpses from his Archives.* Helen Dukas and Banesh Hoffmann, eds. Letter to Hoffmann and Dukas, 1946, p.39. Princeton University Press.

Gish, Duane. 1978. *Evolution? The Fossils Say No!* San Diego: Creation-Life Publishers.

Gould, Stephan Jay. 2002. *Rocks of Ages: Science and Religion in the Fullness of Life.* New York: Ballantine Books.

Huse, Scott. 1992. *The Collapse of Evolution.* Grand Rapids, MI: Baker Book House.

Jones, John E., III. 2005. Kitzmiller v. Dover Area School District. Memorandum Opinion. 400F. Suppl. 2d 707 (M. D. Pa 2005). US District Court for the Middle District of Pennsylvania. www.pamd.uscourts.gov/kitzmiller/kitzmiller_342.pdf.

Krauss, Lawrence M. 2006. "How to Make Sure Children Are Scientifically Illiterate." *New York Times,* August 15, 2006. www.nytimes.com/2006/08/15/science/sciencespecial2/15essa.html.

Madison, James. 1785. "Memorial and Remonstrance Against Religious Assessments. Statement introduced into the General Assembly of Virginia in opposition to a bill to levy an assessment for the support of teachers of religions. Memorial and Remonstrance against Religious Assessments, [ca. ... (archives.gov)

Morris, Henry. 1970. *Biblical Cosmology and Modern Science.* Phillipsburg, NJ: Presbyterian and Reformed.

Morris, Henry. 1974. *Scientific Creationism.* San Diego, CA: Creation-Life Publishers.

National Center for Science Education. 2018. "Ten Major Court Cases About Evolution and Creationism." https://ncse.com/library-resource/ten-major-court-cases-evolution-creationism.

Numbers, Ronald. 1992. *The Creationists.* New York: Knopf.

Sagan, Carl. 2006. *The Varieties of Scientific Experience: A Personal View of the Search for God,* edited by Ann Druyan.

Scott, Eugenie C. 2001. "Antievolution and Creationism in the United States." National Center for Science Education. www.ncseweb.org/resources/articles/4550_antievolution_and_creationi_2_13_2001.asp.

Scott, Eugenie C. 2004. *Evolution vs. Creationism.* Berkeley, CA: University of California Press.

Shermer, Michael. 2006. *Why Darwin Matters: The Case Against Intelligent Design.* New York: Henry Holt & Co.

Tedlock, Dennis translator 1996. *Popol Vuh: The Mayan Book of the Dawn of Life.* New York: Simon & Schuster.

Walker, Jim. 1997. "Little-Known U.S. Document Signed by President Adams Proclaims America's Government Is Secular." *The Early America Review* (Summer). www.earlyamerica.com/review/summer97/secular.html.

Chapter 3: Scientific Method

What Is Science?

Some years ago, several colleagues and I submitted a research proposal to the National Science Foundation for the funds to purchase a micro x-ray fluorescence machine. The equipment is used to perform nondestructive analysis of the chemical composition of substances such as rock, soil, clay, paint, and other things of concern in the field of materials research. Many of the studies we proposed to conduct with the new equipment were archaeological in nature. While working on the proposal, I had in my office the manufacturer's brochure detailing the equipment specifications. A colleague from the chemistry department stopped by to view the specifications, and when he was finished, he asked, "Do you really do this sort of analysis in archaeology?" When I assured him that we do, he replied, "Wow, you should be in the College of Sciences!" (He meant rather than Liberal Arts, as is the case at our university.) The tacit view revealed by this remark is that science is what researchers do in certain disciplines, those commonly identified as the hard or physical sciences. This view is incorrect.

Science is not a discipline or a group of disciplines. It is an approach to knowledge—a method for learning and knowing about the world around us. It is the commitment to seek logical, naturalistic explanations of natural phenomena, through the testing of one's ideas against empirical evidence (Diamond 1987). It may be more challenging to explain phenomena that can't readily be measured in a laboratory, but such activities make up much of the research in fields such as ecology, evolution, animal behavior, psychology, economics, history, government, and human behavior. Certainly, such an approach can be applied to questions involving human antiquity, human behavior, and the relationship of humans to the environment.

If professional scientists sometimes reveal unintentional misunderstandings of the breadth of science and the inclusion of human behavior within its purview, it's easy to understand how laypersons could be confused about the nature of science.

This chapter provides an introduction to the scientific method, the general approach that scientists use to learn about, understand, and make predictions about the world. Students should be able to understand the basic terminology of science and grasp the philosophical bases behind logical arguments as revealed in the discussion of concepts such as parsimony and uniformitarianism.

Q&A: How can evolution be both a fact and a theory?

Evolution means species change over time; that is the fact of change. There are several related explanations for the fact of change; the explanations are the theory.

Indirect Evidence and Uniformitarianism

For many students reading this text, it is probably the first time they've been exposed to the real meaning of and evidence for biological and cultural evolution. As you might imagine, these topics generate many questions and lively discussions among students. A few years ago, one student sent me a written note in which he asked how we could know anything about the ancient past. Specifically, he asked, "How can we know the earth is 4.6 billion years old if there was no conscious mind present to record the event?" This is a very interesting and important question and one that I encounter fairly regularly, as it is commonly included in creationist critiques of the theory of evolution. In fact, this very argument was made by Mr. John Bacon, one of the Kansas state school board members who favored removing evolution from the state science curriculum. He was baffled by the objections of scientists: "I can't understand what they're squealing about. I wasn't here, and neither were they" (Krauss 2006). This view reveals a remarkable misunderstanding of the nature of the scientific method. The implication is that any alleged past event must be witnessed and recorded by a conscious being; otherwise we can't know it actually happened. If this were true, all the fields of science involving phenomena older than recorded history (and those involving things that are very small or very far away) would be studies in futility. Clearly, this is not the case, but how should I discuss the use of indirect evidence with my students?

The next morning as I was preparing to take my daughter (then a fourth grader) to school, I found a way to explain it to my class. We live on the west side of the Franklin Mountains (a narrow range that divides El Paso into east and west sides), and when we leave for school in the morning, our house is still in the shadow cast by the mountains. I asked my daughter, "We live on the west side of the mountains, and we can't actually see the sun come up, so how can you tell that sunrise has happened?" After thinking about it for a few seconds, she answered, "The stars fade, the sky gets lighter, and the birds start to sing." I thought this was an excellent, insightful answer, but I persisted: "Those are all good observations, but how do you know that they indicate the sun has risen?" Her response was great: "Duh, Dad; it always happens that way!" It always happens that way—a very common-sense idea that is the essence of uniformitarianism, the principle that allows us to study phenomena we didn't witness through the examination of indirect evidence.

Uniformitarianism is the idea that the present is the key to the past; the natural principles that shaped the earth during ancient times were the same principles that are at work in the natural world today. Because the processes are still at work today, we can observe them in operation and apply our understanding of them to the past. The idea was first articulated by the French scholar Georges Buffon in 1774 and advanced by geologists James Hutton (*Theory of the Earth,* 1788) and Charles Lyell (*Principles of Geology,* 1872). As originally conceived, *uniformitarianism* meant that the natural processes acted slowly and uniformly (thus the term), but as geologists continued to gather field data, it became apparent that the intensity or rates of various geological processes varied over time. In 1802, John Playfair (*Illustrations of the Huttonian Theory of the Earth*) recognized that the rates of geological change could vary over time and yet still operate according to the same natural laws. (That is, one didn't need to invoke supernatural causes as many catastrophists did.) In other words, natural laws are constant, but the rates at which they operate (how quickly erosion or deposition occurs, for example) are not. This idea later became the twentieth-century version of uniformitarianism, sometimes known as *actualism.*

Modern uniformitarianism or actualism states that the earth's geologic record is a product of both slow and gradual processes and *natural* catastrophes such as earthquakes, hurricanes, and meteorite impacts.

> . . . actualism simply recognizes that the laws of chemistry and physics (thermodynamics, gravity, radioactive decay, etc.) have not changed, at least not during the Earth's history. However, the rates of macroscopic processes (such as the erosion of a landform) can vary widely, depending on the presence or absence of storms, droughts, volcanism, earthquakes, asteroid impacts, and other natural phenomena (Henke 2003).

So, we know that land can sometimes move relatively quickly, as a result of volcanoes or large earthquakes, and that hurricanes or major floods can erode land relatively quickly. But these phenomena are still the result of natural processes, evidence of which can be seen in the geological deposits of the earth. If we know how modern sand dunes are formed and we know what their cross-bedded layers look like, we can recognize ancient sand dunes in the earth's rocks. Even if the prehistoric dunes were larger than their modern counterparts, we can still document the fact of their occurrence and make reasonable inferences about how they were formed. For example, Figure 3.1 shows a series of *cross-bedded* sandstone layers exposed in Red Rock Canyon near Las Vegas, Nevada. Sand dune cross-beds are caused when the layers within sand dunes are laid down at an angle to the main bedding planes, resulting in horizontal units with inclined layers within them. We don't need to have witnessed the formation of the dunes in order to recognize their diagnostic features in the geological record.

Figure 3.1: Cross-bedded sandstone deposits at Red Rock Canyon National Conservation Area near Las Vegas, Nevada, indicative of prehistoric sand dune formation. The Aztec Sandstone contains the fossilized remains of massive dunes laid down in the early Jurassic period (about 180 million years ago), extending from the Dakotas to Mexico. This section is hundreds of feet thick; hikers in the upper right corner provide a sense of the scale of the cross-bedded deposits.

It is useful to extend this thinking exercise by taking an imaginary walk through the forest. I'm sure you've heard the old question, "If a tree falls in a forest, but no one is there to hear it, does it make a sound?" Let's examine this possibility in some detail. As we walk through the forest, how could we know whether a tree has fallen in our absence? Well, we might observe that one tree is lying on its side, with the roots sticking up in the air. But how does that indicate it has fallen? It indicates a fallen tree because it differs from the normal condition of trees: trunks vertical with roots still in the ground. ("Dad, it always happens that way.") Moreover, even if we are not botanists, we know something about why the trees normally grow the way they do: leaves at the top so chlorophyll can access the sunlight, roots in the soil to transfer nutrients to the rest of the tree, etc. We know, at some level, that the growth habit of the trees serves a function, so when we observe an individual that diverges from the general pattern, we can infer that it has fallen.

Ok, so a tree fell; can we reasonably infer that it made a sound even if no conscious being was there to hear it? Yes, we can. We might observe that the branches of neighboring trees were snapped off as our tree fell, and we know that a snapping branch makes a sound when we observe it in person. Even if you are not a camper who has snapped twigs and branches for use as firewood, you will almost certainly have some prior experience with breaking pieces of wood that provides the necessary, albeit informal, understanding that the breakage produces a sound. The same goes for the thump when the trunk hits the ground and the crackling of splinters when the trunk shatters.

What do we know about how sounds are made? It is the displacement of air (or other media, such as water) and the generation of sound waves. If sound waves are produced in the air when we witness a tree falling, isn't it reasonable to infer that similar sound waves will be produced even if we're not there? Absolutely. Isn't it reasonable to conclude that the squirrels nesting in the treetop heard sounds when the tree fell, even though they were incapable of recording the event for us? Certainly. Once we know the principles behind the generation of sound waves, we know they are produced independently of the presence of receptors, the species of the receptors, or the receptors' ability to record the event for humans who might come along later. The basic principles are at work in nature, at all times and in all places.

Where does this all lead us? It is not logical to claim that an event never happened simply because a conscious mind did not directly experience and record it. An event may be too small, too far away, or too ancient to be observed directly, but it may well produce indirect evidence. The use of indirect evidence is common in many fields. You have never seen an electron, but electrons can still be studied in physics. One can see the path of an electron when a radioactive element is placed in a cloud chamber because the invisible particle leaves a visible path through the cloud. We cannot see planets in other solar systems, but astronomers have demonstrated that such planets exist, by observing the effects of the gravitational pull they exert on the suns (i.e., stars) they orbit. In many murder cases, there are no witnesses to the crime, but forensic anthropologists can often connect the perpetrator to the crime scene by indirect evidence, such as fingerprints, hair, blood, fiber from fabrics, and footprints.

It is indeed possible to know about the past as long as we are willing to accept the idea that nature operates according to knowable principles. Those principles operate during the day and at night, in the summer and the winter, in the United States and in Scotland, sometimes faster and sometimes slower. They operated yesterday, and thousands of years ago, and they will be operating tomorrow. The challenge is to determine what unobserved past events and processes produced the indirect evidence left behind. That's exactly what the scientists working in such fields as astronomy, geology, paleontology, geophysics, archaeology, and paleoanthropology are trying to do. Indeed, there would be no modern science without the principle of uniformitarianism.

Hypotheses and Theories

One of the most common misconceptions about science relates to the definition of the word theory. In everyday, nonscientific usage, theory is often taken to mean a hunch, guess, an opinion, or a speculation. The use of the term theory to mean a guess or unproven fact is a common ploy in creationist critiques of evolution. This sort of usage also indicates ignorance of science and the scientific method and/or a willingness to deceive the reader who doesn't understand scientific theories. In everyday conversation, one may hear statements such as "It's my theory that Hoffa was murdered" or "It's my theory that O.J. did it and dropped the bloody glove in the trash." These are hunches, not theories in the scientific sense. A scientific *theory* is not a hunch; it is a logical explanation or model of the way some natural phenomenon works that is capable of being tested through empirical observation. A scientific theory is a well-supported (warranted) explanation of a set of facts observed in nature. The theory of evolution is a well-tested and well-supported explanation for biological change.

In science, theory and fact are complementary concepts. An apple that falls off a tree will drop toward the earth, illustrating the fact of gravity. Theories used to explain this fact are Newton's theory of universal gravitation and Einstein's general relativity theory. Similarly, the fact of evolutionary change can be observed in the laboratory; theories used to explain the fact of change include Darwin's natural selection and punctuated equilibrium, described by Niles Eldredge and Stephen Jay Gould. Let's consider this relationship between facts and theories in greater detail.

The process of building scientific explanations for natural phenomena involves several steps that are repeated as part of what can be called the *science cycle* (Thomas 1998, 47). The science cycle links our observations with explanations through the construction of logical arguments. The empirical world can be conceived of as consisting of two parts: the world of facts and the world of generalizations or explanations (Figure 3.2). The facts of nature, such as sunrise, gravity, cloud formations, sound waves, and fossilization, exist independently of our ability or desire to explain them. Facts are not proven, but observed, and they don't become theories when they are repeatedly observed. Instead, theories are separate parts of the science cycle developed to explain the facts that simply exist. There are no such things as alternate facts. There can be alternative interpretations of facts, but a phenomenon is either factual or it isn't.

The first step in the science cycle is observation; one observes a pattern in the world of facts, a phenomenon that one is interested in explaining. Hypotheses are then generated to explain the phenomenon, and they are tested against additional data observed in the world of facts. If the hypothesis (or a group of hypotheses) is repeatedly confirmed, it may come to be regarded as a theory—that is, as a well-tested and well-supported explanation for the phenomenon. Hypothesis testing is the mechanism through which theories are evaluated.

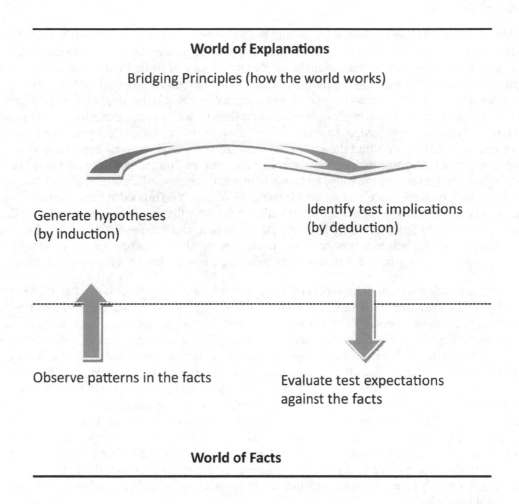

Figure 3.2: The science cycle. Adapted from Thomas (1998) and Kemeny (1959).

A *hypothesis* is a testable statement accounting for a set of observations (Shermer 1997, 19). Our theories about how the world works provide the basis for generating hypotheses that may explain detailed facts observed in nature. The reasoning goes something like this: if our understanding of how the world works (our theory, or the bridging principles in the testing of our hypothesis) is correct, then the expectations deduced from our hypothesis will be consistent with further observations of the facts. If the expectations (predictions) of our hypothesis are not met, we may have to revise our understanding of the principles at work in the problem we are studying. Most of us do this sort of reasoning and problem solving in our daily lives. Let me paraphrase an anecdote provided by Robert Root-Bernstein and Donald McEachron (1982) as an everyday example of the scientific method at work.

Suppose you return home one night after work, but when you open the door to the front hall and turn on the light switch, the lights do not come on. You observe that this result differs from the normal pattern of things, so you have identified an anomaly or problem to be solved (i.e., explained). One of the first things you might do is jiggle the switch to see if that might resolve the situation. What have you done? You have generated and tested the hypothesis that a faulty switch may be the reason the lights are not illuminated. Although you are not an electrician, your consideration of the possibility of a faulty switch as the cause is related to your general understanding about how the electrical system in your house works (i.e., how the world works). You are aware at some level that switches can become worn, cease to make good contact, and therefore interrupt the electrical circuit. If you jiggle the switch and the lights still do not come on, you have eliminated that possibility. But you haven't solved the main problem, so what do you do? You consider another hypothesis.

Maybe there has been a power failure and the entire neighborhood is without lights, and you just didn't notice it as you opened the door. To test this possibility, you step back out onto the porch and find that your neighbors' lights are on, thus eliminating that hypothesis as well. Perhaps the circuit breaker has been tripped. So you try the lights in the living room, and they turn on as expected, so you can conclude the problem is not with the circuit breaker, right? Wrong. The living room lights might be on a different circuit than the hall lights. In science, you must test your assumptions as well as your explanations. So you stumble from the hallway into the dark garage, tripping over all the piles of important stuff you have stored there, to retest your last hypothesis. You find the circuit breakers are all normal, so your hypothesis is still wrong. Returning to the front hall, you conclude that the bulb must be burned out, so you drag out the ladder; remove the globe from the light; remove the bulb; replace it with a new, energy-efficient fluorescent one; and throw the old bulb away. You have explained the problem, right? Wrong. You missed at least one more possibility. The bulb could have been loose in the socket. (Don't ask me how that happens, but we know it does.) The appropriate test of that hypothesis would have been to screw in the bulb to see if it was loose, but as the bulb has been removed, discarded, and broken in the trash, that possibility can no longer be readily tested. I suppose one could retrieve it from the trash and examine the filament, but hopefully you get the point.

The point is that we know, in a general way, how this reasoning process works. Our expectations (the test implications of our hypotheses) are based on our general understanding (theory) of how the electrical circuits in houses operate. Even if we're not electricians, we generally have some sense of how these things work. Certainly, there are other ways of knowing about our world and, therefore, other ways of responding to the light bulb problem. We might choose to believe that there is an evil witch in the neighborhood who has placed a spell on our house. Or perhaps an extraterrestrial alien has landed in the neighborhood and the arrival of the alien craft caused an electromagnetic pulse that is interfering with the flow of electricity in our house. Maybe our lighting problem is simply an act of God. (If you don't think this is invoked as a cause for some natural events, you might want to review your homeowner's or renter's insurance policy.) The advantage of the scientific method is that the incorrect hypotheses are eliminated, and the problem can be solved. In the other ways of knowing, we are more or less powerless. Our only real option is to sit in the dark hall waiting for God or the alien or the witch to change their minds and make our light work again. One could argue that sometimes we might actually be truly powerless, but it needn't be so in the case of the light bulb.

The Principle of Parsimony

People bring interesting things to my office all the time. As an employee of a public university, I am readily accessible to the general public, and it has been my pleasure to view many interesting items over the years. People have asked me to examine fossilized bones, meteorites, a jade mask, classic Mayan pottery, and a meterlong stone pestle from Mexico that the owner identified as a fossilized Neanderthal club. However, one of the most interesting items was the incredible alien ring discovered in the desert east of El Paso.

A few years ago, a community member (whom I'll refer to as Bob) contacted me with an amazing story of discovery, one that he imagined would change the way humanity views our place in the universe. While hiking in the desert along the Carlsbad highway at the edge of town, Bob discovered a ring, but he was convinced it was more than that: a remarkable artifact that provided proof of contact with extraterrestrial aliens. He asked if he and his father could bring the ring to my lab and examine it under one of our microscopes. I agreed, and we all viewed the ring and discussed their interpretation of the find. The ring itself was unimpressive. It had an adjustable band made of soft, pliable metal, and it contained a greenish plastic "stone"; it looked like a mood ring one might obtain from a gumball machine. It was definitely not a piece of fine jewelry. On the inside of the ring, we could see a series of small, more or less parallel scratches. To Bob, these looked like pictures of Phoenician cuneiform writing he had seen in *National Geographic*. Yet, they were so small . . . How could humans create a cuneiform inscription so small that we would need a microscope to view it? He concluded that aliens from outer space must have done it. His interpretation of the ring was that the aliens intended to contact us and chose to do so by inscribing a ring and then discarding it in the desert east of El Paso, where it waited until the right appropriately insightful person found it. All we had to do now was translate the inscription, and much would be revealed!

How satisfying is this explanation? Hopefully you have already identified several problems with Bob's interpretation, but this case allows us to consider the more general question of how we evaluate alternative explanations (hypotheses) in science. Hypotheses are evaluated by reference to criteria of adequacy—that is, a set of traits that indicate the explanation is naturalistic, viable, useful, etc. These criteria include such things as the testability, productivity, scope, and simplicity of the proposed explanation (Schick and Vaughn 1995, 200–211). The alien ring story provides a useful vehicle with which to consider the concept of simplicity. In science, the preference for simplicity is expressed in the *principle of parsimony*. This logical principle is also known as Ockham's razor, named for the medieval philosopher William of Ockham with whom it is associated because he often cited it in his writings.

William of Ockham (ca. 1285–1349) was born in Ockham (or Occam), England; studied at Oxford; and became a Franciscan theologian. Through his writings on philosophy, he can be viewed as the leader of the thirteenth-century nominalists, who contrasted the empirical nature of things with the conceptual nature of scientific ideas (i.e., the world of facts vs. the world of explanations). It has been suggested, on the basis of his contribution to this intellectual position, that Ockham was the pioneer of modern epistemology (Fieser 2003, 2). As used by Ockham, the principle of parsimony states that "plurality should not be posited without necessity," or one should not increase, beyond what is necessary, the number of entities required to explain anything (Carroll 2002). In modern terms, we might say that the best explanation is the simplest, the one involving the fewest assumptions.

So, is Bob's explanation of the amazing ring in the desert simple or parsimonious? No, it is not. And for that reason, it's not a very compelling or satisfying explanation. For Bob's explanation to be correct, a whole series of unsupported propositions must be true. First, we must accept the idea that there are in fact extraterrestrial aliens in the universe and that such beings are sophisticated enough to find us. Of course, this is an assumption because the existence of aliens has yet to be demonstrated. We must also subscribe to the notion that these aliens are interested in contacting us, have the ability to do so, and have the benevolent intent of communicating with us. Assumptions again; it would seem just as likely that aliens, if they exist, would be here on a hunting trip or in search of natural resources (as in the movies *Predator* and *Independence Day*). Next, we would have to agree that aliens from a sophisticated civilization were not only capable of interstellar travel, but also actually succeeded in making a journey to earth. And when they arrived here, they tried to communicate with us not in their own language or the language of mathematics, but in a dead prehistoric human language. Furthermore, while they have technology beyond our own and manufacture metal alloys we have never seen, they chose to write the microscopic inscription on a toy ring made of cheap, soft metal of the sort we find in gum ball machines, not meteorites. And we would have to agree that even though the aliens were here on Earth long or often enough to learn cuneiform and find a toy ring to engrave, they left no other evidence of their presence. Finally, they chose to place the amazing ring in the desert east of El Paso, instead of at the White House, NORAD, Livermore Lab, or the Vatican. Each of these assumptions must be true for Bob's interpretation to be correct; if any of them is incorrect, the entire explanation falls apart. In other words, the extraterrestrial alien explanation is very weak.

Can we think of a more parsimonious explanation for the ring? We certainly can. Imagine a human child accompanying their family as they shoot off fireworks in the desert east of town (because of the ban on fireworks within the city limits). While playing, the child drops an inexpensive ring purchased from a gum ball machine, and the ring is lost in the sand dunes. The soft metal is easily scratched by the windblown sand, and after some time it is re-exposed and discovered by Bob. It is just a lost toy ring, not a message from outer space. This is a more parsimonious explanation because it is much simpler and doesn't require extraneous assumptions; it fits with what we know about how the world works. Now, we can't say for sure that a child deposited the ring, but such an interpretation is certainly far more likely than Bob's explanation; it is more parsimonious.

Being good scientists, we should consider other possible scenarios and test them further by studying things like the average size of children's fingers relative to the circumference of the ring, the depth of scratches caused by windblown sand on a sample of the soft metal, etc. Nevertheless, by applying Ockham's razor, we have cut away or shaved off the unnecessary assumptions Bob made, and as a result, we have identified a more fruitful avenue to a likely explanation. A similar reasoning process is appropriate when considering a proposition such as claims that evolution didn't happen, that it is a hoax being perpetrated by scientists from around the world, and that God created fossils of animals and plants that never existed, made them appear old, and placed them in sediments appearing to be old, all to test our faith. Clearly, science is not the only way to know about such things, but it often provides the most simple and productive explanation of natural phenomena. It certainly yields the most testable explanations.

References and Further Reading

Berra, Tim M. 1990. *Evolution and the Myth of Creationism: A Basic Guide to the Facts in the Evolution Debate.* Palo Alto, CA: Stanford University Press.

Carroll, Robert T. 2002. *"The Skeptic's Dictionary." http://www.skepdic.com/.*

Diamond, Jared. 1987. "Soft Sciences Are Often Harder than Hard Sciences." *Discover* (August): 34–39.

Fieser, James, ed. 2003. *"The Internet Encyclopedia of Philosophy." https://iep.utm.edu/.*

Henke, Kevin R. 2003. "Actualism versus Outdated Young-Earth Creationist Views of Niagara Falls." ww.noanswersingenesis.org.au/henke_niagara_falls.htm

Kemeny, John G. 1959. *A Philosopher Looks at Science.* New York: Van Nostrand Reinhold.

Krauss, Lawrence M. 2006. "How to Make Sure Children Are Scientifically Illiterate." *New York Times,* August 15, 2006. https://www.nytimes.com/2006/08/15/science/sciencespecial2/15essa.html.

Root-Bernstein, Robert, and Donald L. McEachron. 1982. "Teaching Theories: The Evolution-Creation Controversy." *The American Biology Teacher* 44, no. 7 (October): 405.

Schick, Theodore Jr., and Lewis Vaughn. 1995. *How to Think about Weird Things: Critical Thinking for a New Age.* Mountain View, CA: Mayfield Publishing Company.

Shermer, Michael. 1997. *Why People Believe Weird Things: Pseudoscience, Superstition, and Other Confusions of Our Time.* New York: W. H. Freeman and Company.

Thomas, David Hurst. 1998. *Archaeology. Belmont, CA:* Wadsworth Publishing.

Chapter 4: Evolution, the Modern Synthesis

The Philosophical Challenge of Evolution

Evolution is change in populations of organisms over time. Darwin referred to it as *descent with modification,* although today we might refer to it as *change in gene frequency over time.* The central point, however, is the understanding that biological species are not fixed and that populations of organisms change over time. This fact of biological change is the fundamental organizing principle of modern biology. It is accepted by virtually all scientists working in such fields as biology, ecology, epidemiology, microbiology, biochemistry, genetics, geology, paleontology, and anthropology, to name a few. Much research in these fields is concerned with understanding how, when, and why particular changes occurred. The reality of evolutionary change itself is not in doubt. Nevertheless, many members of our society remain unfamiliar with the basics of evolution and how it operates, and some even deny that evolution happens at all. It is interesting to consider why this level of misunderstanding or skepticism should still persist more than 150 years after the discovery of the principle of natural selection by Charles Darwin and Alfred Russel Wallace.

Paleontologist Stephen Jay Gould makes the case that evolution, especially natural selection— Darwin's and Wallace's theory for how species change occurs—is still uncomfortable for many members of our society because it contradicts many of our social hopes and cultural biases (Gould 1997). He argues that the theory of natural selection is not especially difficult, but that we as a society don't want to accept it because it is philosophically radical (as is, by extension, the modern synthesis of which it is a part).

Q&A: How can organisms with fully functional designs evolve at random?

Evolution is not random; it involves natural selection, which is a nonrandom process.

Evolution is challenging because it is explicitly materialistic and rigidly naturalistic. Natural selection (or any scientific theory) doesn't explicitly deny the existence of a god, but it doesn't require one either. It provides a way to explain the diversity of life observed in nature without supernatural agency. This is a difficult notion for a society steeped in the tradition of dualism, in which life consists of both material and spiritual parts, with the spiritual being the more important. We would like to believe that a benevolent creator has designed harmonious ecosystems that benefit humans and that change takes the form of progress, with humanity as the result of that progress. Even among those who don't feel the need to appeal to a creator, many still have the expectation that species change represents progress, species are becoming better, and evolution leads inevitably and predictably to humans. Natural selection is philosophically challenging because it undermines all of these expectations.

The main force behind natural selection is the unconscious struggle of individual organisms for reproductive success (Gould 1997). It is very mechanical and impersonal. There is no principle of the harmony of ecosystems. There is no principle of progress; species may become better adapted to a particular environment, but they don't become "better" in some absolute sense. There is no overall grand design leading inevitably to humanity. These uncomfortable findings of evolutionary biology can be difficult to reconcile with our views of how we would like to think the world operates. They probably also contribute to the misunderstandings that many still have about evolution.

This chapter starts with a consideration of some of the most common misunderstandings about what evolution is and how it works. Students will then be provided with an overview of Darwin's perspectives on natural selection, followed by a discussion of some of the non-Darwinian evolutionary processes that contribute to our modern understanding of evolution. At the end of the chapter examples of recent and ongoing evolution will be presented from research on several species, including humans. Learning objectives for this chapter are to become familiar with the basic principles of evolution and to understand how they are still in operation today.

Common Misunderstandings about Evolution

The University of California Museum of Paleontology and the National Center for Science Education have partnered to develop a very interesting and useful website on evolution (https://evolution.berkeley.edu/evolibrary/home.php). Among the wide range of topics addressed and resources provided on the website is a long list of common misconceptions about evolution that indicate a substantial degree of confusion on the part of the general public about the nature of evolution. Students are encouraged to visit the website to peruse the entire list, but we will briefly consider a few of the most problematical. The incorrect views are shown in red, followed by a short response or correction. Phrases and views highlighted in green are understood to be correct.

1. **Evolution is just a theory.** Evolution *is* a theory, but it is not "just" a theory. When people say that evolution is "just" a theory, what they generally mean is that evolution is a hunch, a guess, or an idea that we're not sure is correct. This is not what a theory means in science. To scientists, a theory is a well-tested and well-supported explanation for some set of data or observations in nature. Our current understanding of evolution, the modern synthesis, combines several well-supported explanations for change, linking the findings of genetics with natural selection to explain how populations of organisms change over time.

2. **Evolution is a random process that happens by chance.** Some people claim that evolution cannot be real because the complexity of nature could not result from a random process. It is important to understand that natural selection is not random. If it were, perhaps it would be called *natural randomness*, but it is not. Natural selection is a selective process. Aspects of the environment within which organisms live (such as rainfall patterns, food sources, predators, etc.) serve to select those traits that help individuals adapt to the local environment and reproduce more effectively. Mutation, the source of genetic variation in species, is random, but natural selection is not. It is the accumulation of many selected traits that results in species becoming adapted to their local environment.

3. **Natural selection involves organisms trying to adapt.** Neither species nor individual organisms *try* to adapt. The species don't "know" how the environment is changing or what traits they might "need" in order to adapt to those changes. There is no conscious agency involved at all. Rather, natural selection is a mechanical process that is one of the possible outcomes of what is actually happening: individuals are simply attempting to reproduce successfully. Those that produce more offspring will transmit more of their genes to the next generation.

4. **Evolution is survival of the fittest.** Evolution is not "survival of the fittest." Darwin did not use this phrase, and it is a misrepresentation of his theory. Herbert Spencer actually first used that phrase, as a way to justify social inequality in human society, but this is not what Darwin's theory is about. It is simply differential reproductive success, or survival of the best adapted. The traits that confer an adaptive advantage—camouflage, for example—may have nothing to do with strength, speed or ferocity, etc.

5.   **Evolution results in progress.** Evolution is nonprogressive. Darwin was careful to avoid labeling organisms as higher or lower forms. At most, natural selection is about organisms' adaptations to changing local environments. An organism could become better adapted to a particular environment, but if the environment changes in the future, what was once an advantage could become a disadvantage. Many organisms are facing precisely this challenge as a result of global climate change. Most organisms that have existed on the planet are extinct; it is hard to see how that fact can be viewed as a result of a principle of progress.

Darwinian Evolution

Charles Darwin made two primary and quite distinct contributions to our understanding of biology. First, he demonstrated beyond a reasonable doubt the fact of change in populations of organisms. This may not seem like a big deal today, but to those who believed that all kinds of animals were created recently, in their present form, his idea of change was indeed challenging. Yet, he was not the first to recognize the evidence for species change. Darwin meticulously documented many examples of change over time, thereby demonstrating beyond a doubt that species were not static. Second, he proposed natural selection as a mechanism to explain the fact of species change. Several researchers had made earlier attempts to explain the changes they saw in the fossils or groups of related organisms, including Jean-Baptiste de Lamarck and Georges Cuvier, but Darwin's explanation has proven to be correct.

Scientists do not simply accept natural selection as dogma. Any proposed scientific explanation must be closely examined and tested, and it is important to understand that alternative hypotheses were tested and found wanting. In 1796, the French zoologist Georges Cuvier demonstrated that the fossils found in geological strata are the remains of extinct animals. Prior to that time, it was generally believed that extinction was impossible because God's creation was perfect. Cuvier found different groupings of animals in separate layers and concluded that the species represented in each layer must have become extinct as a result of major catastrophes, such as floods or volcanoes. He also surmised that the earth must be very ancient, at least several million years old. He argued that the geologic record reflected a succession of different faunas and a series of extinctions, but his explanation for the appearance of new faunas after extinction events was not convincing. Although Cuvier was instrumental in demonstrating the fact of extinction, his suggested mechanism of cyclical creations didn't square with the geological evidence for the operation of smaller-scale processes in the geologic record that have since been regarded as the result of uniformitarian principles rather than catastrophes.

Jean-Baptiste de Lamarck also recognized the fossil evidence for species change, but he proposed a different mechanism, called *inheritance of acquired traits*. He suggested that characteristics acquired by a parent during its lifetime (such as large muscles, long neck, etc.) could somehow be transmitted to the offspring. He felt that the habits or actions of the organism caused the changes to occur. This effort was noteworthy because it was the first serious attempt to explain the passing of physical traits from parents to offspring; the only thing wrong with it was that it is wrong. We now know that an individual's characteristics are inherited in one's genes, not determined by what one's parents accomplished during their lifetime.

Early Concepts of Evolution: Jean Baptiste de Lamarck

https://evolution.berkeley.edu/evolibrary/article/history_09

One of Lamarck's colleagues, Étienne Geoffroy Saint-Hilaire (1772–1844), also accepted the evidence for species change. He formulated the concept of "unity of composition," having observed that animals share one basic structural plan with variations in its parts. He was a deist, believing in God, but he also accepted a universe of natural laws, functioning without supernatural intervention. He proposed still another alternative mechanism for change, suggesting that the environment causes direct induction of change, that the organism somehow knows what it needs to change. Again, knowledge of the principles of genetics undermines this idea.

Darwin did not work in a vacuum. He was aware of earlier research that demonstrated the fact of extinction and suggested an ancient earth. Moreover, he was familiar with the work of his contemporaries in other disciplines. Charles Lyell provided geological evidence for the great antiquity of the earth and for the view that natural processes acting gradually over long periods of time could result in large changes. Thomas Malthus was a demographer who introduced the idea that the environment could accommodate only a certain number of organisms, resulting in competition among individuals. He provided the concept that there could be some characteristics that would be advantageous for survival in the context of such competition. Adam Smith was an economist who championed a free-market economy. He argued that the operation of a free market would allow competition among companies and individuals; the successful ones would balance each other, and the unsuccessful ones would go out of business. The resulting economy would have the appearance of orderliness, the appearance of planning, without any explicit plan—without the "guiding hand" of government. All of these ideas were influential in Darwin's formulation of natural selection.

So how does Darwin's explanation for species change work? *Natural selection* is a principle of differential individual reproductive success that may lead to populations adapting to changing local environments. It follows logically and directly from three simple ideas: 1) more offspring are produced than can be supported by nature, resulting in competition; 2) there is variability among the individuals in a population, and at least some of that variability is inherited; and 3) individuals who have advantageous characteristics will be more successful at reproduction, thereby producing more offspring with the advantageous trait. Over time, this results in a shift in the population, in the direction of the more advantageous trait, or adaptation to the local conditions for which the trait confers advantages. Darwin drew an analogy to the process of *artificial selection* (a term he also coined), in which the farmer or stock grower selects for desirable traits; but in natural selection it is the environment that identifies or selects the most useful traits.

Darwin discovered and developed the principle of natural selection in the context of trying to explain variation among the 13 different species of finches in the Galapagos Islands. He observed variation in body size and form of the birds' beaks and noted that there appeared to be geographical patterns in the distribution of these traits. He reasoned that details of local habitats, such as the kinds of foods available, led to the development of different beak forms in different areas. Furthermore, he recognized that all the finch species were derived from a single common ancestor that had originated on the mainland of South America 600 miles to the east. After that ancestor somehow reached the Galapagos, its descendants split into multiple populations on different islands, eventually leading to the evolution of a series of related species, via a process Darwin called *adaptive radiation*. Adaptive radiation results in the differentiation and spread of many closely related species in a relatively short period of time, as they adapt to different local environments or ecological niches. (See Quick Link to the research by Peter and Rosemary Grant later in this chapter.)

Another commonly cited example of natural selection at work is the famous case of the peppered moth in Great Britain. Peppered moths (*Biston betularia*) are usually light-colored with black spots on their wings (Figure 4.1). The color patterning on these light moths provides camouflage against the lichen on the trees in which they are found. There is also a genetic variant in the moth population that results in wings that are black instead of peppered in appearance. Against the light-colored lichen, the black moths are more visible and more susceptible to predation by birds and therefore less common in the population. However, starting in the mid-1800s, naturalists found that the black moths were actually more common in the vicinity of towns and cities. Increasing use of coal to fuel the Industrial Revolution resulted in air pollution that killed much of the lichen and blackened the trunks of trees in industrial towns. In that environment, the light moths were more visible and more susceptible to predation, so the black moths became more common in urban areas. In Manchester, the first black moth was noted in 1848, and by 1895 nearly all the moths in the city were of the black variety. In the mid-twentieth century, after air pollution controls were instituted, tree trunks became lighter, and the light-colored moths became more common again. It is generally accepted in the scientific community that differential bird predation is the primary selective mechanism that drove the observed evolution in peppered moths (Majerus 1998; Walton and Stevens 2018). The change from light to dark moths and back again did not involve speciation; both color varieties are versions of the same species. Instead, the change in the percentages of each variety is an example of micro-evolution, or change within a species, by means of natural selection.

Figure 4.1: Pepper moth as an example of natural selection. Light and dark phases of Peppered moths shown against light and dark backgrounds.

Natural selection is a principle of differential individual reproductive success. Individual organisms cannot choose to evolve during their life; they either have the advantageous traits, or they don't. If they do, they are statistically more likely to produce more offspring, and the advantageous traits will be more common in the following generations. It is the population that evolves (or in Darwin's terms, descent with modification happens in populations, not individuals). Individuals are the units of selection, but it is populations or species that actually evolve.

So what does natural selection explain? It explains the resemblances among different, closely related organisms—as a result of their descent from a common ancestor. It explains the diversity of life, or why the differences among different organisms have proliferated over time—as a means of adaptation. It accounts for the fossil evidence of changes in organisms over long periods of geologic time, and for the fact that most species that ever existed are already extinct; they didn't adapt to environmental change (Botanical Society of America 2003).

Darwin made important contributions, but there was much that he did not know. Even he understood that natural selection was not the whole story:

> Furthermore, I am convinced that natural selection has been the most important, but not the exclusive, means of modification (Darwin 1859).

Darwin didn't know what causes the variability within populations of organisms or how traits are transmitted to the next generation; natural selection doesn't explain these details. Other researchers added these and other important parts of the puzzle. The work of other researchers since his time has not disproven Darwin's theory of natural selection; instead, it has repeatedly confirmed the importance of his work. But they have also added many of the details that eluded Darwin, and they have identified several other processes that can contribute to change in gene frequency over time—to evolution.

The Rest of the Story

As brilliant as Darwin was, and as relevant as his ideas continue to be today, it is inaccurate to equate evolution with Darwin (as implied by the term *Darwinism*). Our contemporary view of evolution is often referred to as the evolutionary synthesis, or modern synthesis. Three great biologists, Theodosius Dobzhansky, George Gaylord Simpson, and Ernst Mayr, were the architects of the modern synthesis, and their reconciliation of evolutionary theories with the processes of genetic inheritance didn't happen until the latter half of the twentieth century. There are a whole series of process that are sometimes known as *non-Darwinian* evolutionary principles. They include the principles of genetic inheritance, mutation, genetic drift, and punctuated equilibrium. Some of these processes operate at the cellular level, some at the individual level, and some at the level of entire populations. All are processes that contribute to change in gene frequency over time, but by mechanisms other than natural selection. A very brief overview of how these principles contribute to evolution is presented below.

Our basic understanding of the *principles of inheritance* comes from the work of the Augustinian friar Gregor Mendel. Through his experiments on pea plants, he was able to work out several important concepts behind the transmission of traits from one generation to the next. Contrary to the popular view that inheritance involves a blending of traits received from each parent, Mendel reasoned that the inherited material must be some sort of particle, capable of being joined in various combinations to produce different outcomes. If this were not the case, if blending were really occurring, after many generations all members of a population would share the same blended traits. What happens instead is that an offspring receives a unit of inheritance from each parent, and those units are combined during sexual reproduction. But when the offspring later reproduces, those same units are uncombined and then recombined, thereby maintaining the diversity of the population. We now refer to these units of inheritance as genes. So, Mendel discovered the *particulate nature of inheritance*, a pretty amazing accomplishment for him to have achieved in the garden outside his rectory.

Mendel's work can be summarized by the three laws of inheritance he developed. *The Law of Segregation of Alternate Factors* shows that discrete factors (i.e., genes) are responsible for inherited traits; the genes are paired (but not blended), and they separate during reproduction and are recombined upon fertilization. The *Law of Independent Assortment* reflects the observation that the condition of one trait doesn't influence the occurrence of other traits; they are inherited independently. In his experiments, this meant the form of the seed coat on peas was transmitted independently of the color of the flower on the pea plant. For humans, this principle has enormous implications for our understanding of the meaning of race, as discussed in the next chapter. *The Law of Dominance* involves the discovery that alternate forms (*alleles*) of some genes exist that are expressed differently depending on the combination in which they occur. Some are *dominant* and will be expressed if they are received from at least one parent, while others are *recessive* and will be expressed only if they are received from both parents.

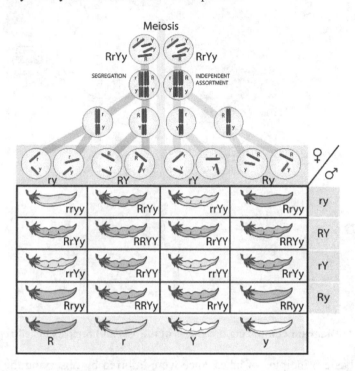

Figure 4.2: Diagram illustrating Mendel's Laws of Segregation and Independent Assortment in pea plants

The bottom portion of Figure 4.2 shows how Mendel's three laws of inheritance work together to maintain variability within populations of organisms. In this example, the pea plants produce either green or yellow pods that may be either wrinkled or smooth. The gene responsible for pod color is indicated by R and r (dominant and recessive alleles), and the gene for wrinkling is indicated by Y and y (Y = wrinkled and y = smooth). The recessive conditions, yellow pods or smooth pods occur only when an individual plant receives that form of the gene from both parents (rr and yy), the homozygous recessive condition. When the dominant allele is received from both parents (the homozygous dominant condition), the pods are green and wrinkled. Because green color and wrinkled pods are the dominant traits, when an individual receives a dominant allele from one parent and a recessive from the other (the heterozygous condition), the dominant trait will be expressed (Rr and Yy). Knowing which traits are dominant and recessive allows us to predict their occurrence in the population. In this case, we can see that 75% of the combinations result in wrinkled pods, and 75% are green pods. The most common phenotype (the outward expression of the genes) involving both traits is green, wrinkled pods (56%), and the rarest condition will be smooth, yellow pods (rryy), which account for only one-sixteenth (6.25%) of the population. Note that the two traits considered here, pod wrinkling and color, are not linked; wrinkled pods can be of either color, and vice versa. The traits are inherited independently.

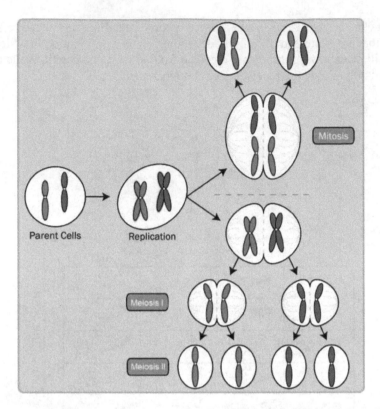

Figure 4.3: Diagram comparing the stages of mitosis and meiosis in cell replication

Although the basic principles of inheritance were inferred by observing the outcome of Mendel's careful breeding experiments, the mechanisms occurring at the molecular level to bring about cell division (and recombination) were identified by other researchers. *Cell division* was first observed under a microscope by Hugo von Mohl in 1835, but the process was first photographed in progress in 1943 by Kurt Michel, who used a phase-contrast microscope, which didn't require killing and staining the cells in order to see them. The sequence of changes observed during cell division are illustrated in Figure 4.3.

Organisms generate new cells all the time, through the process of cell division. Two different sorts of cells are made, somatic (body tissue) cells that are replaced as part of regular growth, and gametes or sex cells as part of reproduction (Matisoo-Smith and Horsburgh 2012, 26). Somatic cells are made by the process of *mitosis*, while sex cells are made by *meiosis*; the processes are similar but not identical. When body tissue cells divide during mitosis, the chromosomes in the nucleus undergo replication, producing a complete set of double-stranded chromosomes. In the next phase, the doubled chromosomes split and move apart, and the cell divides, producing two new cells with a complete set of identical chromosomes (Figure 4.3, top right). Meiosis starts out the same, with the replication of chromosomes. But instead of one cell division, meiosis involves two; the first produces two daughter cells with the full complement of chromosomes. The second meiotic division yields gametes (eggs and sperm) that contain only half of the chromosomes of the parent cell. When the gametes are combined during reproduction, the resulting zygote contains the complete number of chromosomes. In essence, cell division by meiosis shuffles the existing variation being carried in the parent cells, resulting in new combinations; each egg and sperm will contain different combinations of inherited genes, some of which might be useful to the organism as it adapts to changing local environments. Indeed, the maintenance of genetic variability is perhaps the primary biological benefit of sexual reproduction (as opposed to cloning).

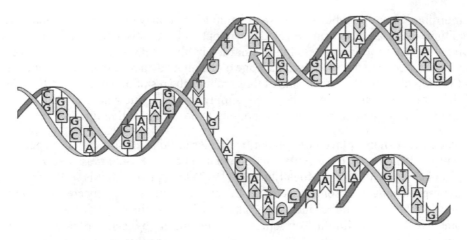

Figure 4.4: Pair bonds and DNA replication

Although mutations, the ultimate source of variation in populations of organisms, were discovered by Hugo de Vries in 1901, it was not until many years later that we learned how they occur. *Mutation* is a random, permanent change in the coding of the DNA base sequence. This understanding was predicated on the discovery of the structure and functioning of the DNA molecule by Francis Crick and James Watson in 1953 (Watson 1968). Chromosomes are made of DNA, molecules that carry the information necessary to build proteins. Proteins are composed of sequences of amino acids, the building blocks of which consist of four bases: ATCG, adenine, thymine, cytosine and guanine. In the DNA molecule, adenine always binds with thymine, and cytosine binds with guanine. During replication, the DNA molecule unzips, and each strand generates a copy of the missing, matching strand by linking up with the appropriate base retrieved from the cell cytoplasm. The unzipped molecule produces a mirror image of itself, an exact copy of the hereditary material to be passed to daughter cells (Figure 4.4). When a random error in coding of the base sequence happens during replication, the resulting protein can be altered either slightly or radically. When this occurs in a sex cell, the resulting offspring can have new and different biological traits. This process provides the variability which is acted upon by natural selection.

Random changes in the gene frequencies within populations may occur due to the accumulation of chance events of several different sorts. Collectively, these processes are referred to as *genetic drift*. One type of genetic drift is called *gamete sampling*. In sexual reproduction, there are an enormous number of possible combinations; regardless of which sperm fertilizes the egg, there will be a large number of potential combinations that are never realized. The effect on the gene frequencies of the ensuing generations is real, but it is not related to the adaptive fitness of the traits involved because it is produced at the time of fertilization, before natural selection has a chance to act upon the variation being expressed in an individual organism.

Another kind of genetic drift involving sampling at the population level (rather than at the cellular level) is called the *founder effect*. The founder effect occurs when a small portion of a population becomes isolated from the parent group and forms a new population. Because the founder group is so small relative to the original group, it usually will not have all of the genetic variability contained in the larger population. Therefore, natural selection will have different sets of variations upon which it can act, and if they remain isolated, the populations can diverge fairly quickly.

One final example of genetic drift is the effect of random events that result in differential mortality. In various parts of the country, efforts have been made to reintroduce or maintain native vegetation that has been lost due to farming or residential development. One of the ways this is done is to establish corridors for wildflowers and native grasses along highway easements. While this may be a good strategy for propagating native plants, it can produce problems for the animal species that are adapted to those habitats. Suppose there is a family of rabbits living among the wildflowers in the corridor along a highway in central

Illinois. One morning, when the rabbits awake and begin to feed, they go to the right and move up into the adjacent agricultural field, feeding on alfalfa all day without incident; it is a good day for all, except perhaps the farmer. On a different morning, the rabbits are startled by the sound of an approaching vehicle and they scatter. Some of them dodge to the left, reach the edge of the highway pavement and are run over by a farmer driving a Ford F150 pickup truck. Is the death of those rabbits the result of natural selection? Were they less well adapted than the other rabbits? No; they were simply unlucky. Their demise will certainly affect the genetic makeup of the next generation, but it has nothing to do with adaptive fitness.

An analogous scenario played out on a much larger scale could affect entire species or groups of species, especially if it involved large scale environmental change. *Punctuated equilibrium* is a concept developed by Stephen Jay Gould and Niles Eldridge (1977) to explain patterns in the fossil record which seem to indicate rapid changes in some species. In punctuated equilibrium, species are viewed as making only minor adjustments to the environment (via natural selection) for most of their history. These long periods of homeostasis or equilibria are sometimes punctuated by short periods of relatively rapid environmental change, requiring organisms to make relatively rapid adjustments that appear to leave limited evidence of transitional forms in the fossil record because the changes occur over a relative short time span. An example of this sort of change is the extinction of dinosaurs and the subsequent expansion of mammals. It is now widely accepted that the extinction of dinosaurs was the result of a meteor impact that altered the atmosphere for many years. As the dinosaurs became extinct, that opened up new ecological niches for the diminutive early mammals that had existed in their shadows up to that point. The mammals adapted relatively rapidly to the newly available niches, developing many new forms through the processes of natural selection and adaptive radiation. But did they outcompete the dinosaurs? No; the dinosaurs (except for the ones that evolved into birds and reptiles) were removed by a chance event.

To summarize, we can organize the various aspects of the modern synthesis of evolution by reference to four primary forces or processes of evolution: mutation, natural selection, genetic drift, and gene flow. Mutation, the random change in the DNA base sequence, is the source for new genetic variation within a species. New variation is constantly being generated, and it has nothing to do with what a species may or may not "need" to assist in their adaptation. It is just the mechanical process of coding errors occurring during cell replication. Natural selection acts upon the variation that already exists in a population, through the process of differential reproductive success. Traits that contribute to more successful reproduction will be transmitted to subsequent generations, thus becoming more common throughout the population. Individuals with beneficial or deleterious traits may be selected for or against, but they don't evolve; populations evolve.

Genetic drift refers to several sorts of chance events that can result in change in gene frequency over time. These include gamete selection, which occurs at the cellular level; random loss of individual organisms, at the individual level; and the founder effect, which involves populations (albeit usually small ones). Genetic drift usually increases the variation between populations, because the chance events that occur within one population are unlikely to be experienced the way by other populations. Gene flow, or the movement of genetic material from one population to another, generally has the opposite effect. When members of one population migrate and interbreed with members of other populations, the exchange of genes decreases the differences between the populations.

Finally, a few words on how all these processes can lead to speciation, the development of new species. If two populations are isolated from each other, due to geographical, environmental, or behavioral barriers to mating, genetic drift will make the populations more genetically different. Mutations that occur in one population won't be passed to the other. If the two environments are slightly different, natural selection will favor different characteristics and result in different gene frequencies for those traits. If the isolation lasts long enough, speciation will occur. This process is called *cladogenesis*, the splitting of one lineage into two or more lineages. Even if separate populations do not exist, evolution can still occur. A single species may change significantly over time while still remaining a single lineage. Parent populations and much later descendant populations may look very different and be given different species names.

Examples of this sort of pattern are evident in the evolution of modern horses and modern bison from their prehistoric ancestors. This process of evolution within a lineage is called *anagenesis*.

Now let's consider a few examples of recent or ongoing evolution, including some cases in which evolution can be observed within a human lifetime.

Examples of Evolution at Work

Bacterial Resistance to Antibiotics

It should be of great interest to the general public that many of the wonderful innovations in medicine and agriculture are derived from biological research based on evolutionary theory (Thorp 2006). Some of our greatest medical challenges are also evolutionary issues. Natural selection explains why we are once again at risk from diseases we thought had been defeated decades ago. Bacteria that cause pneumonia, dysentery, meningitis, ear infections, gonorrhea, and tuberculosis are becoming resistant to antibiotics (Consumer Reports 1995, 492). That is, the bacteria are evolving by means of natural selection. A drug can cure an illness (relieve our symptoms) without killing all the bacteria. The bacteria that survive are the ones most resistant to the drug, and when they reproduce, the next generation of bacteria will share the drug resistance. Because they reproduce so quickly, in a matter of hours, the drug resistance can evolve in a few days or a week. Many bacterial diseases that we thought were defeated years ago have returned and are now immune to all but a few antibiotics (Neu 1992).

Rapid Evolution in Darwin's Finches

Researchers continue to study Darwin's finches on the Galapagos Islands, the species that inspired Darwin's formulation of natural selection more than 180 years ago. Beginning in 1972 and continuing to the present, biologists Peter and Rosemary Grant have observed some 20 generations of finches, identifying each individual and tracking their breeding behavior and reproductive success and documenting changes in body size and beak form (Weiner 1995). They have documented changes in body size and beak shape in response to variation in rainfall and changes in the kinds of foods that are available in wet vs. dry years. In some cases, natural selection has produced changes in these traits, and resulted in reproductive isolation in as few as three generations, or two to three years (Lamichhaney et al. 2018).

A short video illustrating the nature of the Grants' research activities may be viewed at https://www.hhmi.org/biointeractive/the-origin-of-species-the-beak-of-the-finch.

Rapid Evolution in Fish Populations

In part because of the importance of seafood to the American diet, and also because of the increasing demands of water use by a growing population in a period of climate change, there has been quite a bit of research conducted on evolution among various fish populations in North America. Researchers have identified several different triggers of evolutionary change in fish populations, and some of those changes have been surprisingly rapid. Four examples will be summarized here.

Although climate change denial is still fashionable in Washington, D.C., the scientific reality of it has been settled for many years. One of the ways in which climate change affects fish behavior is by its effect on the timing of fish migration and spawning. In a recent University of Alaska study (Kovach et al. 2012), it was reported that climate change has selected for pink salmon that migrate upriver earlier, spawning before river water temperatures reach their increasingly warmer summer peak. A DNA marker inserted in late-migrating fish in the 1970s had nearly disappeared by 1993. In other words, the late-migrating fish have become increasingly unsuccessful, thus removing that genetic marker from the population and increasing the percentage of early-migrating fish. It has also been discovered that some runs of pink salmon are now migrating from their natal streams to the sea two weeks earlier, a change that has occurred over the past 40 years.

The Understanding Evolution website (https://evolution.berkeley.edu) features some of the research conducted by David Conover of Stony Brook University.

Conover notes that most fishing regulations restrict harvests to fish above a certain size. In commercial fishing, the size requirement is implemented by the use of nets with appropriately sized mesh. Normally, in nature, larger fish would be favored by natural selection, as they produce more eggs than smaller fish. But commercial fishing, with its focus on larger fish, has shifted the advantage to the smaller fish that can escape the commercial nets. Over the past few decades, many fisheries have been overfished to the extent that the harvest is 80 to 90 percent of the target populations. Under such intense selective pressure, the overall size of the fish harvested has declined by 30 percent over the past 40 years. Harvesting the largest fish has selected for not only fish that are smaller, but also fish that grow more slowly, reach sexual maturity more quickly, and are smaller at maturity. Selecting for smaller body size (by harvesting larger fish) also results in the production of fewer eggs, smaller eggs, and smaller larvae with higher levels of mortality. All of these trends contribute to a loss of genetic variability and make it more difficult for overfished populations to recover. Even if the decision were made to discontinue harvesting, the genes for producing the larger fish may now be much reduced or even absent in many of today's populations.

Speciation may occur when organisms exposed to different circumstances become reproductively isolated because of their adaptation to the different conditions. Many of the widely recognized trout species evolved because ancestral populations were split by natural processes such as avalanches that separated different sections of streams or lakes, by portions of rivers drying up after the last ice age, by the buildup of ice dams, etc. Some biologists have been studying how quickly reproductive isolation can occur, and the results are surprising.

In one study in northern California, a riverine population of rainbow trout was compared to the ancestral stock of anadromous steelhead trout (those that mature in the ocean but return to the river for spawning) from lower elevations in the same river. The origin of the riverine population was already documented; it was known that some of the steelhead had been transplanted upstream above several waterfall barriers by humans 70 years ago. When some members of the riverine population were reintroduced below the barriers, they maintained their reproductive isolation; hybridization has been limited. After being separated for only 70 years, the populations were not only behaviorally separated, but also genetically distinct (Pearse et al. 2009).

In another study at Lake Washington near Seattle, researchers documented the split of a single population into two varieties of Sockeye salmon within the same watershed, even in the absence of physical barriers. The parent population of Sockeye was introduced into Lake Washington between 1937 and 1945, and it grew into a self-sustaining population that spawned in Cedar Creek, a tributary of the lake. In 1957, a new sockeye population was documented in the lake, breeding on a beach 7 kilometers north of Cedar Creek. Otoliths (ear bones) were used to identify the place of birth of salmon from both lineages, and it was determined that reproductive isolation has already occurred. Some of the beach breeders are immigrants from the river spawners, but the beach breeders don't spawn in the river. Furthermore, the body sizes and proportions of both sexes of salmon have diverged in response to the different demands of breeding in the disparate microenvironments, such as heavier currents in the stream vs. calmer on the beach and challenges of moving silt while building redds (spawning beds) in the river, which is unnecessary on the beach. So, over a period of 57 years or less, there is already evidence of reproductive isolation evolving (Hendry et al. 2000).

Recent Evolution in Humans

You may be surprised to learn that humans are still undergoing biological evolution and that some of the characteristics observed among modern humans developed relatively recently. Here we will consider four such traits starting with *skin color*. The earliest modern humans appeared in East Africa about 160,000 to 200,000 years ago, and because they evolved in the tropics, it is likely that they had dark-colored skin. Indigenous populations living near the Equator generally have darker skin because the higher levels of melanin provide protection against excessive exposure to UV radiation (Figure 4.5). Darker skin is an advantage because it helps reduce the likelihood of getting skin cancer. Excessive ultraviolet (UV) radiation can also break down folic acid, which is required for normal embryo development and sperm production, so darker skin is related to greater reproductive success in equatorial regions (Feder and Park 2007, 345.) However, UV radiation is also needed for vitamin D production, and in higher latitudes where UV radiation is less intense, dark skin hinders the body's ability to make vitamin D. So, populations who left Africa and adapted to northern latitudes eventually evolved lighter skin to assist in vitamin D production (Anemone 2011, 99–102). Recent DNA studies of Cheddar Man and other Mesolithic skeletons in Europe suggests that light skin didn't evolve in Europe until about 10,000 years ago, much more recently than had been previously thought (Brace et al. 2018). In response to the gradual change in UV radiation at different latitudes, skin color varies gradually across the landscape as well. This sort of gradual change in the distribution of a trait is called *clinal variation* (Figure 4.5).

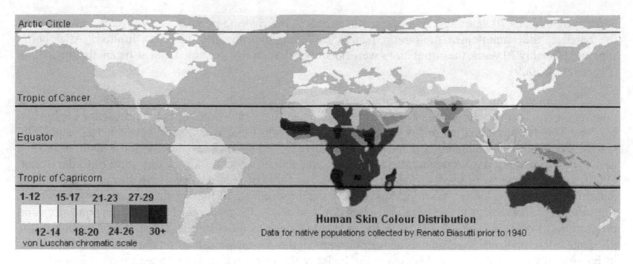

Arctic Circle

Tropic of Cancer

Equator

Tropic of Capricorn

1-12 15-17 21-23 27-29

12-14 18-20 24-26 30+
von Luschan chromatic scale

Human Skin Colour Distribution
Data for native populations collected by Renato Biasutti prior to 1940

Figure 4.5: Clinal distribution of skin color in relation to latitude

Modern humans have also evolved in response to living at high altitudes, where levels of atmospheric oxygen are lower, resulting in a condition called *hypoxia* (Anemone 2011, 111–114). Some populations, such as Tibetans, have developed a biological response that counters the effects of hypoxia. They have genes that cause them to produce fewer red blood cells, thus reducing the likelihood that their blood will thicken and clot at high altitude. They also have genes for higher oxygen saturation in their hemoglobin, a trait that facilitates the body's access to oxygen even when they have thinner blood with fewer red blood cells (Larsen 2017, 151). Thicker blood is linked to slow fetal growth and high rates of fetal mortality, so the ability to obtain more oxygen from thinner blood results in women having more surviving offspring. This is a clear example of natural selection (Beall et al. 2010), and it seems to have occurred very recently. Genetic research on Tibetan populations suggests they split off from related Chinese populations and moved into the Himalaya highlands less than 3,000 years ago. This suggests that their genetic adaptation to high altitude evolved in about 100 generations, one of the most rapid cases of evolution documented in humans (Yi et al. 2010).

Some of you probably experience the discomforts associated with *lactose intolerance*. The rest of you may have been fortunate enough to inherit a trait called *lactase persistence*. Lactose is the main carbohydrate found in mother's milk, and when consumed by young mammals, it is broken down in the digestive system by the enzyme lactase. After weaning, most mammals no longer have access to milk, and the intestines stop producing lactase. This is the ancestral mammal condition, and it is characteristic of humans as well. However, in a few parts of the world, such as northern Africa, the Middle East, and northern Europe, humans became increasingly dependent on the production of livestock and the consumption of milk products. Under these conditions, it became advantageous to continue to consume milk after weaning, and when a mutation occurred that caused lactase persistence, the continued production of lactase into adulthood, that mutation was favored by natural selection. Today, people whose ancestry comes from those regions and populations where dairy products were commonly consumed now have high levels of tolerance for lactose. This is a good example of biocultural evolution, in which human behavior (such as dietary and lifestyle choices) and natural selection acted in combination to produce the observed changes (Anemone 2011, 135). DNA research on Neolithic skeletal remains suggests that lactose tolerant populations evolved in Europe in the past 7,000 years (Burger et al. 2007).

You may be surprised to learn that the Dutch are the tallest people in the world. Dutch men are the tallest in the world, averaging 6 feet (ft) tall, and Dutch women are the second tallest in the world at 5 ft 6 inches (in.) tall. In comparison, the average heights in the United States are 5 ft 9 in. for men and 5 ft 3 in. for women. According to family friends and archaeological colleagues living in the Netherlands, the tall average height of their fellow citizens is a fairly recent phenomenon which has developed in only the past 150 years, during which time the average height of Dutch men has increased by almost 8 in. (20 centimeters).

Researchers have now confirmed this observation, and it seems that natural selection is at least partially responsible (Stulp et al. 2015, NCD Risk Factor Collaboration 2016). There are probably several factors involved, including excellent health care, good nutrition, and sanitation, but these things don't account for the magnitude and rapidity of the change in average height over such a short time period. Natural selection is probably at work, through a mechanism called *sexual selection*. That is, Dutch men and women often choose to marry and mate with tall people, thus increasing the likelihood that their children will be tall.

Additionally, taller women in the Netherlands are having more children than shorter women, an indication of differential reproductive success, or the very definition of natural selection. So, despite our heavy reliance on modern technology that mediates humanity's interactions with nature in these modern times, humans are still evolving. Of course, we are not becoming a new species, so the sorts of changes mentioned here are examples of microevolution at work.

References and Further Reading

Allendorf, Fred W., and Jeffrey J. Hard. 2009. "Human-Induced Evolution Caused by Unnatural Selection Through Harvest of Wild Animals." *PNAS* 106, no. 1 (June 16, 2009): 9987–94.

Anemone, Robert L. 2011. *Race and Human Diversity: A Biocultural Approach*. Boston: Prentice Hall.

Beall, Cynthia M., Gianpiero L. Cavalleri, Libin Deng, Robert C. Elston, Yang Gao, Jo Knight, Chaohua Li, Jiang Chuan Li, Yu Liang, Mark McCormack, Hugh E. Montgomery, Hao Pan, Peter A. Robbins, Kevin V. Shianna, Siu Cheung Tam, Ngodrop Tsering, Krishna R. Veeramah, Wei Wang, Puchung Wangdui, Michael E. Weale, Yaomin Xu, Zhe Xu, Ling Yang, M. Justin Zaman, Changqing Zeng, Li Zhang, Xianglong Zhang, Pingcuo Zhaxi, and Yong Tang Zheng. 2010. "Natural Selection on *EPAS1 (HIF2a)* Associated with Low Hemoglobin Concentration in Tibetan Highlanders." *PNAS* 107, no. 25 (June 7, 2010): 11459–64. https://doi.org/10.1073/pnas.1002443107.

Botanical Society of America. 2003. "Botanical Society of America's Statement on Evolution." *Skeptical Inquirer* (July/August): 12–4.

Brace, Selina, Yoan Diekmann, Thomas J. Booth, Zuzana Faltyskova, Nadin Rohland, Swapan Mallick, Matthew Ferry, Megan Michel, Jonas Oppenheimer, Nasreen Broomandkhoshbacht, Kristin Stewardson, Susan Walsh, Manfred Kayser, Rick Schulting, Oliver E. Craig, Alison Sheridan, Mike Parker Pearson, Chris Stringer, David Reich, Mark G. Thomas, and Ian Barnes. 2018. "Population Replacement in Early Neolithic Britain." BioRxiv.org. February 18, 2018. https://doi.org/10.1101/267443.

Burger, J., M. Kirchner, B. Bramanti, W. Haak, and M. G. Thomas. 2007. "Absence of the lactase-persistence-associated allele in early Neolithic Europeans." *PNAS* 104, no. 10 (March 6, 2007): 3736–41. https://doi.org/10.1073/pnas.0607187104.

Consumer Reports. 1995. "Antibiotics: How to Use Them Wisely." *Consumer Reports* (July): 492–93.

Darwin, Charles. 1859. *On the Origin of Species by Means of Natural Selection, or, The Preservation of Favored Races in the Struggle for Life*. London: John Murray.

Dawkins, Richard. 2004. *The Ancestor's Tale: A Pilgrimage to the Dawn of Evolution*. Boston: Mariner Books, Houghton Mifflin.

Feder, Kenneth L. and Michael Alan Park. 2007. *Human Antiquity, An Introduction to Physical Anthropology and Archaeology*, 5th edition,: 345. Boston: McGraw-Hill.

Gould, Stephan Jay. 1977. *Ever Since Darwin: Reflections in Natural History*. New York: W. W. Norton & Co.

Gould, Stephan Jay, and Niles Eldredge. 1977. "Punctuated Equilibria: The Tempo and Mode of Evolution Reconsidered." *Paleobiology* 3 (Spring 1977): 115–51.

Hendry, Andrew P., John K. Wenburg, Paul Bentzen, Eric C. Volk, and Thomas P. Quinn. 2000. "Rapid Evolution of Reproductive Isolation in the Wild: Evidence from Introduced Salmon." *Science* 290, no. 5491 (October 20, 2000): 516–18. https://doi.org/10.1126/science.290.5491.516.

Kovach, Ryan P., Anthony J. Gharrett, and David A. Tallmon. 2012. "Genetic Change for Earlier Migration Timing in a Pink Salmon Population." *Proceedings of the Royal Society B: Biological Sciences* 279, no. 1743 (September 22, 2012): 3870–78. https://doi.org /10.1098/rspb.2012.1158.

Lamichhaney, Sangeet, Fan Han, Matthew T. Webster, Leif Andersson, B. Rosemary Grant, and Peter R. Grant. 2018. "Rapid Hybrid Speciation in Darwin's Finches." *Science* 359, no. 6372 (January 12, 2018): 224–28. https://doi.org/10.1126/science.aao4593.

Larsen, Clark Spencer. 2017. *Our Origins: Discovering Physical Anthropology.* New York: W. W. Norton & Co.

Majerus, M. E. N. 1998. *Melanism: Evolution in Action. Oxford, UK:* Oxford University Press.

Matisoo-Smith, Elizabeth, and K. Ann Horsburgh. 2012. *DNA for Archaeologists.* Walnut Creek, CA: Left Coast Press.

NCD Risk Factor Collaboration. 2016. "A Century of Trends in Adult Human Height." *Epidemiology and Global Health,* July 26, 2016. https://doi.org/10.7554/eLife.13410.

Neu, Harold C. 1992. "The Crisis in Antibiotic Resistance." *Science* 257 no. 5073 (August 21, 1992): 1064–73.

National Academy of Sciences. 2008. *Science, Evolution and Creationism*. Washington, DC: National Academies Press.

Pearse, Devon E., Sean A. Hayes, Morgan H. Bond, Chad V. Hanson, Eric C. Anderson, R. Bruce Macfarlane, and John Carlos Garza. 2009. "Over the Falls? Rapid Evolution of Ecotypic Differentiation in Steelhead/Rainbow Trout (*Oncorhynchus mykiss*)." *Journal of Heredity* 100, no. 5 (September-October 2009): 515–25. https://doi.org/10.1093/jhered/esp040.

Stulp, Gert, Louise Barrett, Felix C. Tropf, and Melinda Mills. 2015. "Does Natural Selection Favour Taller Stature among the Tallest People on the Earth?" *Proceedings of the Royal Society B* 282, no. 1806: 20150211. DOI:10.1098/rspb.20150122

Thorp, Holden. 2006. "Evolution's Bottom Line." *New York Times,* May 12, 2006. https://www.nytimes.com/2006/05/12/opinion/12Thorpe.html.

University of California Museum of Paleontology. 2004. Understanding Evolution." https://evolution.berkeley.edu.

Walton, Olivia C., and Martin Stevens. 2018. "Avian Vision Models and Field Experiments Determine the Survival Value of Peppered Moth Camouflage." *Communications Biology 1, no. 118*. DOI: 10.1038/s42003-018-0126-3DOI: 10.1038/s42003-018-0126-3.

Watson, James D. 1968. *The Double Helix.* New York: Athenaeum.

Wiener, Jonathan. 1995. *The Beak of the Finch: A Story of Evolution in Our Time.* New York: Vintage Press.

Wilson, David Sloan. 2007. *Evolution for Everyone: How Darwin's Theory Can Change the Way We Think about Our Lives.* New York: Random House.

Yi, Xin, Yu Liang, Emilia Huerta-Sanchez, Xin Jin, Zha Xi Ping Cuo, John E. Pool, Xun Xu, et al. 2010. "Sequencing of 50 Human Exomes Reveals Adaptation to High Altitude." *Science* 329, no. 5987 (July 2, 2010): 75–8. https://doi.org/10.1126/science.1190371.

Chapter 5: Race: Humanity's Most Dangerous Myth

The Only Human Race: Le Tour de France

Most people in the United States have been raised to believe that races are actual biological subdivisions of the human species and that racial differences are real. And even though we know it is widely considered politically incorrect to do so, many among us regularly judge people on the basis of their skin color. African Americans are often harassed—and worse, the harassment can be for driving their own cars, entering their own homes, and napping in their own college dorms. Mexican Americans, Native Americans, and Muslim Americans have been detained simply because their mere presence made a white person nervous or afraid. We are in a period of backlash against affirmative action. Calls for securing our borders (actually, mainly the southern one) against immigration are on the increase. Much of this country's past has involved racial thinking and the stereotyping of individuals according to their appearance, and such behavior is still surprisingly common today. Consider the following example.

On August 3, 2019, the residents of El Paso, Texas, were shocked and saddened by the senseless tragedy of a mass shooting at a Walmart store adjacent to Cielo Vista Mall in the eastern part of town. The shooting was the deadliest attack on Hispanics in recent US history, killing 23 people and injuring 23 more. A white male shooter confessed to driving more than 600 miles from the Dallas area with the specific intent to seek out and kill Mexicans. According to a racist manifesto attributed to the shooter, the attack was planned as a response to the Hispanic "invasion of Texas." It's as if we've taken several giant steps backward, to the times before the civil rights movement or back to the lawless days of the old western frontier.

It might be tempting to think that racial stereotypes and the hatred they spawn contain some kernels of truth that could explain some people's desire to act on their racial hatred, but there is no biological justification for such attitudes. The more we learn about the nature of variability within the human species, the clearer it is that race does a poor job of characterizing that variability. For generations we have used race as an excuse to discriminate against those who are perceived as being different or competing for assets of one sort or another. But it is important to know that there is simply no biological basis for such discrimination.

Q&A: How many human races are there?

There is only one human race: Le Tour de France. In other words, there are no human races.

There are no biological races in humans; there is just one species, without subspecies, in which we all share something like 99 percent of the total variation. The variation within the human species that many people refer to as race is actually known to anthropologists as *ethnicity*. Ethnicity is a culturally constructed identity, not a biological characteristic, as race would be if that term were used precisely.

If races were real biological phenomena, what would they actually be? In biological terms, *if races were to exist, they would represent subspecies*. In other words, they would each represent a large cluster of populations diagnosed as distinct from other such clusters, although still capable of interbreeding. Such natural divisions of the human species do not exist, and this fact has been recognized for a long time, perhaps as far back as 1865 (Marks 1995, 106–107). People who engage in racial classification and/or stereotyping are often making several kinds of errors from among those discussed below.

Figure 5.1: Where would we draw the line? This image represents the range of skin tones among some well-known people who identify as African American. It illustrates the arbitrariness of boundaries between human populations based on skin color.

Common Misconceptions about Race

Leonard Lieberman (2004) refers to race as a *syndrome*, in the sense of a set of symptoms that characterize a disease. He argues that referring to race as a concept would bestow on it an apparently precise definition and perpetuate the mistaken belief that race is a scientific fact. It is not. Instead, the race syndrome is comprised of a series of dysfunctional and invalid ideas, many of which were refuted 100 years ago. Lieberman (2004) provides this list of ten commonly held but mistaken beliefs about race. The mistakes are shown in red, followed by the addition of brief comments about why they are wrong.

1. **There are a few major biological divisions of *Homo sapiens.*** The many attempts to classify humans into a few groups have failed because variation within the species is continuous throughout populations, and one trait doesn't determine the others. Choosing a different trait (other than skin color) results in entirely different groupings.

2. **Each population is separated by identifiable boundaries.** Biological traits show clinal variation: gradual change in frequency across the landscape. Therefore, geographical boundaries between so-called races are largely arbitrary.

3. **Each population is genetically homogeneous.** There is more genetic variation within each of the so-called races than there is between them (Anemone 2011, 6).

4. **Cultural behavior is determined by genes.** Cultural behavior is learned, not inherited.

5. **Racial differences are the result of independent evolution.** Different populations of humans have not been isolated long enough to undergo independent evolution.

6. **Cultural behavior of the races varies in a hierarchy from superior to inferior.** All modern humans have the same basic capabilities; behavioral differences are largely a matter of different adaptations, not innate superiority or inferiority.

7. **The culture of a race is unchanging because it is biologically based.** Culture can and does change—and relatively quickly, too—because it is learned, not inherited. For example, how else would anyone know how to operate a computer, or any other new technology that wasn't available to our grandparents, if culture didn't change? Additionally, the groupings that some consider to be "races" also change over time because they are culturally and socially defined, not biologically real (Gannett 2004, 341).

8. **Inferior races will become extinct.** Although cultures can become extinct, most of the biological makeup of any group is shared with other populations.

9. **Offspring of two different races results in disharmonic body and inferior behavior.** Humans have been highly mobile and good at "interbreeding" for a long time, perhaps as long as we've been a species. The more we study individuals' DNA, the more apparent it is that we are all "mixed" to some degree. Such mixture is good for the species, as it maintains variability.

10. **Racial differences justify discrimination.** The most important differences among humans do not correspond to skin color, cannot be used to define races, and do not justify discrimination.

Ten Things to Know about Race

More recent attempts to define races actually involve abstractions based on behavioral traits assumed to represent socially defined groups. There are several reasons why the idea of biological race is incorrect, but before discussing them, let's consider another list, "Ten Things Everyone Should Know about Race" (PBS 2003):

1. Race is a modern idea. Ancient societies certainly practiced discrimination, but they did so according to traits such as class and religion. The term doesn't even enter the English language until 1508; therefore, it seems silly to argue that the idea reflects ancient natural divisions of the species.

2. Race has no genetic basis. Not one characteristic, trait, or gene distinguishes all the members of one so-called race from the members of another race (Anemone 2011, 77).

3. Human subspecies don't exist. Modern humans haven't been around long enough or isolated enough to have evolved into separate subspecies or races. We are one of the most similar, most homogeneous of all species.

4. Skin color really is only skin deep. Most traits are inherited independently from one another. The genes influencing skin color are not linked to the genes influencing eye form, hair color, blood type, musical talent, etc.

5. Most variation is within, not between "races." Of the small total amount of variation among humans, about 85 to 90 percent exists within any of the three major continental populations (Jorde and Wooding 2004).

6. **Slavery predates race.** Due to a unique set of historical circumstances, the system of slavery developed in the United States was the first in which all the slaves shared similar physical traits. The existence of a "Black" slave class did not reflect the natural existence of such a race or the inferior traits attributed to it. These ideas were constructed by those in power.

7. **Race and freedom evolved together.** The United States was founded on the idea that "all men are created equal," but our early economy was based on slavery. The new idea of "race" helped justify why some people could be denied the rights and freedoms enjoyed by others.

8. **Race justified social inequalities as natural.** This is not to say that such a view is actually justifiable, but as the idea of race became widely accepted in the United States, so did the notion of White superiority, which in turn was used to justify Manifest Destiny, including the genocide of Native Americans, the taking of land from Mexico, and the passage of anti-immigration laws based on race.

9. **Race isn't biological, but racism is still real.** Race is a powerful social idea that gives people differential access to opportunities and resources. Our social institutions have created advantages that disproportionately channel wealth, power, and resources to white people.

10. **Colorblindness will not end racism.** To combat racism, we need to identify and remedy social policies and practices that advantage some groups at the expense of others.

The Lack of Biological Races in Humans

There are several kinds of arguments that can be made to demonstrate that race is not biologically valid. Several of these points of discussion derive directly from a basic understanding of the principles of genetics, as discussed in the preceding chapter. Others have to do with the way perceptual biases can affect the design of research and with the influence of the environment on behavior that has been mistakenly identified as biologically determined. Students are encouraged to access the Understanding Race webpage on the American Anthropological Association's (AAA) website for an engaging presentation of the history of the concept of race and articles about how continued acceptance of the idea of race affects members of the general public. A useful entry point into the website information might be taking the quiz on race in sports or reading about the Lived Experiences of race.

Understanding Race

www.understandingrace.org/index.html

In examining the problems inherent in the concept of biological race, let's recall one of Gregor Mendel's most important contributions to our modern understanding of evolution, the *law of independent assortment*. This principle acknowledges the fact that most physical traits are inherited independently. That is, one trait is usually not linked to another, so skin color doesn't determine any other trait within an individual. This is a powerful idea, for it directly undermines what would be the common-sense expectation about race. If there were such a thing as real biological races, they should reflect clusters of traits, recognizable as different from other groups. That this simply doesn't happen, because of the effects of a well-known principle of genetics, is an exceedingly strong argument against race. Choosing a different trait besides skin color to define races would yield entirely different groupings and boundaries from the ones we have been led to believe are real. This alone is reason enough to reject race, but there are other kinds of evidence that lead to the same conclusion.

We know that physical variation in any given trait tends to occur gradually across the landscape. It is not possible to draw lines around different populations that delineate the presence or absence of certain traits, because different groups share most traits to greater or lesser degrees. The gradient in variation of traits is called a cline, and each separate trait has a different pattern of clinal variation (because the occurrence of one trait doesn't determine the occurrence of another). The *clinal variation* of a trait is often the result of adaptation to local environments via natural selection. The distribution of the sickle cell condition of hemoglobin is an adaptive response to the endemic distribution of malaria. As we saw in Chapter 4, the distribution of skin color by latitude is an adaptation to the amount of ultraviolet (UV) radiation at different latitudes. Any line we draw around a geographically defined population will be arbitrary, and the populations so defined will share most of the same traits, but in different percentages, in response to the different regional environments to which they are adapted.

Another example of clinal distribution resulting from natural selection is provided by the occurrence of the sickle cell trait in humans. The sickle cell trait is a genetic blood disorder that causes malformation of the hemoglobin cells in the blood. The abnormal cells are long, thin, and curved, like a crescent moon, making it more difficult for them to pass through the smaller blood vessels. The sickle cell trait affects approximately 1 to 3 million Americans, most of whom are African Americans, although it is also common among Hispanics. Because the trait is more common in African Americans, people sometimes believe that it is linked to skin color, or "race," but it is not.

When the gene for sickle cell, Hemoglobin S, is inherited from both parents, the offspring develop sickle cell disease which is potentially very debilitating. Symptoms may include anemia, organ damage, lung problems, bone damage, increased risk of stroke, and reduced lifespan (average life expectancy of 42 to 47 years; American Society of Hematology 2019). One would think that such a deleterious trait would have been quickly removed from the gene pool by natural selection. However, although individuals who are homozygous recessive for hemoglobin S face many physical difficulties, those who inherit the gene from just one parent (are heterozygous) are more resistant to the effects of malaria. In other words, the population as a whole benefits from having carriers of the sickle cell trait, despite the negative effects for those who develop sickle cell disease. The occurrence of the gene is not linked to or determined by skin color, but by the geographic regions where malaria is present (Figure 5.2).

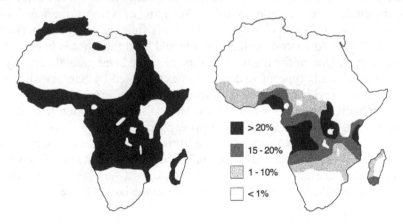

Figure 5.2: Distribution of malaria (left) and the sickle-cell trait (right) in Africa

We also know that humans have been highly mobile species for a very long time and that most groups are very effective at interbreeding with one another. In other words, humans have maintained a *high degree of gene flow* throughout the entire range of occupied lands. This means that we share most of our genetic diversity. In fact, biologist Richard Lewontin has calculated that there is more genetic variation within one so-called race than between that race and another. Only 6 percent of the genetic differences among humans can be correlated with their "racial" classification (Begley 1995, 67). This means that two Koreans selected at random may be as different genetically as a Korean and an Italian. It also means that any two "blacks" selected at random probably have fewer genes in common than one of them will with a randomly selected "white" person. The more we know about genetics, at the species and individual levels, the clearer it is that racial classification is flawed.

It is now possible to obtain information on our individual genetic background by submitting samples for DNA testing. Some of the results have been quite unexpected. Debra Anne Royer thought she had Middle Eastern or Southeast Asian traits, but her DNA indicates a Native American ancestry. Wayne Joseph has identified himself as black for his entire life; that identity has affected many important choices in his life, such as what college to attend and, whom to marry, etc. He has even written about being black for *Newsweek*, but he recently learned from his DNA test that he has no African blood at all. Catholic priest Father Bill Sanchez from northern New Mexico learned that he has genes linking him to the Jewish Cohan priesthood lineage and some members of the African Lemba tribe (Kalb 2006). Such findings provide strong evidence of extensive mobility and gene flow, processes that work against the development of biological races.

Q&A: What do IQ tests measure?

They don't measure innate intelligence. The scores reflect cultural literacy and a variety of environmental effects on test performance in addition to learned skills.

Failed Attempts to Quantify Differences among Races

Craniometry

A number of nineteenth-century researchers explored craniometry as a way to measure differences among so-called races, ultimately with the goal of demonstrating the inferiority of non-white groups. This was such an important goal in some circles (for example, to justify the taking of Native American lands) that the Army Surgeon General issued standing orders to the cavalry units fighting Native Americans in the western territories to decapitate Native Americans killed in battle and send their heads back to Washington, D.C., where they would be studied. One of the main traits to be measured was cranial capacity, or the volume of the brain cavity in the skull. This type of research was exemplified by Samuel Morton's (1839) *Crania Americana* and later works in which he attempted to document differences in brain size among Native Americans and between Native Americans and whites. Morton's work suffered from conscious bias, and it is also known that he fiddled with the numbers to fit his expectations. Nevertheless, his actual data showed no statistical difference between Native American and Euro-American cranial capacity. Other nineteenth-century researchers found similar results, and by the end of the century most scientists had moved on to other techniques in an effort to measure racial differences. One of the most persistent and damaging of such efforts has been the application of intelligence quotient (IQ) testing to the issue of race.

IQ Testing

French psychologist Alfred Binet pioneered the use of psychological methods to assess intelligence, after abandoning his own research on cranial size. In 1908 Binet developed a scale of mental age based on a series of everyday tasks graded by difficulty to abstract children's general potential. His purpose was to identify students whose lack of success in the classroom suggested the need for what we would today call special education. He declined to speculate on the meaning of the score, as he recognized that intelligence is too complex to be described with a single number. He advocated its use only for a limited practical purpose, to identify students with learning disabilities. Binet greatly feared the potential perversion of intelligence testing and cautioned against its general use for purposes for which it was not intended.

Binet died in 1911 and his cautions didn't receive the attention they deserved. In 1912, German psychologist W. Stern developed what we now know as the intelligence quotient. He divided the mental age from Binet's system by the chronological age of the test subject and multiplied by 100 to obtain the IQ score. This score has been used ever since, often with the assumptions that it actually measures a real trait called *intelligence* and that the score or level of intelligence is genetically determined. Both assumptions have proven to be grossly wrong, but not before enormous damage had been done by using test results to influence social policy in the United States.

IQ Testing and Social Policy

H. H. Goddard popularized the use of the Binet scale in the United States in the early twentieth century. During the teens and 1920s, he tested immigrants arriving at Ellis Island in New York City.

As Goddard described the scene, a fog hung over New York harbor that day and no immigrants could land. But one hundred were about ready to leave, when Goddard intervened:

> We picked out one young man whom we suspected was defective, and through the interpreter, [we] proceeded to give him the test. The boy tested 8 by the Binet scale. The interpreter said, 'I could not have done that when I came to this country,' and seemed to think the test unfair. We convinced him that the boy was defective (Gould 1981, 165).

Following this initial "success," Goddard applied his testing to larger numbers of immigrants. The results were astounding. After testing samples of immigrant Jews, Russians, Hungarians, and Italians, he found that between 79 and 87 percent of each population were scored as feebleminded. Even Goddard was surprised: "Could anyone be made to believe that four-fifths of any nation were morons?" (By this, he was referring to the fact that they scored less than 70 on the Binet scale.) These results should have been a red flag, an indication that something was wrong with the testing, but because the outcomes supported Goddard's prior beliefs, he convinced himself that the test was accurate. Perhaps his views would not have mattered much if they had languished in obscurity, but they did not. Goddard believed that morons (the term he coined for "high-grade mental defectives") should not be allowed to mate. He even suggested that they be confined or sterilized in order to prevent the production of more mental defectives in the United States. His views were influential in the passage of anti-immigration laws targeting those populations who scored low on the IQ tests, mainly people from Southern and Eastern Europe and Asia. One result of these laws was the expulsion from the United States of the Chinese laborers who built the railroad from California to El Paso. Another result was the turning away of many Jews fleeing the impending German holocaust when they attempted to immigrate to the United States. Perhaps most shocking of all, many US citizens were incarcerated because of their low scores on IQ tests.

A recent book by Michael D'Antonio (2005) explores the dark history of the eugenics movement in this country. Beginning in the 1920s, hundreds of thousands of American children were locked away in government institutions because they had been labeled feebleminded, idiots, or morons on the basis of their IQ scores. Mainly, they were just poor and uneducated. These children were housed in more than one hundred "schools" around the country, where they experienced physical, emotional, and sexual abuse but received little education. The system persisted until 1960, when the shameful practices were revealed to the public by the rebellion of residents at the Fernald School in Massachusetts. In 1994 it was revealed in Senate hearings that the residents of Fernald had been used as human guinea pigs. In the early 1950s, a group of boys were fed oatmeal with radioactive milk in a nutritional study for Quaker Oats. The boys were included in the study without their knowledge or consent, in clear violation of the Nuremberg Code, written only ten years earlier in response to Nazi war crimes, in which such experiments were determined to be unacceptable without the informed consent of the study subjects.

IQ Testing and Race

Robert Yerkes administered IQ tests to Army recruits during the first two decades of the twentieth century. His work was focused on the effort to document IQ differences between black and white recruits, and in one sense, he was successful. Yerkes documented a 10-to-15-point difference between the scores of whites and blacks. Other researchers have since replicated this disparity, but Yerkes didn't really explore the possible reasons for the difference. He was convinced that he already knew the reason: the intellectual inferiority of the black race. Yerkes's findings were influential in leading to the widespread use of IQ testing in the US educational system and using the results to deny African Americans and other people of color access to higher education.

Yet, because of his racial biases, Yerkes actually overlooked patterns in his own data that pointed to a different interpretation. The IQ scores of blacks from the northern United States were higher than those of southern whites. This indicates a significant degree of environmental influence on the scores, something that has been repeatedly demonstrated over the years (Gould 1981). Aside from the many methodological problems in Goddard's and Yerkes's work (detailed in Gould 1981), it has become very clear that like any other test, the IQ exam is culturally biased; to a large degree, it measures acculturation to and success within mainstream US society. Follow-up tests of immigrants in New York City found that IQ scores increased by an average of 20 points after immigrants had been in the United States for seven to nine years. If the trait being measured were genetic, this could not happen. Orphans have shown up to a 35-point increase in IQ scores when they are relocated to positive, stable foster homes. Students in an Appalachian test case improved their scores by an average of 20 points after becoming familiar with the test (i.e., practicing).

I'm sure many of you have heard statements to the effect that IQ tests, and even other kinds of tests, are culturally biased. It may be fairly straightforward to imagine the difficulty we might have with a test involving knowledge we lack, such as repairing an internal combustion engine, building an aerodynamic wing, or explaining the actions of subatomic particles. How much more difficult would it be to pass an exam about an unfamiliar culture, in a different language, as Goddard's immigrant populations were expected to do? In order to get a sense of what he was expecting of them, try answering the questions on the test of Aboriginal knowledge on the next page. How did you do? Would it seem fair if your treatment by government officials, businesses, and fellow residents were determined by your score on this test?

Test of Aboriginal Australian Knowledge (Source Unknown)

These items relate to the culture of the Edward River Community in Far North Queensland, Australia.

1. What number comes next in the sequence: one, two, three, _____?

2. How many lunar months are there in a year?

3. Wallaby is to *animal* as *cigarette* is to _____.

4. Which three of the following items may be classified with saltwater crocodile?

    a. marine turtle; b. brolga; c. frill-necked lizard; d. black snake

5.   Which items may be classified with sugar?

    a. honey; b. witchetty grub; c. flour; d. water lilies

6.   We eat food, and we _____ water.

7.   Sam, Ben, and Harry are sitting together. Sam faces Ben, and Ben gives him a cigarette. Harry sits quietly with his back to both Ben and Sam and contributes nothing to the animated conversation going on between Sam and Ben. One of the men is Ben's brother; the other is Ben's sister's child. Who is the nephew?

    a. Sam; b. Harry; c. Ben

8.   Suppose your brother, while in his mid-forties, dies unexpectedly. Would you attribute his death to:

    a. God; b. fate; c. germs; d. no one; e. someone; f. your brother himself

9.   You are out in the bush with your wife and young children, and you are all hungry. You have a rifle and bullets. You see three animals all within range: a young emu, a large kangaroo, and a small female wallaby. Which should you shoot for food?

    a. young emu; b. large kangaroo; c. small female wallaby

10. Why should you be careful of your cousins?

See the next page for answers.

Answer Sheet

1. One, two, three, *many*. The *kuuk thaayorre* counting system goes only to three: *thana, kuthir, pinalam*, and then *mong*; *mong* is best translated as "many," which can mean any number between four and ten. Larger numbers would be *yurr mong*, or "very many."

2. *Thirteen* would be correct in European terms, but not in Edward River terms. The speakers of *kuuk thaayorre* recognize lunar menstruation and believe that the lunar month is calculated as the time between one phase of the moon and the next appearance of that phase. However, they have no precise word for 13, so the correct answer would be *yurr mong*, or "very many." The year is identified by natural environmental cycles rather than fixed divisions of time. Thus, the year is the time between the onset of one wet season and the beginning of the next wet season, and as wet seasons can be early or late, who can be precise?

3. The correct answer is *tree*. This stems from the *kuuk thaayorre* speakers' early experience with tobacco, which was stick tobacco, therefore classified with *tree*.

4. Crocodiles, turtles, birds, and frill-necked lizards are all classified as *minh* (animals). Snakes and eels are classified as *yak*, which may be translated as "snakelike creatures."

5. All the items are classified with sugar and belong to the class known as *may*, or vegetable food. Even witchetty grubs that are found in the roots of trees are in this category, as is honey, which is found in trees and therefore associated with fruit. Flour fits into the category because it resembles processed native plant foods (such as yams).

6. *Eat* is the correct answer. *Kuuk thaayorre* speakers use the same word for eating and drinking.

7. An avoidance taboo operates between mother's brother and sister's son, and politeness requires that sister's son should never directly face mother's brother or talk to him directly when in the company of others. Sam and Ben are obviously brothers because they conversed openly, while Harry showed respect by turning his back to both uncles.

8. Among *kuuk thaayorre* speakers, God has been equated with a mythological character who is not malevolent. Fate and germs are foreign concepts in the *kuuk thaayorre* belief system. No one dies without a reason, and suicide is unknown in their society, so the correct answer is "someone," a person who has practiced sorcery.

9. *Small female wallaby* is the correct answer. Emu is a food that may be eaten only by very old people. Large kangaroos may not be eaten by parents or their children. If this taboo is broken, everyone knows the children will get sick.

10. Because some of your cousins need to be avoided. For example, a male must avoid his father's sister's daughter or anyone classified with her. Such relations are called *poison cousins* in Aboriginal English.

So, what does an IQ score measure? It measures literacy and performance in the white-oriented public school system. It measures past exposure to and acceptance of the concepts and motivations appropriate to testing situations. It is influenced by familiarity with test taking, the subjects' understanding that tests are important, and their motivation to do as well as possible on all such tests.

Ironically, some of the most motivated students today, who rank among the highest according to IQ test scores, are students of Jewish and Asian descent, the very groups that were discriminated against in the past on the basis of low IQ scores. If intelligence were a real, simple, genetically transmitted entity, this could not be so. It has been estimated that about 20 to 60 percent of the variation in IQ scores can be attributed to environmental factors, especially during the first 15 years of life, when growth is most rapid, or when socially disadvantaged populations are being measured. Also, there is no single entity called *intelligence* that is measured by the IQ test. The exam doesn't test for divergent thinking, three-dimensional spatial skills, or creativity in the arts or music. I know someone whose high school counselor suggested she not attend college because her IQ score wasn't high enough. Yet, she received a bachelor's degree from the top finance school in the country and went on to earn a master's degree in public administration. Fortunately, she didn't listen to that misinformed counselor; everyone should be cautious about how IQ testing results are interpreted. It is especially important to understand the nature and sources of variability in the scores before using them as a basis for social policy-making decisions.

Reification of Race in Science

It is widely understood and accepted by scientists in a variety of disciplines that biological races do not exist in humans (Gannett 2004, 323; Anemone 2011, 4). Nevertheless, there are some researchers, especially in biomedicine and forensic sciences, who still seem to treat their research populations as if they are races, even if inadvertently (Soo-Jin et al. 2001, 54). The use of racial groups for medical testing or the attribution of forensic evidence to particular racial groups are examples of the fallacy of misplaced concreteness, or the *fallacy of reification*, described long ago by Alfred Whitehead (1929, 11). Reification in this context refers to the tendency to assume that categories developed or perceived by researchers actually conform to biological realities in the natural world. It is intuitively appealing and easy to conclude that if we can measure differences between two or more groups of people, such as so-called "races, then the groups and the separation among them must be real. In biomedical research, this sort of expectation constitutes circular reasoning; study groups are defined with the expectation that there will be differences between them, then researchers use statistics to find differences (Soo-Jin et al. 2001, 55).

There are several other methodological problems with the use of such groups as well. As Duster (2005) has noted, studies of human genetic diversity often involve comparisons among a relatively small number of individuals thought to be representative of the various "racial" groups being compared. The groups of individuals chosen to represent different regions are often chosen because of the convenience and accessibility of samples from existing databases and repositories (Duster 2005, 1050). It is inappropriate to assume that the sampled individuals are representative of the genetic diversity within their respective so-called races. It is also important to recognize that the samples may not have any relationship to an actual geographically or socially defined breeding population (Duster 2005, 1051; Gannett 2004, 340). Therefore, it would be inappropriate to characterize the entire population (i.e., so-called racial group) on the basis of the database samples.

The DNA Identification Act of 1994 called for the linkage of various DNA data banks from around the country, and the Combined DNA Index System (CODIS) was launched in 1998. The system includes DNA profiles for different racial groups that are used to estimate the probability of racial matches with forensic evidence. There is more genetic variability within the groups than between the means of different groups, but separate databases have been developed for four racial or ethnic populations: Caucasian-American, African American, Hispanic American, and Asian American. The statistical groupings essentially define "races" by attributing biological parameters to what are actually socially defined groups (Gannett 2004, 340–41), not actual, real biological populations.

Office of Management and Budget (OMB) racial categories are also used in the context of the US census, but those categories are not fixed biological categories either; they are socially defined categories that have changed over time. During the twentieth century, the US census has used 26 different classifications to describe racial identity (Soo-Jin et al. 2001, 43). Some of the changes to the system were so drastic that ethnic groups that at one time were considered non-white (such as Ashkenazi Jews) are now counted as white. The OMB categories also don't account for those individuals who identify with more than one racial or ethnic group. In the 2010 census, those people amounted to 2.9 percent of the population, or more than 9 million people (US Census 2012). In sum, researchers who caution against reification of race argue that the use of race wrongly imposes putative biological boundaries onto continuous patterns of variation among people. Duster (2005, 2052) goes so far as to suggest that population genetics studies should include a caveat stating that genetic differences between groups of humans should not be assumed to reflect racial categories.

Race in Sports

One other application of racial thinking deserves mention here—the widespread notion that athletes of African descent dominate the world of sports. This is, of course, another common misconception, one that is essentially no more than popular mythology or folklore. But let's consider it for a moment. Do African athletes dominate sports? It might be tempting to say yes, but it would be wrong. Do African athletes dominate baseball, tennis, swimming, cycling, gymnastics, soccer, golf, skiing, ice skating, or the martial arts? No, they don't. Students may be interested in following the link to the AAA's webpage section entitled "White Men Can't Jump and Other Assumptions about Sports and Race." How many of the answers did you know?

Exhibition—RACE: Are We So Different?

www.understandingrace.org/lived/sports/index.html

Many people, including some well-known, influential public figures, harbor the belief that black athletes' performances in sports are related to physical prowess inherited by virtue of being of African descent. This was certainly the underlying belief reflected in Howard Cosell's comment during a 1983 broadcast of *Monday Night Football*: "Look at that little monkey run!" Cosell made this comment in reference to Washington Redskins receiver Alvin Garrett (Wiley 2003). Others seem to believe that African Americans are better at sports because physical strength was bred into them during their slave ancestry. Jimmy "The Greek" Snyder is infamous for his 1988 comments to this effect, alleging that blacks "jump higher and run faster" because of their "high thighs and big size" (Shermer 2000, 44). Another variant of this line of argument is Rush Limbaugh's 2003 insinuation that black quarterbacks are good athletes but lack the intelligence to run complicated National Football League offenses (Wiley 2003). Fortunately, the racist comments of these on-air personalities led to their firing from television sports coverage.

But why are such views so common that anyone would feel justified in stating them in public? Even some African American athletes have bought into the racial determinism implicit in this argument. The answer is the logical fallacy known as *confirmation bias*. Confirmation bias is the tendency to seek evidence that supports our preconceived beliefs and ignore evidence that would contradict those beliefs. So, one might use Michael Jordan's success in basketball to support the contention that "white men can't jump," while forgetting that white high jumper Dwight Stone held the American and world records. And before him, the world record was held for ten years by "white" Russian high jumper Valeri Brumel. As noted on the Understanding Race website, there are some biological traits that seem to influence certain aspects of athletic success at the most elite levels, but those patterns are more nuanced than a simple correlation with skin color. Michael Shermer has some thoughts about why we often tend to overlook the nuances.

> Yes, there are black-white differences in sports, and there may even be good physical reasons for some of these differences. But . . . the vast majority of sports are not dominated by blacks. Why don't we hear about them? Because they don't interest us, or they do not support our preconceived notions about the importance of black-white race questions. Out of literally hundreds of popular sports played in the world today, blacks dominate only three: basketball, football, and track-and-field. . . . Why do we focus on those three? Because we live in America where the black-white issue has bedeviled our experiment in democracy from the beginning, and where basketball, football, and track-and-field are the big sports which pay the big bucks (Shermer 2000, 48).

It is now widely understood that performance in sports, like many types of human behavior, is conditioned by both genetics and environmental factors. It is true that black athletes dominate the sprinting events in track-and-field. There is no physical reason why they shouldn't also dominate speed skating and cycling, given that the training in those sports is similar to that for the sprints. Yet, they do not, and the reason is almost certainly cultural. Skating, swimming, cycling, tennis, golf, hockey, and skiing , etc. have traditionally been, in the United States at least, "country club" sports, or those that require special facilities and which provide limited access at the junior level, especially for working- class and inner-city athletes. At the elite levels, individual coaching is also critical, creating further financial challenges to prospective athletes. These cultural or environmental influences are a big part of why these sports are not dominated by black athletes.

It may surprise you to learn that African Americans didn't always dominate basketball. In the 1920s, 1930s, and 1940s, Jews dominated the professional ranks of the sport. Basketball was an inner-city, blue-collar immigrant game dominated by Jews, the oppressed ethnic group of the time, who went into professions and joined sports open to them. Thinking about it today, we should recognize that social models of success, discrimination, and financial barriers can best explain Jewish dominance of the sport, but that's not what the sports writers of that era thought. They came up with all sorts of explanations for why Jews were so good in basketball:

> It was suggested that they had an advantage because short men have better balance and more foot speed. They were also thought to have sharper eyes, which of course cut against the other stereotype that they suffered from myopia and had to wear glasses. And it was said they were clever. "The reason, I suspect, that basketball appeals to the Hebrew . . ." wrote Paul Gallico, sports editor of the *New York Daily News* and one of the premier sports writers of the 1930s, "is that the game places a premium on an alert, scheming mind, flashy trickiness, artful dodging and general smart aleckness" (Entine, cited in Shermer 2000, 47).

This type of statement is an example of another logical fallacy called *hindsight bias*. However things turn out, we tend to look back and justify the present circumstances as somehow predicted or justified by our perception of the past, of the sequence of events leading up to the present. Thus it was that sports writers could allege that Jews were especially suited to dominate the sport of basketball. Evolution didn't shape African American bodies for success in modern-day basketball, just as it didn't shape Jewish bodies for dominance of 1930s basketball. The realities that led to each group attaining excellence in the sport are largely cultural.

Now, as you may have noticed on the AAA webpage sports quiz, there are some patterns of sports dominance that may be real and may be partly genetic, such as African American dominance of sprint events in track and Kenyan dominance of long-distance events. However, even in these instances, it would be inaccurate to say that runners of African descent dominate. There are possible regional patterns that are obscured by generalizing African athletic success to the entire continent of Africa. For example, Jon Entine (2000, 33) reports that Kenya produces more top distance runners than any other country. Moreover, the

Nandi District of Kenya has the highest *per capita* number of top runners in the world, more than seven times higher than the next highest region of Kenya and twenty times higher than most of the rest of Africa. What could account for such a pattern?

Well, the university where I work has a very good track team, often ranked in the top ten in the nation. I regularly have track athletes enrolled in my classes, many of whom are very good students. A few years ago, one of my students was a scholarship athlete and a distance runner from Kenya. When I was discussing race in sports, he raised his hand and asked if I wanted him to explain to the class why his people dominate the distance running events. "Yes, by all means," I replied. My student told the class this: "In my village, we run ten miles to school in the morning, we run while at school during team practice, and then we run home ten miles after school. We do this every day, at high altitude. We know that success in running is the way for us to leave the village and get a good education." Is there athletic ability involved? Certainly. Are there significant environmental and cultural factors at work too? Absolutely.

To summarize, in genetic terms, all humans, regardless of their place of origin or ethnicity are more than 99.9 percent the same, largely because of our common ancestry. Indeed, genetics researcher Svante Pääbo has noted that all humans are Africans, either residing there or recently exiled from there (Gannett 2004, 325). Nevertheless, scientists do not claim that humans are all the same or that there are no biological differences among humans. What most anthropologists would say is that so-called racial categories do not accurately represent the variation that we know about, nor do they explain that variation.

Again, let us make clear what we are *not* saying. We are not saying that biological differences among human groups do not exist or that racial differences are insignificant. Differences among human groups do indeed exist, but they do not sort the species into a small number of biologically fairly discrete groups. And racial differences are very significant, though not biologically. The question is whether the categories we set up to recognize those differences adequately reflect the biological patterns—or whether they are categories of a different kind. We acknowledge differences among human groups as socially defined and symbolically marked categories, but it is very unclear what underlying biology those categories represent.

. . . It is the discreteness of these racial categories, in defiance of the biology of the people who are being classified that makes racial categories fundamentally non-biological. They are social constructs (Marks 1995, 112).

There is more variation within the so-called races than between them, because of processes such as natural selection, gene flow, high levels of mobility, and the fact of our common ancestry. Boundaries between the "races" are arbitrary because we know that human traits occur as clinal distributions across the landscape. Such distributional patterning is a result of adaptation and mobility, and there are different clinal patterns for each trait. Why? Mendel's Law of Independent Assortment tells us that skin color is not linked to any other trait, nor does it determine any other traits. People at lower latitudes have darker skin than those in northern latitudes. This fact is the result of natural selection; darker skin provides protection from UV radiation in the equatorial regions, while lighter skin at higher latitudes assists the body in producing Vitamin D. Efforts to quantify differences between so-called racial groups have failed because traits such as IQ are affected by a variety of environmental factors. The very definition, boundaries, and membership of the so-called races are social constructs, not biological realities. When we see differences among human populations, we are not seeing race; it is simply variation (Moses 2008, 101).

References and Further Reading

American Anthropological Association. 1998. "AAA Statement on Race." www.aaanet.org/stmts/racepp.htm.

American Anthropological Association. 2007. *"Race: Are We So Different?"* www.understandingrace.org/.

American Society of Hematology. 2019. Clinical Practice Guidelines on Sickle Cell Disease. www.hematology.org/education/clinicians/guidelines-and-quality-care/clinical-practice-guidelines/sickle-cell-disease-guidelines

Anemone, Robert L. 2011. *Race and Human Diversity: A Biocultural Approach.* Upper Saddle River, NJ: Pearson.

Begley, Sharon. 1995. "Three is Not Enough: Surprising New Lessons from the Controversial Science of Race." *Newsweek*, February 13, 1995, 67–9.

D'Antonio, Michael. 2005. *The State Boys Rebellion.* New York: Simon & Schuster.

Duster, Troy. 2005. "Race and Reification in Science." *Science* 307, no. 5712 (February 18, 2005): 1050–51.

Entine, Jon. 2000. "Breaking the Taboo: Why Black Athletes Dominate Sports and Why We're No Longer So Afraid to Talk about It." *Skeptic* 8, no. 1: 29–35.

Gannett, Lisa. 2004. "The Biological Reification of Race." *British Journal for the Philosophy of Science* 55: 323–45.

Gould, Stephen Jay. 1981. *The Mismeasure of Man.* New York: W. W. Norton & Company.

Jorde, Lynn B., and Stephen P. Wooding. 2004. "Genetic Variation, Classification, and 'Race.'" *Nature Genetics* 36 (suppl. 1: S28–S33.

Kalb, Claudia. 2006. "In Our Blood." *Newsweek*, February 6, 2006, 47–55.

Lieberman, Leonard. 2004. "The Race Syndrome," in *Anthropology Newsletter* no. 45 (December 2004).

Marks, Jonathan. 1995. *Human Biodiversity: Genes, Race, and History.* New York: Aldine De Gruyter.

Marks, Jonathan. 2008. "Race: Past, Present and Future." In *Revisiting Race in a Genomic Age,* edited by Barbara A. Koenig, Sandra Soo-Jin Lee, and Sarah S. Richardson, 21–38. New Brunswick, NJ: Rutgers University Press.

Montague, Ashley. 1942; 1998. *Man's Most Dangerous Myth: The Fallacy of Race.* 6th ed. Lanham, MD: AltaMira Press.

Moses, Yolanda. 2008. "Thinking Anthropologically about 'Race:' Human Variation, Cultural Construction, and Dispelling Myths." In *Thinking Anthropologically: A Practical Guide for Students,* edited by Philip Carl Salzman and Patricia C. Rice, 94–105. Upper Saddle River, NJ: Prentice Hall.

PBS. 2003. *Race: The Power of an Illusion.* Three-part documentary series produced by California Newsreel. Additional interactive resources are provided on the companion website. www.pbs.org/race/000_General/000_00-Home.htm.

Shermer, Michael. 2000. "Blood, Sweat, and Fears: Why Some Black Athletes Dominate Some Sports and What It Really Means." *Skeptic* 8, no. 1: 44–50.

Soo-Jin Lee, Sandra, Joanna Mountain, and Barbara A. Koenig. 2001. "The Meanings of 'Race' in the New Genomics: Implications for Health Disparities Research." *Yale Journal of Health Policy, Law and Ethics,* 14, no. 44 (May 24, 2001): 33–76.

United States Census. 2012. "The Two or More Races Population: 2010." www.census.gov/prod/cen2010/briefs/c2010br-13.pdf.

Whitehead, Alfred N. 1929. *Process and Reality*. New York: Harper.Wiley, Ed III. 2003. "Rush Limbaugh Brings Racism to ESPN/NFL." Black Entertainment Television, September 30, 2003.

Chapter 6: Nonhuman Primates

Why Anthropologists Study Nonhuman Primates

Although the discipline of anthropology is about the study of humans, some anthropologists conduct research on nonhuman primates, including both living species and their prehistoric ancestors. This research deals mainly with the evolutionary relationships reflected in the anatomy, adaptation, and behaviors of different species of primates and the implications those details have for understanding early human ancestors. In other words, anthropologists try to distinguish human ancestral forms from nonhuman ancestral forms. If I allege, as I did in Chapter 1, that humans share an ancestry with apes, what would constitute the evidence for such a statement? If the shared ancestry claim is true, we should expect to find some ancestral fossil forms that are transitional, that share both apelike and humanlike traits. But how can we know what traits or conditions are transitional if we haven't examined the details of ape and human anatomy and behavior? This is one of the main reasons we study primates—to facilitate detailed comparisons with human ancestors.

Q&A: Is warfare a uniquely human behavior?

No. Gang warfare has been documented among wild chimpanzees in the Gombe National Park in Tanzania.

Comparative anatomy is studied to identify which structural traits evolved first, under what conditions, and which came later as part of new adaptations. Researchers also try to determine which structures are shared because of a common evolutionary source (*homology*) and which similarities are the results of similar functions (*analogy*). Because most of this sort of information comes from the fossil record, the evolutionary trees or taxonomies presented throughout your textbook are based mostly on patterns of shared skeletal traits.

Like anatomy, behavioral comparisons can also be used to identify those behaviors that are shared due to close evolutionary relationships and those that reflect specific adaptations. The goal is to determine which behaviors (e.g., group size, mating patterns) were advantageous in certain circumstances. Even more importantly, if we can identify which behaviors (if any) are uniquely human and which are shared with other primates, we may be able to suggest behaviors that would also be shared by our ancient human ancestors. If so, that would allow us to flesh out the evolutionary framework presented by the fossil evidence.

Figure 6.1: Portrait of a female Western Lowland Gorilla (*Gorilla gorilla*) caught in what seems to be a pensive moment; Taken at Brookfield Zoo, Chicago

During your work on this unit, you should gain a basic understanding of what it means to be a primate, in terms of anatomy and behavior. You should learn and be able to discuss the range of complex behaviors, once thought to be uniquely human, that have now been documented in our nearest primate relatives. Finally, you should develop an awareness of the threats to the survival of nonhuman primates in the wild and some of the ethical issues related to the use of captive primates in medical research.

Conservation Efforts

The primates initially evolved in tropical forest environments, and nearly all living primates are adapted to and live in equatorial forest areas, with the exception of a few species, such as Japanese and Barbary macaques, in Japan and Gibraltar, respectively (Figure 6.2). Unfortunately for nonhuman primates, tropical forests are among the most heavily pressured environments in the world, and deforestation, habitat loss, and development are endangering most species of nonhuman primates. Our nearest relatives among the primates are the species collectively known as the *greater apes*, including the common chimpanzee, bonobo chimpanzee, gorilla, and orangutan. All of these species are severely endangered in the wild, and their continued survival is in grave doubt due to the effects of hunting, deforestation, human warfare, and capture for sale to animal traffickers. Three of the species have been relatively well studied in the wild over the past several decades, most famously by Jane Goodall, Dian Fossey, and Biruté Mary Galdikas. As part of their efforts to study these animals and educate the world about their behavior and the threats to their survival, international foundations have been established to communicate the results of the activities undertaken on their behalf.

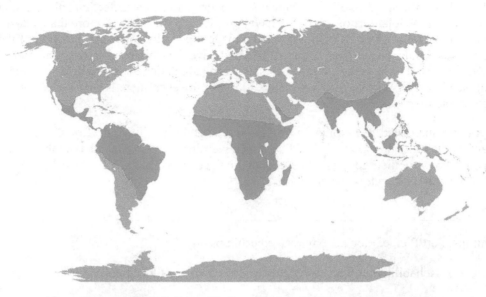

Figure 6.2: Global distribution of living nonhuman primates

Please visit the websites for the following foundations and browse the materials posted there. You should pay special attention to the photographs and videos that show the animals in the wild and the discussions of the current threats to their survival, including the two gorilla video clips by Anderson Cooper.

- Jane Goodall Institute, which supports wildlife research, education, and conservation (www.janegoodall.org)

- Dian Fossey Gorilla Fund International (www.gorillafund.org)

- Orangutan Foundation International, Biruté Mary Galdikas, president (www.orangutan.org)

Many students find the information on our primate relatives to be the most interesting, endearing, and compelling aspect of the class. The more one learns about the complexity of primate behavior, the harder it is to think of them as merely animals; certainly, it is difficult to think of them as lab animals. The similarities of their behaviors and abilities to those of humans are in some ways so striking that we can be confident they are thinking beings. From that perspective, it is difficult to justify the poor treatment that captive primates have often received. Anthropologists generally do not condone biomedical experimentation on primates, especially the great apes; indeed, many anthropologists advocate for the rescue and rehabilitation of primates held in captivity for medical research.

Many of the monkeys and chimps in this country were obtained for military or medical research, either by capturing them in the wild as infants (and killing the adults of their social group in the process) or by breeding in captivity. Many have been held in filthy, cramped cages or cells while being purposely infected with diseases (such as hepatitis and HIV) and subjected to various toxicology experiments. In many cases, little or no effort was made to address their psychosocial well-being. In response, a number of groups have been formed to advocate on behalf of captive primates, rescue them from the laboratory when possible, and rehabilitate them for restoration into a healthier environment.

Holloman Air Force Base in southern New Mexico used to house one of the largest primate colonies in the country. Between 1980 and 1993, the facility was operated by New Mexico State University, but after hosting a well-publicized visit from Jane Goodall during which she voiced her concerns about the animals' welfare, the university divested itself of the lab, and the animals were transferred to the Coulston Foundation in Alamogordo, New Mexico. By the late 1990s, the foundation's facility held more than 600 chimps and hundreds of monkeys, the subjects of toxicology research, drug trials, and infectious disease studies. After being cited for repeated violations of the Animal Welfare Act and the death of more than a dozen animals, the Coulston Foundation transferred many of the chimps to other labs under the direction of the National Institutes of Health. Coulston went bankrupt in 2002, and Save the Chimps purchased the property and the remaining 266 animals. The Save the Chimps foundation is rehabilitating the animals for eventual transfer to their tropical, seminatural sanctuary in Fort Pierce, Florida. However, there is still a need for assistance at the Alamogordo facility.

If you are interested in helping any of the rescue and rehabilitation efforts, you could start by contacting any of the following groups. In addition, their websites provide many details about the conditions primates face in captivity, their general poor treatment in the context of medical research, and stories about some of the rescues and laboratory closures.

Save the Chimps, Fort Pierce, Florida: www.savethechimps.org

Wildlife Rescue & Rehabilitation, Inc., San Antonio, Texas: www.wildlife-rescue.org

Project R&R: Release and Restitution for Chimpanzees in US Laboratories: www.releasechimps.org/labs/labs-closed/the-coulston-foundation

---

What Is a Primate?

Primates can be defined as mammals that are (or whose ancestors were) adapted to life in the trees. Their *arboreal adaptation* is reflected in a set of anatomical traits that is unique among mammals. These traits are detailed below. In addition, primates are omnivores, and their dentition is adapted to consuming a variety of different types of foods, a condition called *dietary plasticity*. Finally, primates have few offspring but invest a great deal of parental effort to see their offspring through to adulthood (Larsen 2017, 169). In many species of primates, *parental investment* is assisted by complex group social structures and social behavior.

The species classified as primates are grouped together because they share a whole series of anatomical traits relating to their present or former arboreal adaptation (Figure 6.3). These traits or evolutionary trends occur in all the species because they share an ancient evolutionary history—that is, the traits were inherited from ancient common ancestors. Although the primate evolutionary trends are interrelated, it is convenient to discuss them according to anatomy (postcranial, dentition, skull) and behavior patterns. Let's consider each of these four aspects of the primate adaptation in turn.

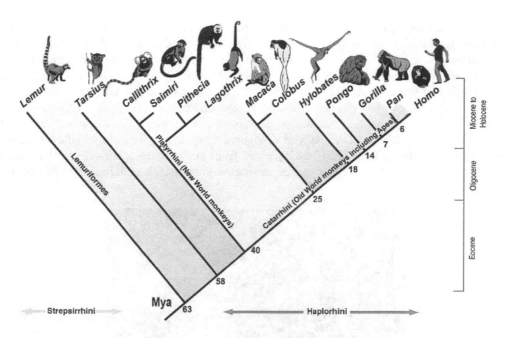

Figure 6.3: Taxonomic diagram of the major subdivisions of primates

The *postcranial skeleton* (trunk and limbs) of primates retains characteristics that are understood to have evolved in the context of living in the trees. The trunk is erect, and the placement of the *foramen magnum* (where the spine enters the skull) is more centrally located than is the case on other mammals. Primates have retained the ancestral mammal condition of five digits on the hands and feet, but the claws have been replaced (with a few partial exceptions) by fingernails and the development of soft, padded fingertips. The hands are thus prehensile, capable of grasping in a way that is different from and more precise than other mammals. In most of the primate species, the feet are prehensile as well. The other main feature is the retention of a clavicle, essentially a floating shoulder joint. As some of you may already know, the clavicle (or collar bone) is prone to injury; it is not the strongest or most stable joint. Why should it be that way?

Figure 6.4: Juvenile orangutan brachiating in trees

It is a compromise, involving the evolution of the ancestral mammal joint into a new configuration to accommodate *brachiation*: moving, or locomoting by hanging and swinging from the arms in the trees, as demonstrated by this juvenile orangutan (Figure 6.4). Notice how both the feet and hands are prehensile, allowing the orangutan to climb or stay suspended in the tree while grasping twigs and leaves with the left foot. The positioning of the torso and the mobility of the shoulder joint allow primates to reach above the head in ways that other mammals cannot, allowing brachiators to suspend their weight by the arms and swing through the forest canopy. This adaptation is perhaps best developed in the lesser ape species, such as siamangs and gibbons, which have evolved elongated arms to facilitate brachiation (Figure 6.5). In humans, the shoulder mobility and flexibility inherited from our primate ancestors are what allows us to throw a ball, use a tennis racket, or do gymnastics; most other mammals do not have that degree of shoulder flexibility.

Figure 6.5: Gibbon family group showing male offspring at lower left. Note the long length of the forelimbs in comparison to the legs, especially clearly visible on the light-colored female individual.

The *dentition* of the primates is similar because they are indicative of a generalized, omnivorous dietary capability. Although the specific number of each kind of teeth varies in different parts of the world, all primates have four different kinds of teeth: molars, premolars, canines, and incisors. Rather than being specialized for tearing flesh like a lion or shearing grass like a cow, primate dentition is generalized, accommodating a wider variety of food types.

Figure 6.6: Common marmoset (*Callithrix jacchus*), Showing distinctive facial markings, reduced nose, and forward placement of the eyes

The skulls of primates reflect *reorganization of the brain* and senses, a shift away from the ancestral mammal condition. The nose is shorter, in keeping with a reduction in the importance of the sense of smell. Instead, primates have an increased emphasis on vision. The eyes are on the front of the skull (rather than the sides), resulting in overlapping fields of vision (Figure 6.6). This means primates have binocular, stereoscopic vision, providing depth perception, a trait important to a successful arboreal adaptation. Primates also have color vision, which most mammals do not. It is understood that color vision plays a role in the food search, the identification of group members, mating, and other sorts of visual communication. Many nonhuman primates, such as the mandrill baboon (Figure 6.7), colobus monkeys (Figure 6.8), and the François' langur (Figure 6.9), have bold color patterns in facial hair or skin colors to facilitate visual communication by focusing attention on the face and its expressions. In other species, distinctive facial features serve the same function, such as the prominent noses of the proboscis monkey (Figure 6.10). All these sensory changes are reflected in the brain as well. Compared to most other mammals, the brains of primates are more complex, and the areas associated with sensory functions are expanded.

Figure 6.7 Mandrill baboon (*Mandrillis sphinx*), Chicago Zoological Park (Brookfield Zoo). The vivid coloration makes the face very distinctive.

Figure 6.8: Black and white colobus monkey (*Colobus guereza*), aka Mantled guereza, Seattle Zoo. Note the mask-like facial markings.

Figure 6.9: François' langur (*Trachypithecus francoisi*), closeup view of facial markings

Figure 6.10: Proboscis Monkey (*Nasalis larvatus*), showing the prominent nose for which it is named

The fourth aspect of the primate evolutionary trends involves a set of *behavioral traits* common among primates. Primates experience a prolonged period of gestation and a relatively long life span. Offspring have a prolonged period of infant dependency, and there is a greater investment, by mothers and other group members, in rearing and teaching offspring than is the case for most mammals (Figures 6.11 and 6.12). This greater investment in raising offspring is accompanied by a decrease in the number of offspring borne by a given female; the primates don't have litters, as many mammals do. Primate social groups are more complex than those of many other animals, and there is a tendency toward group permanence; even males often maintain permanent associations with their natal group (Figure 6.13). Because group interactions and social structures are complex, there is a greater emphasis on learned behavior. Recent research has shown that some of these behaviors are quite remarkable.

Figure 6.11: Proboscis monkey female with young

Figure 6.12: Female Western Lowland gorilla and juvenile in a reassuring embrace, Brookfield Zoo, Chicago

Figure 6.13: Small group of Hamadrayas baboons (*Papio hamadryas*), Serengeti National Park, Tanzania

Types of Primates

The broadest subdivisions within the primate order are the suborders *Strepsirrhini* and *Haplorhini* (see Figure 6.3). The species classified as *Strepsirrhini* are sometimes referred to as the *lower primates*, but that doesn't mean they are inferior or less interesting. Rather, the designation refers to their wet nose (rhinarium), an earlier-evolved, ancestral condition shared with non-primates and primate ancestors such as tree shrews (Figure 6.14). The strepsirrhines include lemurs, galagos, pottos, lorises, and aye-ayes. Most are arboreal, and they generally have smaller brains than members of the other suborder, the *Haplorhini*. The haplorhines are identified by their dry noses, and most are classified as higher primates. The suborder includes the tarsiers and simians (New World and Old World monkeys and the apes).

The primates can be further organized into four broad categories: prosimians, New World Monkeys, Old World monkeys, and apes (including humans). The prosimians were the earliest of the primates to evolve, and they are generally understood to have evolved from earlier arboreal mammals resembling modern-day tree shrews. Tree shrews bear some outward resemblance to squirrels, with their long tails, claws on the digits of the hands and feet, eyes on the sides of the head, and an elongated wet rhinarium (Figure 6.14). The earliest primates are represented today by lemurs, galagos, and tarsiers. They share most primate characteristics but retain a few ancestral traits as well, such as the rhinarium (hairless wet nose) and a well-developed sense of smell (Larsen 2017, 182). The prosimians are usually small, mostly arboreal, and about half the species are nocturnal. Their hands are prehensile, but some have claws on some digits and their fingers move together rather than being individually opposable with the thumb (Feder and Park 2007, 119). Some species, such as the ringtail lemur (Figure 6.15) have a prominent snout, but they and the other prosimians, such as tarsiers (Figure 6.16) and bush babies (Figure 6.17), exhibit forward-facing eyes and the loss of claws.

Figure 6.14: Tree Shrew, a model of the mammalian ancestor of early primates. Note the prominent nose, side-facing eyes, and claws on digits.

Figure 6.15: Ring-tailed lemur (*Lemur catta*), Seattle Zoo. Note distinctive facial and tail markings that are used for visual communication.

Figure 6.16: Tarsier (*Carlito sp.*). Note forward-facing eyes, reduced snout, and loss of claws.

Figure 6.17: Bush baby (*Galago sp.*) Showing forward-facing eyes, loss of claws, and large eyes and ears that are part of its nocturnal adaptation

New World monkeys are so named because they occur only in the western hemisphere. They have several characteristics that distinguish them from Old World monkeys and the apes. Their taxonomic name, *Platyrrhini*, refers to the shape of their noses; they are flat with widely spaced nostrils, as modeled by a golden lion tamarin (Figure 6.18). New World monkeys also have more teeth than their Old World counterparts, with 12 premolars instead of six. Perhaps the best-known distinguishing trait, however, is related to their locomotive pattern. Some species (especially those best well known to the public) have evolved prehensile tails that act like a fifth limb to help them move through the forest canopy. Examples of New World monkeys include marmosets, howler monkeys (Figure 6.19), and spider monkeys (Figure 6.20).

Figure 6.18: Golden lion tamarin (*Leontopithecus rosalia*)

Figure 6.19: Red howler monkey (*Alouatta puruensis*), Tambopata Park, Peru

Figure 6.20: Black-headed spider monkey (*Ateles fusciceps*) using prehensile tail to grasp tree limb

Old World monkeys are in the superfamily *Cercopithecoidea*. They have noses shaped like all the Old World primates, including our own. Most species have tails, but they are not prehensile. Males tend to be significantly larger than the females, a condition known as *sexual dimorphism*. They are more widespread across different environments than the New World monkeys; some macaque species are adapted to the desert region in northwest Africa and cold snowy regions in northern Japan (Figure 6.21). While many species maintain an arboreal adaptation, some groups, such as the macaques and baboons, live mainly on the ground. Those that do generally have larger social groups, apparently for protection from predators. Among the Hamadryas baboons, sexual dimorphism is expressed by the larger body size of the mature males, who protect the social group. Figure 6.22 shows a typical male agonistic display, which serves as a warning to rivals and/or predators.

Figure 6.21: Group of Japanese macaques, aka snow monkeys (*Macaca fuscata*) warming in the hot springs at Jigokudani Monkey Park, Nagano, Japan. The females of the group develop a social hierarchy in which dominant females prevent lower ranking females from accessing the springs, thereby reducing their reproductive success.

Figure 6.22: Hamadryas baboon male exhibiting an agonistic display involving piloerection (hair standing up), the baring of his large canines, and the whites of the eyelids displayed

The superfamily *Hominoidea* includes the apes and humans. It is commonly divided into two families, the *Hylobatidae,* or the lesser apes, and the *Hominidae,* including the greater apes and humans. The hylobatids include the gibbons and siamangs, species who are arguably the gymnasts of the nonhuman primate world. Although all the primates have some characteristics related to an arboreal evolutionary history, both these species are specialized brachiators; they move through the trees while swinging from their elongated arms, grasping with their elongated fingers. They are adapted to life in the upper canopy of the tropical rainforests of Southeast Asia and live in small family groups characterized by pair bonding, a social pattern that is rare among nonhuman primates.

Figure 6.23: Male Bornean orangutan (*Pongo pygmaeus*) at Brookfield Zoo, Chicago

Aside from humans, the rest of the *Hominidae* are comprised of the *greater apes*, classified into the subfamilies *Ponginae* (orangutans; Figure 6.23), *Gorillinae* (gorillas; Figure 6.24), and the tribe *Panini* (chimpanzees and bonobos). By *greater apes*, we mean larger apes. Because of their size, they spend more time on the ground than do the lesser apes, and their locomotion pattern is different as a result. The greater apes walk on all fours using a technique called *knuckle-walking* in which much of the body weight is supported by the arms. But unlike the Old World monkeys who walk on their palms, in apes the hand is partially closed, and the weight is borne on the knuckles (Figure 6.25). The orangutans live in Southeast Asia, and the other greater apes are from Africa. Contrary to popular misconceptions, gorillas are vegetarians, and chimpanzees are largely vegetarian (but, see further discussion below). Like almost all of the nonhuman primates, their survival in the wild is threatened by habitat loss and by being hunted by humans.

Figure 6.24: Highland gorilla (*Gorilla beringei*) silverback male, Seattle Zoo

Figure 6.25: Common chimpanzee (*Pan troglodytes*) illustrating the opposable great toe typical of the apes, long arms, and the long, stiff metacarpals that facilitate their knuckle-walking form of locomotion

'Human' Behaviors Exhibited by Apes

When I was a beginning anthropology student, we were taught that there were a series of traits that clearly distinguish humans from the rest of the primates. The list included tool use, cooperative hunting, food sharing, complex social organization, warfare, self-awareness, bipedal locomotion, and language (Hockett and Ascher 1964; Simons1972). Language was widely considered to be an especially important human trait. Although it was recognized that other animals have communication systems, certain features of human language were considered unique to our species. These properties or design features of human language include displacement (the ability to talk about things that are not physically present); productivity (the ability to create new messages by combining existing signs); duality of patterning (meaningful words are made from meaningless parts); prevarication (ability to make false statements, to lie); reflexivity (ability to refer to one's self); and learnability (users of a language can speak to each other; Hockett and Altmann 1968).

As amazing as it may seem, over the past three or four decades, anthropologists have observed nearly all these behaviors and abilities in one or more species of great apes, either in the wild or in captivity. Only two traits are rare or nonexistent in apes. One of these is upright bipedal locomotion, but even that has been recently observed among orangutans. The other is spoken language. Clearly, none of the other primates can speak like humans, but a number of chimps and gorillas have been taught various forms of sign language and have been shown to possess the other (nonverbal) language capabilities that had been considered uniquely human. As a general statement, therefore, it would be fair to say that most of the abilities we used to consider unique to humans are actually shared to some degree by our nearest primate relatives. Therefore, it is reasonable to propose that our ancient common ancestors would have shared some of these traits as well.

Let's consider some of the evidence for the sorts of abilities that have been discovered through observations made in the wild and in the laboratory. Jane Goodall initiated one of the truly groundbreaking efforts in primate studies in 1960 in what is now the Gombe National Reserve in Tanzania (Goodall 1990). Dr. Goodall is world-famous because her long-term, up-close-and-personal approach to studying chimpanzees allowed her to record some remarkable behaviors never before observed in the wild. In fact, some were entirely unanticipated from nonhuman primates. She learned that chimps live in stable family groups in which the offspring know their mothers (but not fathers) and interact with them and siblings throughout their lifetimes. They have a dominance hierarchy based in part on size and aggressiveness, but at least one chimp (Mike) increased his social ranking by learning to intimidate the others by making noises by banging empty kerosene cans.

One of Goodall's most important early observations was that chimps learn how to make and use tools. She observed the older chimps selecting certain twigs, stripping them of leaves and bark, and using them to probe into termite mounds to extract the termites and eat them. They also used wads of chewed leaves as sponges to extract water from cavities in tree trunks where they couldn't reach with their mouths. Some of the males also used sticks as clubs to intimidate baboons living in the same area. In all these cases, the behavior was taught to younger chimps, who learned by imitation. Learned behavior is very important in chimp society, even with regard to activities such as child-rearing, something that most people thought would be instinctual.

Figure 6.26: Common chimpanzees (*Pan troglodytes*) using sticks to fish for termites

Goodall also observed male chimps engage in cooperative hunting, working together to surround and kill monkeys in the treetops and then sharing the meat of their kill. Hunted meat is the only food item the Gombe chimps share. The long-term study also facilitated tracking the growth and movement of two different bands of chimps living in the Gombe reserve. Over time, the smaller, southern band was displaced by the larger and growing northern band. When males from the northern band encountered individuals from the southern band, they were observed to beat them to the point of serious injury and even death. This example of aggression is essentially a form of gang warfare, apparently initiated for no other reason than to control territory, much as human warfare is often intended to do. So, here are at least four of the traits traditionally identified as unique to humans (tool use, cooperative hunting, food sharing, and warfare), observed in the wild among chimps who had no prior exposure to humans.

Perhaps just as remarkable are the examples of antisocial behaviors that can really only be described as mental illness. One of the adult females and her daughter (Passion and Pom) began stealing and eating infants born to other females in the band. Over a period of about a year, they may have killed and eaten as many as ten infants. When Passion died, her daughter stopped making any further attacks. There seems to have been no reason for this aberrant behavior, an unprecedented example of cannibalism among chimps. Another heart-rending sequence of events unfolded as Goodall followed the aging of Flo, one of the oldest females in the band, and her infant son Flint. Flint grew extremely attached to and dependent upon his mother, so much so that he failed to make the normal transition to juvenile independence along with the other chimps of his age. Even after Flo gave birth to another infant, Flint forced himself on her, continuing to breastfeed, and riding on Flo's back, despite his increasing size and her weakening condition. Flo died of old age, and Flint refused to leave her corpse; he grew depressed, and within the period of three-and-a-half weeks, he also died. The very suggestion that one could use the terms *overly dependent* and *depression* in reference to a wild chimp is remarkable.

Goodall's work inspired other researchers who have gone on to observe different bands of chimps in other parts of Africa, and the amazing findings continue to accumulate. Bonobo chimps make and use tools, but they have different sorts of tools that serve entirely different purposes than the Gombe chimps. They make rain hats from leaves, and they drag branches to initiate group travel and indicate the direction of travel. Bonobos have also been observed to make simple stone tools and to teach that use to other members of the group. They hunt only rarely and show no evidence of cooperative hunting, and females sometimes do the hunting. They do more food sharing than the Gombe chimps, and sharing extends to plant foods in addition to meat.

Figure 6.27: Common chimpanzee females using a sharpened stick as a spear for hunting smaller primates in the hollows of tree trunks

More recently, several researchers reported new observations about chimpanzee tool use in the wild in other parts of Africa (Iowa State University 2007; Hooper 2007). Chimpanzees in Senegal are regularly making and using wooden spears to hunt other primates such as galagos. The study, funded by the National Geographic Society, is the first to report habitual tool use by nonhumans while hunting other vertebrates. Researchers documented 22 cases in which chimps fashioned spears to stab into the hollows of tree trunks where the nocturnal galagos hide during the day. Although most of the hunting by this group of chimps is undertaken by males, the use of spears is almost entirely a female approach to hunting. The authors suggest that this novel approach is a response to the demands of living in a drier, harsh environment, unusual for chimpanzees. The chimps even come down out of the trees to gather food and rest in caves during the hot season. This is also the first time anyone has reported chimps living in caves.

New research from the Tai National Park in Ivory Coast suggests that prehistoric chimps were making and using stone tools at least 4,300 years ago (Bower 2007; Whipps 2007). In other words, a prehistoric site has been discovered that seems to have been made by chimps, not humans. The stones, used for cracking nuts, are often larger than humans can readily manipulate, and they bear the residue of the same nuts used today by local chimps but not humans. This is the first discovery of a prehistoric tool used by nonhuman great apes (i.e., by primates not ancestral to humans), and it suggests that prehistoric stone tool technology is not unique to humans (see the video link below). As if these findings were not remarkable enough, some of the observations of captive chimps have blurred the lines between chimpanzee and human behavior even further.

Chimpanzees' Sophisticated Use of Tools—BBC Wildlife

www.youtube.com/watch?v=5Cp7_In7f88

Dr. Diana Davis is a psychologist who works with at-risk youths. As part of her doctoral research at the University of Oklahoma, she worked for several years with Washoe, the first and most famous of the chimpanzees that learned American Sign Language. Dr. Davis asks us to consider what makes humans unique. Many people would say our capacity for thought, our intellect, and our ability to feel and express emotions make us unique. Yet all of these traits were observed and documented in the behavior of Washoe and the other chimps with whom she lived. The chimps go through the same developmental maturation sequence as humans, and they showed clear individual personalities. Washoe was initially raised by human parents and thinks of herself as human; she refused to socialize or hang out with the other chimps, interacting only with the "other humans."

Chimps experience the same emotions as humans, including anger, depression, joy, laughter, joking, and even love. Washoe actually developed a romantic attraction to one of the male students working on the project, and he had to be let go because he was injured by one of her amorous advances. Another chimp, Pancho, liked going on field trips outside the lab so much that he got very excited, even agitated, at the prospect. Adult chimps are much stronger than humans, so if Pancho got too excited, it would be dangerous to take him on an outing, and he would be returned to his cage. Understanding this, he learned how to do self-calming techniques such as deep breathing and meditation to control his excitement so that he could go on the trips.

The chimps were also studying the researchers, and they were able to understand the pecking order among the researchers (faculty, graduate students, and undergraduates). They understood which students were arrogant toward the chimps, and they would play dumb when it was their turn to observe and record chimp behaviors. When trouble happened in the lab, it was mostly the disrespectful students who got picked on. In other words, the chimps retaliated against those students who treated them poorly.

Chimps can be pensive and can appreciate places and imagery that we would call beautiful, peaceful, and aesthetically pleasing. Late one afternoon, one of the chimps in the outdoor enclosure went missing, and an urgent effort was made to locate him. The researchers discovered he had gone off to an isolated area of the facility and climbed a tree and was watching a particularly pretty sunset. As darkness fell, he climbed down and returned to the lab on his own; he just wanted to enjoy the momentary beauty. Like some captive gorillas, two of the chimps with whom Dr. Davis worked also did artwork, using the paint and colors in distinctly individual styles.

Perhaps most remarkable of all (given the traditional ideas about human traits) is the evidence for sophisticated language abilities among some of the chimps. The researchers taught the chimps a limited number of signs in order to see if they could/would combine them when they needed to communicate about new things or events. Indeed, they could, and they did. The chimps recombined signs to generate new words, such as "water + bird" for swan, "cry + hurt + food" for radish, and "candy + fruit + drink" for watermelon. In addition, the chimps made up their own names for the researchers, different from the ones the researchers had given themselves and taught the chimps. The chimps expressed cussing or name-calling, by signing for "poop" and then pointing to the object of their derision. They also were able to conceive of and communicate about the future (such as Pancho's anticipation of future trips) and the past, and they even had the ability to lie (i.e., to conceive of a fantasy). When new combinations of signs were developed by one chimp, the new "words" were taught to the others and used thereafter in their interactions and communication with the researchers. Yes, they actively communicated with the researchers, asking for things, making comments, expressing emotions, etc.!

Although there is still some debate among scientists about the meaning of all these observations, many researchers would argue that most or all of the supposedly human language traits listed by Hockett are actually exhibited by chimps, with the exception of speech. At the very least, it should be abundantly clear that we are very, very closely related to the great apes, and we should have some idea of what a common ancestor might be capable of doing.

References and Further Readings

Bower, Bruce. 2007. "Chimpanzee Stone Age: Finds in Africa Rock Prehistory of Tools." *ScienceNews* 171, no. 7 (February 17, 2007): 99. https://www.sciencenews.org/article/chimpanzee-stone-age-finds-africa-rock-prehistory-tools.

Dian Fossey Gorilla Fund International. n.d. www.gorillafund.org.

Feder, Kenneth L., and Michael Alan Park. 2007. *Human Antiquity: An Introduction to Physical Anthropology and Archaeology*. 5th ed. Boston: McGraw Hill.

Goodall, Jane. 1990. *Through a Window: My Thirty Years with the Chimpanzees of Gombe*. Boston: Houghton Mifflin.

Jane Goodall Institute. www.janegoodall.org.

Hockett, Charles F., and Robert Ascher. 1964. "The Human Revolution." *Current Anthropology* 5, no. 3 (June 1964): 135–68.

Hockett, Charles F., and Stuart Altmann. 1968. "A Note on Design Features." In *Animal Communication,* edited by Thomas Sebeok, 61–72. Bloomington, IN: Indiana University Press.

Hooper, Rowan. 2007. "Spear-Wielding Chimps Snack on Skewered Bushbabies." *NewScientist,* February 22, 2007. https://www.newscientist.com/article/dn11234-spear-wielding-chimps-snack-on-skewered-bushbabies/.

Iowa State University. 2007. "Chimpanzees Discovered Making and Using Spears to Hunt Other Primates." *ScienceDaily*, February 23. Iowa State University. https://www.sciencedaily.com/releases/2007/02/070222155719.htm.

Larsen, Clark Spencer. 2017. *Our Origins: Discovering Physical Anthropology*. 4th ed. New York: W. W. Norton & Company.

Orangutan Foundation International. www.orangutan.org.

Ottenheimer, H. J. 2007. *The Anthropology of Language: and Introduction to Linguistic Anthropology*. Belmont, CA: Thomson Wadsworth.

Simons, Elwyn L. 1972. *Primate Evolution: An Introduction to Man's Place in Nature. New York:* Macmillan Publishers.

Whipps, Heather. 2007. "Chimps Learned Tool Use Long Ago Without Human Help." Live Science, February 12, 2007. https://www.livescience.com/4354-chimps-learned-tool-long-human.html.

Whipps, Heather. 2007. "Chimps May Have Used Stone Hammers." NBC News, February 12, 2007. https://www.nbcnews.com/id/wbna17121018.

Chapter 7: The Material Record

In previous chapters we have focused on the philosophical arguments and genetic evidence for human evolution. However, much of the evidence for human evolution comes in the form of material remains. These include the preserved remains or fossils of organisms and the material byproducts of human behavior in the form of artifacts. The human species is a product of both biological and cultural evolution, but biological changes played a more prominent role in the early evolution of humans, while cultural changes have dominated the more recent developments that characterize our species. Both biological and cultural changes are documented almost entirely by the physical byproducts of humans and their behavior that comprise the paleoanthropological and archeological records. This chapter will provide an introduction to the basic steps involved in fossilization, an overview of how paleontological and archaeological sites are discovered, and a summary of the types of dating methods that researchers use to determine the age of fossils and sites.

Q&A: How do we know that there were ancient human ancestors?

Fossils provide the evidence for long-term evolutionary change, and scientists use a variety of dating techniques to determine when those ancestors existed.

The Fossilization Process

The process of fossilization is complicated and perhaps fairly improbable, making the formation and discovery of fossils, especially those of terrestrial vertebrate animals, a relatively rare event. There are three different sorts of fossils that are commonly used to study human evolution: true-form fossils, trace fossils, and casts. True-form or replacement fossils are those formed when minerals seep into the remains of a plant or animal and replace the organic remains. This process is sometimes called *petrification*, and petrified wood is a well-known result of such fossilization. The most common fossils, bones and teeth, are also formed by this replacement process (Figure 7.1). Trace fossils are impressions left in soft sediments by plants or animals are subsequently hardened through mineralization. Footprints are trace fossils that may provide important information about the soft tissues of the feet, as well as hints about the social behavior of some humans and human ancestors. Cast or mold fossils are those which result from a negative impression being filled by sediment that is later hardened, producing an imprint of the original surface. Casts of brain surface morphology from the interior of skulls are mold fossils of particular interest in the study of human evolution. There are several steps that are necessary for a fossil to form and become part of the database of biological change. If any of the steps are interrupted or prevented, the remains of the organism will be unavailable to science.

Figure 7.1: Replica of *Homo erectus* Fossil, D-2700, discovered in Dmanisi, Republic of Georgia, and dating to 1.7 million years ago

The first thing that must happen is the preservation of the organism. In most cases, this means the organism must be buried to protect it from the elements. In order to be most useful, burial would need to happen quickly enough to protect the remains from excessive deterioration, but gently enough that the deposition of sediments doesn't cause too much damage. If a body is exposed on the ground surface for any length of time, it will likely be damaged and scattered by scavengers. If it is uncovered for a long period, it will become weathered, often cracking and breaking up into splinters. If it sits on the surface long enough, erosion might even scatter the pieces; eventually, they will completely decompose as a result of weathering. Ideally, sedimentation would occur fairly quickly, but gently. If the organism dies in a high-energy environment, such as along a major river, the carcass or bones may be broken up and scattered by the erosive force of a high-energy flood, incorporating the fragments into the gravels of the streambed, where they will be further damaged. Perhaps the best locations for fossils to form is in low-energy depositional environments, such as swamps, sloughs, lakes, and slowly moving streams, where fine-grained sediments (silt and clay) are deposited gently around the remains without disturbing them. Another sort of deposit conducive to fossilization might be volcanic ash, as long as the organism is near enough to the eruption to be gently buried in ash and far away enough that it is not destroyed by a pyroclastic debris flow.

The next step is the actual fossilization, meaning the replacement of bone or other organic parts by minerals. This process usually involves the dissolving of minerals contained in the surrounding sediments. The minerals in solution then percolate though the sediments and replace the organic parts of the bone molecule by molecule. An alternate and potentially more rapid process may result in fossil casts or prints when organisms are buried by sediments that solidify quickly or when such sediments are imprinted. Examples of the former might be the formation of travertine around tree trunks that leave a cast when they decompose; the latter situation is what preserved the Australopithecus footprints in volcanic ash at the site of Laetoli, Tanzania, and the *Homo sapiens* prints in gypsum mud at White Sands National Park in New Mexico (Figure 7.2).

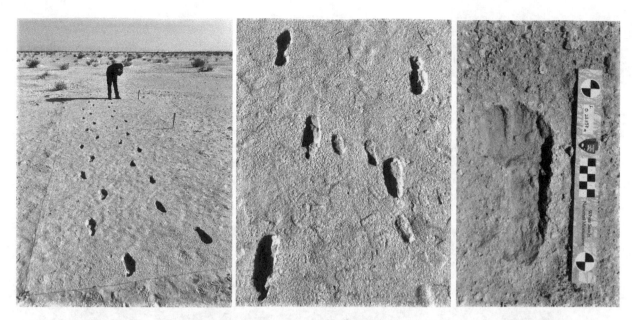

Figure 7.2: Human footprint impressions in fine gypsum sediments at White Sands National Park, New Mexico. The impressions were made during the late Pleistocene when the surface was soft and muddy, and they were preserved after drying and being covered with gypsum sand (National Park Service 2020).

Some kinds of rocks and sediments are more likely to contain fossils than others. Fossilization will be favored when environmental conditions are conducive to the formation of sedimentary rocks that are highly mineralized (containing materials that can be dissolved and redeposited in the fossils). Basalt and other igneous rocks that are deposited as flows are not likely to contain fossils because the organisms would have been melted or burned by the intense temperatures of the molten rock. However, volcanic ash, falling gently at some distance from the volcano, could readily produce fossils. Sedimentary rocks, such as limestone, shale, siltstone, and sandstone, can all contain fossils, but the gentler depositional environments represented by the finer-grained rocks may yield more intact specimens.

After a fossil is formed, usually while deeply buried by the surrounding sediments, it must be uncovered, or re-exposed. The processes involved could include faulting, uplifting, and erosion by wind and water; they must be sufficiently strong to actually expose the fossil, but ideally not so strong that the fossil is crushed, scattered, or carried away from its depositional context.

And finally, the fossil must be discovered by someone who recognizes for what it is and enters it into the fossil database. This final step may seem easy, but it is really not so simple. Imagine looking for a piece of fossilized bone the size of your little finger, distributed amongst thousands and thousands of other rocks and stones scattered across an area the size of several football fields, in the middle of the wilderness, in 120-degree heat and glaring sun. It would be easy to overlook small fragments, especially if they are still partially buried.

What if the fossil were discovered by someone else with different interests? The discovery of *Homo erectus* fossils from Zhoukoudian Cave in China occurred after scientists spotted hominin fossils in the window of a traditional Chinese apothecary shop. The fossils were being sold as "dragon bones," to be ground up and used as an ingredient of aphrodisiac potions. Clearly, someone had been aware of the fossils and the site of their origin for some time, but they were not part of the fossil record of human evolution until researchers studied them.

Given all the steps an organism must go through to become part of the fossil record, it's remarkable that we have as many hominid fossils as we do. You may recall from Chapter 2 that there are only about 36 known specimens of *Tyrannosaurus rex*, or T-Rex. Nevertheless, most of the public has no doubt that T-Rex actually existed. There is much more fossil evidence for our hominin ancestors. As will be discussed in Chapter 8, there are more than 8,000 fossil specimens of hominins, many of which are transitional, exhibiting apelike as well as humanlike characteristics.

How Is Material Evidence Discovered?

In Chapter 3, paleoanthropological and archaeological fieldwork was likened to the forensic analysis of modern crime scenes. In many ways this is a valid comparison, but prehistoric fossil localities and archaeological sites differ from modern crime scenes in several ways. The most important difference is that prehistoric sites have not been identified ahead of time for the investigators, and they may still be buried. That is, the paleontologist or archaeologist must locate the site before any material remains can be recovered and studied. Locating sites, especially in remote undeveloped regions or in areas of extreme natural conditions, can be very challenging. The process of finding and identifying the places containing fossils or human artifacts is usually called *site survey*.

Figure 7.3: Archaeology students recording details of a prehistoric campsite discovered during surface survey of ranchlands near the Sierra Vieja in West Texas

Most archaeological or fossil sites are discovered during pedestrian survey, by simply walking across the land surface and carefully examining the ground for the material remains (Figure 7.3). One would also examine erosional cuts, rodent burrows, and anthills, where evidence of buried materials might be exposed. If one is already familiar with some locational details of the materials being sought—fossils from a certain time period, for example—that knowledge can be used to focus the search on the geological layers containing fossils of the appropriate age. If one knows that early hunter-gatherer groups in the American Southwest tended to locate camps on the downwind side of former lake beds, that observation, referred to as *site pattern recognition*, may be used to identify places where one is likely to find additional examples of such sites. However, if one doesn't have that sort of prior knowledge or if one is interested in learning about other kinds of sites that may occur in different settings, it will be necessary to search more of the landscape.

The landscape is a big place. And as we will see in Chapter 12, prehistoric populations were highly mobile and used large portions of the landscape. Therefore, if one's goal is to understand how people in a particular time and place adapted to their environment, it might be necessary to search entire valleys or drainage basins for evidence of their activities. In these sorts of cases, it is necessary to look at only a portion of the landscape by conducting a *sample survey*.

Samples can be selected in a variety of ways, but we are primarily interested in obtaining a sample that is representative of the areas or sites that are being investigated. To ensure that samples are representative, it is often necessary to examine a *stratified sample*, in which the land areas sampled are distributed among the different landform or terrain features that might contain sites. Some large survey areas may be examined in their entirety, but in most cases only a small fraction of the area will be walked. The surveyed areas will usually be statistical samples contained in grid squares or linear transects (Kelly and Thomas 2014, 41; Judge 1981).

It is increasingly becoming the case, at least in archaeology, that *aerial surveys* are being used to study large project areas. A variety of *remote-sensing* technologies are being used to identify sites when survey areas are very large or very remote or occur in areas of heavy ground cover (Figure 7.4). Low- and high-altitude photography can be effective, with or without infrared recording. Radar techniques such as light detection and ranging (LIDAR) can be used to enhance and map subtle ground features or to record surfaces and sites that are obscured by vegetation. Other methods, such as ground-penetrating radar (GPR) and proton magnetometer survey, can detect buried features that exhibit little or no surface manifestation (Figure 7.5). While remote-sensing techniques can be very useful in locating sites, they do not replace the need to actually visit the sites on the ground to verify their contents after they are discovered.

Figure 7.4: Aerial photograph of the Eaker site (3MS105) near Blytheville, Arkansas. The arrows mark the approximate corners of the site, between which linear patterns indicative of prehistoric wall trenches are visible.

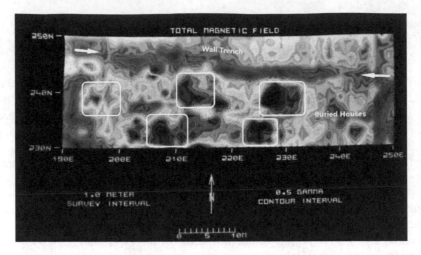

Figure 7.5: False color image of proton magnetometer signatures of a Buried Wall Trench (Arrows) and House Floors at the Eaker Site (Modified from US Air Force 1989)

Although the features delineated in Figure 7.5 were discovered by remote sensing, it was test excavation that revealed the details necessary to identify them as house floors and a wall trench.

How Old Is It?

One of the biggest misconceptions the general public has about paleoanthropology and archaeology is the notion that we can't know the date or age of a fossil or prehistoric artifact. Many people seem to think that scientists make hunches, guesses, or wild speculations about the age of prehistoric materials. Perhaps this misconception is a specific case of the general misunderstandings about the use of indirect evidence that we discussed in Chapter 3. Or perhaps it relates to some people's belief that the earth is only a few thousand years old; for such believers, any scientific evidence for an older earth must be dismissed out of hand, and that perspective has some currency in today's public policy discourse. I'd prefer to think that many people simply haven't been introduced to the science behind geological or archaeological dating, and I hope that when you hear about some of the details, you will be able see how scientists are often able to reliably date prehistoric events and materials.

The geological time scale is completely beyond the personal experiences most people have with the passage of time, so it is hard for most of us to think about ancient time periods. I'm sure most of you reading this book don't remember the Vietnam War. That reality always reminds me how old I'm getting, but it also illustrates that for most of you, the experiences of the 1970s are just things you hear about from your older relatives or read about in history books. For most of us, something our grandparents tell us about their early years is what we might consider old, and if something is so old that our grandparents didn't experience it, then it is REALLY OLD! But, of course, the past hundred years is merely the blink of an eye in geological or archaeological terms. To help people visualize the age of the earth in understandable terms, Carl Sagan (1977) developed the idea of the "cosmic year," which reduces the entire age of the universe down to a single year (Figure 7.6). The cosmic year begins January 1 with the Big Bang and ends with the present on December 31; each day represents 42 million years. On the one hand, we can see that most of what has occurred on the earth happened long before humans or our hominin ancestors even existed; the last 200,000 years, during which time modern humans evolved, represents only the last two minutes of the cosmic year. Nevertheless, 200,000 years, or even 20,000 years, is far older than most people can imagine or comprehend. How can we know about these ages?

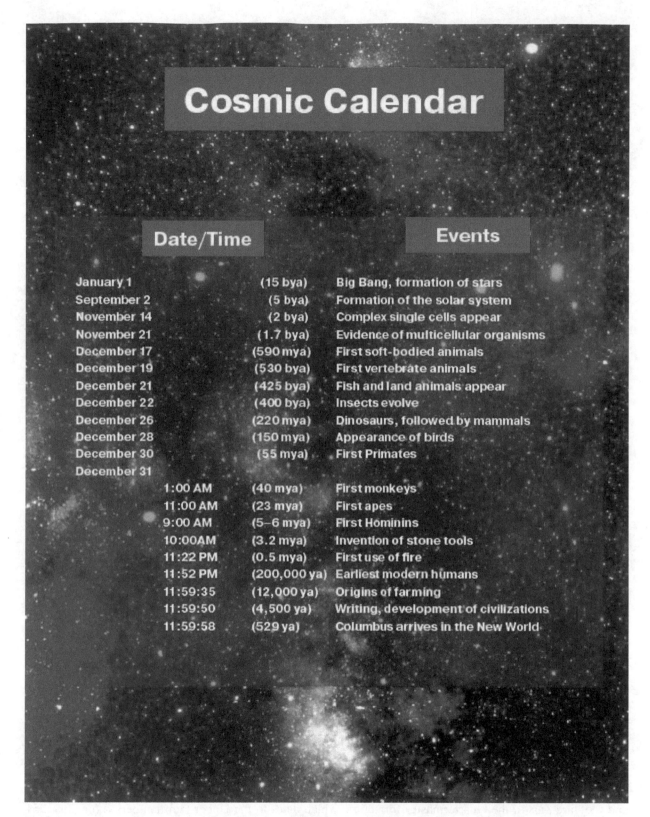

Figure 7.6: The Cosmic Calendar

There are two different kinds or broad categories of prehistoric dating techniques: relative dating and chronometric dating. Relative dating techniques do not provide a definite age in years, but they order events, fossils, and artifacts in a sequence of relative age. In other words, it is possible to know that something is older or younger than something else, without knowing by how much. In contrast, chronometric dating methods provide an estimate of the age of a fossil or artifact in years, often with an error factor that indicates the degree of confidence one has in the estimate. A variety of dating techniques are listed in Table 7.1. Each of these techniques has specific applications, strengths, and weaknesses. However, by using multiple techniques when possible and crosschecking them for consistency, geologists, geophysicists, geochemists, biologists, and anthropologists have built up a global chronological framework about which there is a high degree of agreement and confidence.

Figure 7.7: Stratigraphic section of sediments exposed in Palo Duro Canyon State Park in the Texas panhandle. Strata A and B are part of the Quartermaster formation dating to the Upper Permian, and the overlying sediments belong to the Upper Triassic Dockum group.

Most relative dating techniques are related in one way or another to stratigraphy, so it is useful to briefly mention how that works. Stratigraphy is based on the Law of Superposition, which states that earth's layers (rocks and soils) are deposited with the oldest layers on the bottom and successively younger layers on top of one another. Barring any major disturbance, we can confidently tell which sediments were deposited in what order; by extension, the relative ages of fossils and artifacts contained within the different stratigraphic units can also be inferred. However, even though we know the relative ages of the sediments and their contents, we don't know how old they are in years or precisely how much time has elapsed between the deposition of different layers.

As an example, consider the stratigraphy shown in Figure 7.7. These sediments are exposed by erosion throughout the Palo Duro Canyon State Park in Texas. The layers labeled A and B are the oldest, and they are part of the Quartermaster formation, which dates to the Upper Permian period (ca. 299–251 mya). The overlying layers are part of the Upper Triassic Dockum group from about 237–201 million years ago. They are labeled in ascending order, from bottom to top, to reflect the order in which they were deposited. Initially, the units were defined on the basis of their contents, such as fossils, mineral composition, etc. Only later were the estimated ages in years determined by the use of a chronometric dating technique called *potassium-argon* (K/Ar) dating (International Commission on Stratigraphy 2020).

Geological strata and early fossils are generally dated with the K/Ar technique, which is well suited to dating volcanic materials. Like other radiometric dating techniques, it is based on the rate of radioactive decay of one element into another. Different elements have different half-lives and are therefore appropriate for use on sediments from different time periods. Radiocarbon, or carbon-14 (C14), dating is the preferred method of dating organic materials in archaeological sites dating to the past 75,000 years. It is also the technique about which members of the public are most likely to have heard. Although C14 dating is rather precise and its validity is widely accepted among researchers, it is often misunderstood or misrepresented by members of the general public. So let's go through a brief introduction about how it works.

Radiocarbon dating is commonly misrepresented in at least two different ways. Some researchers refer to C14 and similar dating techniques as "absolute" dating, and people often conclude that dates derived from these techniques must be exact; this is not true. Most *chronometric dating* techniques (my preferred terminology) yield estimates of dates, albeit precise estimates. The other, more common way in which radiocarbon is misrepresented is in the claim that C14 dating simply cannot be correct. This claim is most often associated with young-earth creationist beliefs about the age of the earth being no more than 6,000 to 10,000 years old. Believers in a young earth have made many statements about how and why C14 dating must be wrong, and how scientists are fooling themselves about the age of the earth (and thus the validity of evolution). The failure of such arguments becomes obvious when one knows something about the history of the development of radiocarbon dating (and the other radiometric dating techniques as well).

Table 7.1: Summary of Selected Relative and Chronometric Dating Techniques (Adapted from Larsen 2017)

Method	Basis	Materials	Date Range
Relative Dating			
Stratigraphy	Law of superposition	anything	any
Horizon markers	correlation of strata from different areas	fossils, rocks and artifacts	any
Chemical dating	Fossils absorb chemicals such as fluorine from soil	Fossil bones	<100,000 yrs
Biostratigraphy	changes in animals or plants such as pollen and spores	bones, pollen, spores	any
Chronometric Dating			
Cultural dating	artifacts are time-specific	human technology	up to 3.3 mya
Dendrochronology	annual growth rings of trees	certain tree species	0–8,000+ yrs
Radiocarbon	carbon-14	organic material	<75,000 yrs
Potassium-argon dating	potassium-40	volcanic rocks/ash	>200,000 yrs
Amino acid dating	racemization	bones, shells	40K–1 mya
Fission track dating	fission tracks on rocks	volcanic rock	up to 3 mya
Paleomagnetism	shifts in earth's magnetic	sedimentary rocks	up to 5 mya

Electron spin resonance	concentrations of radioisotopes	bones, teeth	thousands to 1 mya
Thermoluminescence	energy trapped in clay, soils, rocks	ceramics, sediment	up to 800,000

mya: million years ago; yr: year.

Radiometric dating techniques are based on the concept of radioactive decay, a natural process that can be used as a sort of atomic clock. The time range of applicability is determined by the rate of radioactive decay (the half-life) of the element in question—5,730 years, in the case of radiocarbon. Willard Libby was the scientist who initially worked out the rate of radioactive decay for C14. It is significant that Libby's method grew directly out of the work he and other chemists did on the development of the atomic bomb during World War II (Larsen 2017, 254–255). That is, radiocarbon dating is a direct, peacetime application of knowledge gained about subatomic particle physics during the development of the atomic bomb.

From Chapter 3, you know about the principle of uniformitarianism, or actualism. You will recall that uniformitarianism is the idea that the processes at work in nature today are the same as the ones that operated in the past. Another expression of this principle is that natural processes that work in physics and chemistry are also at work in biology and anthropology or any other scientific discipline. So if one denies that radiocarbon dating is valid, one is also denying the existence of the atomic bomb. The two applications are based on the same principles of subatomic particle physics.

One cannot have it both ways; one cannot logically argue that the atomic bomb is real but an ancient earth is not. The physical principles of radioactive decay are either real, or they're not. One doesn't get to choose when they work and when we don't want them to work simply because we may be uncomfortable with the implications (such as an ancient earth). It is even more ironic to use the medium of television or the internet to broadcast such a message, because television and monitor technology is based on subatomic physics, too. Television screens and computer monitors (at least those using pre-liquid crystal display [LCD] technology) contained a cathode ray tube that used an electron gun to spray electrons onto a photosensitive screen to produce the image. The technology is another of the peacetime applications of the knowledge gained about subatomic particles during the development of the atomic bomb. So if the physical principles were not real and understood, the technology wouldn't exist. We humans don't really have that choice in a logical world; the processes of nature work, or they don't. We don't get to decide when we might like to suspend the laws of nature.

So, accepting that archaeologists really can date prehistoric materials using radiocarbon, just what do the dates mean? Simply put, a properly reported radiocarbon date gives an estimate of the date with an error factor, which specifies the degree of confidence in the estimate. We can think of it as something like a voter poll taken during political campaign. Is there a way we can know for certain who wins the election? Yes, we can wait until the election actually happens, do an accurate count of the votes, and announce the winner. Then why conduct surveys and polls before the election? Because someone, such as candidates and their campaign staffers, want to know ahead of time if there are any trends they might need to address before the election. But pollsters can't actually contact all the voters and record their choice (that would be called an election). Instead, they contact a sample of likely voters and make a reasoned estimate of the distribution of the votes, accompanied by an error factor. Because the pollsters are unwilling to wait for the election, their projections are necessarily based on a sample of the voters, and therefore, there are sources of error associated with the estimate.

Similarly, in the case of radiocarbon, the only way to know for certain how much C14 is still contained in a piece of old charcoal would be to wait for all the C14 to decay, counting each release of a radioactive particle as it occurs. But in order to count each one, we would have to be counting for thousands of years. Instead, we count a sample over a period of several days and make an estimate based on that sample. The interpretation or meaning of that estimate can be understood by reference to the normal distribution in Figure 7.8. Let's use a simple date as an example: 1,000+/-50 years before present. What this really means is that the estimate of 1,000 years corresponds to the mean (μ) of the normal distribution. The error factor of 50 years corresponds to the standard deviation around the mean (-1σ and +1σ). The range of values within one standard deviation of the mean corresponds to 68 percent of the area under the curve. Therefore, the reported radiocarbon date really says there is a 68 percent chance that the actual age of the dated sample is between 950 and 1,050 years ago. Now, in statistics, as in weather forecasting, most of us would like to be more than 68 percent confident about our results, so the 95 percent confidence interval is used. By expanding the confidence interval to two standard deviations (-2σ to +2σ), we include 95 percent of the area under the curve. Thus, what this date estimate really tells us is that there is a 95 percent chance that the true age of the sample is between 900 and 1,100 years old.

There are other issues involved in the use of radiocarbon that bear on the interpretation and reporting of dates. For example, radiocarbon dating can only be used on samples containing organic material. If someone tells you that stone tools were dated directly using C14, they are misinformed. Radiocarbon can be used only on samples of organic materials, such as charcoal, wood, plant fibers, shell, soil carbonates, etc. Things like stone artifacts can only be dated *indirectly* by C14 when they are in close association with organic materials. It is also important to remember that radiocarbon dates the death of an organism, not the time when it was actually used by humans. For example, if a timber was cut for prehistoric construction and it is eventually dated by archaeologists, we will get a date on when the tree was killed, not when the timber might have been recycled and reused during later periods of construction.

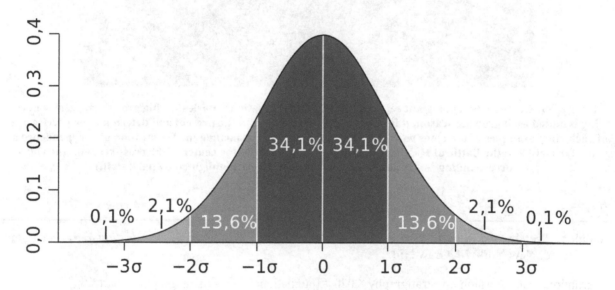

Figure 7.8: Normal distribution and standard deviations as they relate to confidence intervals in radiometric dating techniques

As noted in Table 7.1, there are also time limits to the usefulness of radiocarbon dating. This is because after 50,000 to 75,000 years, the amount of C14 remaining in a sample is so small that it can't be accurately measured. So if someone alleges that bones have been dated to 500,000 years ago using the C14 technique, they are mistaken. Potassium-argon dating could be used on fossils and sediments of that age, however.

We also know there have been fluctuations over time in the concentration of radioactive carbon in the atmosphere and, therefore, in the organisms living at those times. By extensive radiocarbon dating of wood samples of known age (cross-checked with dendrochronology, Figure 7.9), we now know that prior to 1,500 BC, radiocarbon dates are about 150 years too young; by 4,000 BC, they are about 700 years too young. Correction factors have been derived from the dendrochronology dates as far back as about 11,300 years ago (Ashmore and Sharer 2000, 164). While each of these challenges or limitations might seem to make radiocarbon dating less reliable, the opposite is actually the case. As we develop ever more detailed understandings of the advantages and disadvantages of this or any technique, the results that derive from their more informed use are more reliable.

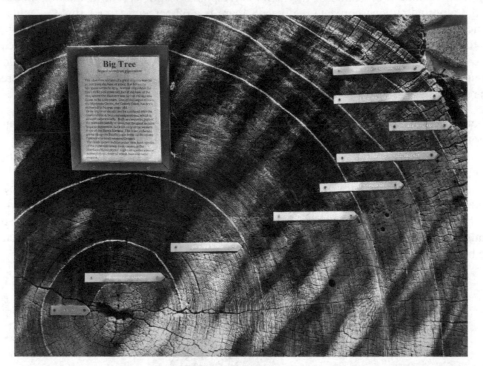

Figure 7.9: Cross-section of a giant sequoia tree in Yosemite National Park showing growth rings. as a new ring is added each growing season, it is possible to count back from the present and determine the precise age of each ring. examples of the rings corresponding to historic events include the Declaration of Independence at the far right and the Battle of Hastings in 1066 just to the right of the center of the cross-section. (the rings corresponding to the dates indicated by labels were highlighted by park staff.)

References and Further Reading

Ashmore, Wendy, and Robert J. Sharer. 2000. *Discovering Our Past: A Brief Introduction to Archaeology.* 3rd ed. New York: McGraw Hill.

International Commission on Stratigraphy. 2020. "International Chronostratigraphic Chart." https://stratigraphy.org/chart

Judge, W. James. 1981. "Transect Sampling in Chaco Canyon: Evaluation of a Survey Technique." In *Archeological Surveys of Chaco Canyon,* edited by Alden C. Hayes, David M. Brugge, and W. James Judge. Washington, DC: Publications in Archeology 18A, Chaco Canyon Studies, National Park Service.

Kelly, Robert L., and David Hurst Thomas. 2014. *Archaeology Down to Earth.* 3rd ed. Belmont, CA: Wadsworth Cengage Learning.

Larsen, Clark Spencer. 2017. *Our Origins: Discovering Physical Anthropology.* New York: Norton.

National Park Service. 2020. *White Sands National Park, New Mexico, Fossilized Footprints.* www.nps.gov/whsa/learn/nature/fossilized-footprints.htm.

Sagan, Carl. 1977. *The Dragons of Eden: Speculations on the Evolution of Human Intelligence.* New York: Random House.

Stringer, Chris, and Peter Andrews. 2005. *The Complete World of Human Evolution.* London: Thames & Hudson.

US Air Force. 1989. *Proton Magnetometer Survey of Site 3MS105, Eaker Air Force Base, Arkansas.* Prepared by Archaeological Services, Western Wyoming College, and Tetra Tech, Inc., San Bernardino, CA. For the US Air Force, AFRCE-BMS, Norton Air Force Base, CA.

Chapter 8: Fossil Evidence for Human Evolution: Origins

You have read about the range of characteristics and complex behaviors that humans share with apes, our closest primate relatives. It is now time to examine some of the differences, especially those anatomical differences that are used to classify the fossil remains that make up the database of human evolution. The general public has often been led to believe that fossil evidence for human evolution is nonexistent or at least not extensive, or equivocal and problematical. Such suggestions are highly misleading, if not outright disingenuous. While there are certainly differences of opinion among scientists about the details of human evolution, the research and debates are based on what is now a very substantial collection of fossils, including many that are clearly transitional between apes and humans.

Q&A: Are humans evolved from monkeys?

No. Humans share a common ancestor with the great apes, dating back to about 6 or 7 million years ago.

Scientists now identify 20 different forms of fossil hominins (Conroy and Pontzer 2012, 105) spanning the last six million years of prehistory. All of these species are represented by at least several specimens, and some are known from more than 500 specimens. There have been 495 specimens of Australopithecine species recovered from the South African site of Sterkfontain since 1966. The site of Koobi Fora has yielded 129 specimens. Nickels (1986) estimated that nearly 1,500 Australopithecine fossils representing 200 to 350 individuals were known to science in 1986, and the numbers of sites and fossils discovered has increased dramatically since 1976. Eckhardt (2000, 8) suggests that the total number of hominid fossils from Africa and Eurasia may now be around 8,000 specimens. The fossil record of human evolution cannot be dismissed as sparse or questionable. Instead, it provides hard physical evidence of change in the animal forms that preceded our species as well as our nearest primate relatives, the Great Apes.

In fact, instead of saying that humans are related to the Great Apes, it might be more accurate to say that we are one kind of Great Ape, the bipedal Great Apes. "We are more similar at the genomic level to chimpanzees and bonobos than these two species are to gorillas. . . . we are more similar to chimpanzees than mice and rats are to each other" (Varki 2018).

This chapter and the next present an introduction to some of the fossils that demonstrate the key changes in hominin evolution and that define our own ancestry in comparison to the apes. Students should be able to identify the key traits that are used to identify and classify animals (fossils or modern) as hominins and how they differ from the panins (apes). You should also be able to describe why the different genera of early fossil hominids are so classified. That is, in what ways do they differ anatomically, and how do scientists think those distinctions reflect different adaptations? Additional illustrations and detailed descriptions of hominin fossils, beyond what those presented in the textbook may be found at the following websites:

- Institute of Human Origins, Arizona State University (www.becominghuman.org/)

- The Talk Origins Archive (www.talkorigins.org/faqs/homs/index.html)

- Darwiniana and Evolution (http://darwiniana.org/hominid.htm)

Hominins Defined: Bipedal Locomotion

A hominin is any member of the taxonomic tribe *Hominini*, which includes modern humans, our ancestors, and a few other closely related prehistoric species. The hominins are often defined in contrast to the taxonomic group known as the *Gorillini* and its subfamily *Ponginae* (orangutans), the subfamily *Gorillinae* (gorillas), and the tribe *Panini* (chimpanzees)—that is, the modern great apes and their ancestors (Figure 8.1). The hominins may be most simply identified as the bipedal primates. Although some of the apes occasionally walk on two feet, only the hominins are habitual bipeds; walking upright is central to the overall adaptation of the hominins, and it influences many details of the skeletal anatomy. In addition to bipedalism, the other defining trait of hominins is *non-honing dentition*—the lack of overlapping canines. All of the other traits we tend to associate with prehistoric humans, such as tool use and language, developed much later (Larsen 2017, 310).

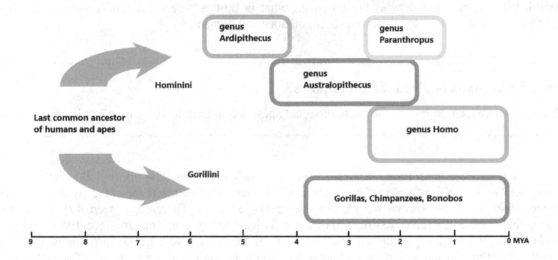

Figure 8.1: General relationship of the hominin lineage to that of the Great Apes

The anatomical details related to bipedal locomotion, and thus to hominin identity, can be organized according to three major areas of the body: the postcranial skeleton, the skull, and the dentition. The relevant details from each of these areas are presented below. In order to best understand them, it will be useful for you to refer to the illustrations of ape and human skeletons.

First, let's consider the *postcranial skeleton*, or that part of the anatomy from the neck down. The human skeleton differs in several ways from that of an ape, in ways that reflect the overall adaptation to habitual upright bipedal locomotion. Starting with the trunk, note the orientation of the gorilla's spine; it is partly horizontal and partly held at a 45-degree angle to the ground (Figure 8.2). The pelvis is long and narrow, extending nearly halfway up the back. The center of gravity is below the rib cage and in front of the hips; the weight of the body is both suspended from the pelvis and spine and supported by the forearms, in what is referred to as a *knuckle-walking stance*. The rib cage is deep, extending far down from the spine; in combination with the abdominal muscles, it forms a sort of hammock within which the internal organs are carried.

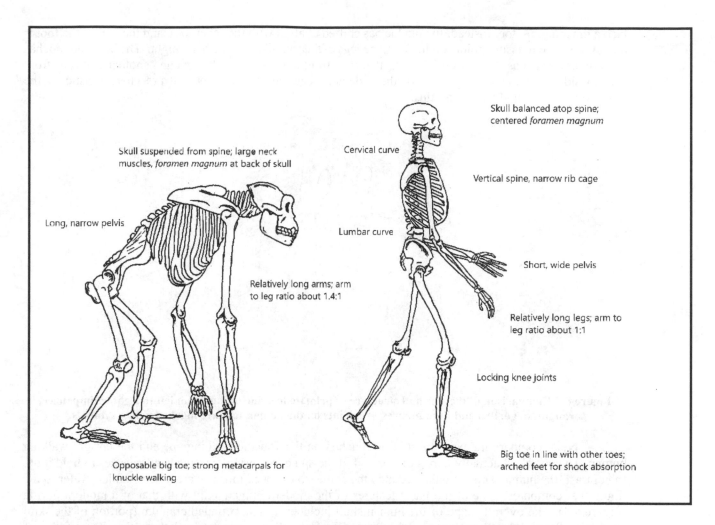

Skull suspended from spine; large neck muscles, *foramen magnum* at back of skull

Long, narrow pelvis

Relatively long arms; arm to leg ratio about 1.4:1

Opposable big toe; strong metacarpals for knuckle walking

Skull balanced atop spine; centered *foramen magnum*

Cervical curve

Vertical spine, narrow rib cage

Lumbar curve

Short, wide pelvis

Relatively long legs; arm to leg ratio about 1:1

Locking knee joints

Big toe in line with other toes; arched feet for shock absorption

Figure 8.2: Comparison of ape (left) and human (right) skeletal anatomy and posture

Contrast that with the human skeleton in which the spine is vertical, allowing for an upright stance. There are two major curves in the hominin spine that reorient the trunk, the lumbar curve at the lower back and a smaller curve in the cervical region, or neck. It is no coincidence that these are areas of common pain and injury in humans, for they are compromises in structural arrangements that represent evolution from the ancestral condition to accommodate the upright bipedal stance. The upright stance results in the center of gravity being repositioned over the hips, facilitating weight bearing and balance. Note also that the pelvis is short and wide rather than long and narrow. The human pelvis actually acts as a "bucket" that supports the internal organs; they are not suspended from our spine, and the chest cavity and rib cage is much shallower (thinner, front to back) as a result. In addition, in humans the limb ratio is different from the apes. In humans, the legs are proportionately longer and heavier and the arms shorter and lighter. The upper legs are angled in from the hip to the knee, in contrast to the bow-legged stance of the apes; this results in the weight of the body being carried through the knee joints rather than between and in front of the knees.

The knees themselves are one of the signature traits of hominins, for they are capable of locking at full extension, allowing us to walk efficiently by straightening the leg with each stride. It was recently discovered that orangutans also have a knee joint capable of locking (Thorpe et al. 2007; Hooper 2007), but that is the only known exception to the rule that locking knees are characteristic of the hominins. The orangutan seems to have this trait because it also moves with a bipedal motion, but on top of tree limbs, rather than on the ground. As a result, the changes in the feet that characterize hominins are not found in orangutans (Figure 8.3). Those changes involve a reorganization of the foot bones and musculature to form an arched tripod that supports the weight of the body and cushions the foot during walking. Unlike the apes, humans lack a grasping big toe. Instead, the big toe has shifted to align with the other toes, and the ball of the foot is one of the three pressure points on the foot, the legs of the tripod that bears our weight. The hominin foot has two arches that act as shock absorbers, one that runs front to back under the foot and another that runs from side to side over the instep. None of these details occur in the apes, but all are characteristic of the australopithecines and later hominins.

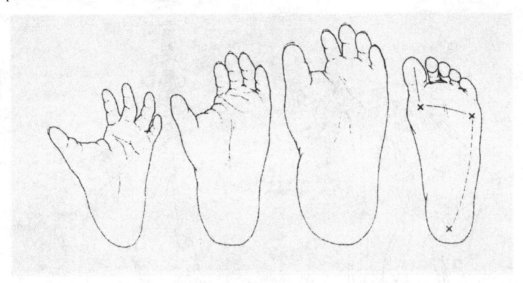

Figure 8.3 Comparison of the size and structure of primate feet, including, from left to right, chimpanzee, orangutan, gorilla, and human. pressure points on the human foot are marked with *x* symbols.

Next, compare the way the skull is attached on the knuckle-walking ape and the upright walking human. The ape skull actually hangs off the end of the spine, requiring massive neck muscles to hold it up. In contrast, the human skull is balanced atop the spine, so the neck muscles are much smaller. Refer to the figure that compares some of the basic features of the modern human skull with that of a modern gorilla (Figure 8.4). The overall shape of the human skull includes a high, rounded cranium (portion of the skull containing the brain) with a developed forehead at the front. The face is flat, such that a line drawn from the forehead to the chin is nearly vertical. Supraorbital brow ridges are relatively small or lacking altogether. Comparing the human skull with the gorilla skull, we can see that the overall shape is quite different. The gorilla cranium is relatively smaller, and there is no forehead; in fact, there is a constriction of the cranium behind the eye sockets. The gorilla has very large supraorbital brow ridges. The lower portion of the gorilla's face extends quite far forward; this condition is referred to as *alveolar prognathism*. Prognathism is very prominent in apes, mostly lacking in later hominins, and intermediate in early hominins, such as australopithecines.

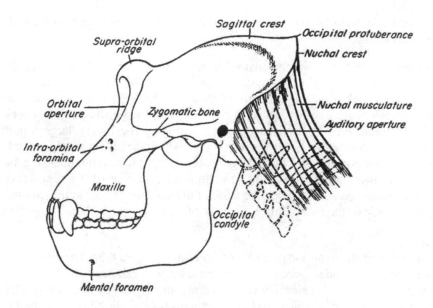

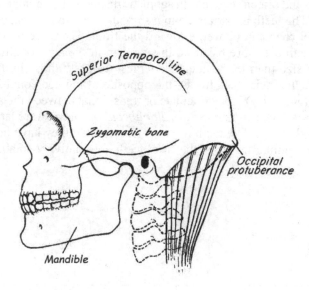

Figure 8.4: Comparison of gorilla and modern human skulls, with emphasis on facial structure, jaws, and muscle attachments

Using the human skull diagram as a guide, place your fingers above one of your ears, about halfway up the side of your head, and clench your teeth. You should be able to feel a thin layer of muscles moving under your fingers when you do this. If you move your fingers higher while continuing to clench and unclench your teeth, you will reach a point where you no longer feel muscles moving. You are now touching just above the superior temporal line. The temporal line is a small raised area on the skull where your jaw muscles attach. From there they stretch down behind the zygomatic arch, the bone that extends from the cheekbones back to your ears. The muscles then spread out around the corner and lower edge of the mandible, or lower jaw. The small size of the temporal line reflects the relatively small jaw muscles it must support. At the back of the skull is a bump just above the hairline called the *occipital protuberance*. It is usually more pronounced in males than females, again because of the size of the muscles that attach there, in this case the neck muscles.

Now, compare these features with the analogous areas of the gorilla skull. Notice that there is no temporal line on the side of the ape cranium. Instead, the chewing muscles attach to the sagittal crest, a bony ridge extending from front to back along the centerline of the top of the skull. Think about that for a minute—while our jaw muscles attach about halfway up the side of our skull, the gorilla has jaw muscles that attach completely above the cranium, on a specially adapted bony ridge. These very large muscles and their prominent attachment point correspond to the enormous jaw, which makes up nearly a third of the skull. There is also a huge zygomatic bone or arch with a large space behind it to accommodate the massive bundle of muscles extending from the sagittal crest to the jaw. Similarly, the rear of the skull lacks an occipital protuberance. Instead, a nuchal crest extends up the back of the skull from both sides, connecting with the sagittal crest high on the back of the skull. This second set of bony ridges is where the gorilla's enormous neck muscles attach.

Finally, let's compare the dentition of apes and hominins (Figure 8.5). The apes, illustrated in this case by a chimpanzee, retain the older, ancestral dental arrangement exhibited by the Miocene apes. The shape of the jaw is rectangular, with the side teeth arranged in more or less parallel rows. The largest teeth are those at the front, the incisors and canines, and there are gaps (canine diastemata) at the front corners of the mouth that accommodate the overlapping canines from the lower jaw, thereby allowing the rest of the teeth to occlude, or make contact. The movement of the canines in and out of the gaps actually hones the canines, keeping them sharp and effective for use in agonistic displays. The human dentition is very different in several important ways. The teeth are arranged in a smooth curve in the shape of a parabolic arch. The side teeth are not in parallel rows but converge toward the front. There are no canine diastemata and no overlapping canines. The teeth are more balanced in size than in the ape condition—that is, the different kinds of teeth are closer in size than in the ape. The largest teeth are those in the rear of the mouth, the molars, and the smallest are the incisors in front—the opposite of the ape condition. Note that the jaw of *Australopithecus afarensis* (aka Lucy) is intermediate or transitional between the apes and human. There is still a small canine diastema, so the canines of *Australopithecus afarensis* were larger than those of modern humans, but they were non-honing. The tooth rows are not parallel; they have begun shifting towards the parabolic arrangement. Also, unlike the apes, the front teeth are relatively small, while the rear teeth are large.

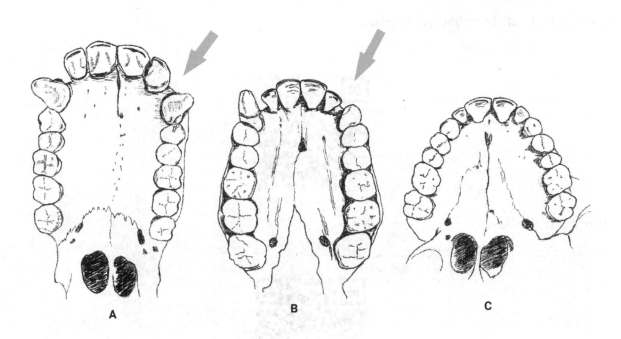

Figure 8.5: Comparison of the maxilla (upper jaws) of a chimpanzee (a), *Australopithecus afarensis* (b), and a modern human (c). the blue arrows point to the canine diastemas, the gaps in the tooth row that provide space for the canines in the lower jaw, thus allowing the jaw to close and the teeth to occlude. note that the canines and diastemas are large in the chimpanzee, very much reduced in A. *afarensis*, and lacking in modern humans.

It is noteworthy that the defining hominin traits, the shift to bipedal locomotion and the behavioral and dietary changes reflected in the teeth affect many parts of the anatomy. Therefore, they can be inferred from bones representing structures such as the hips, knee, feet, spine and skull. It is not necessary to recover an entire skeleton; it is still possible to identify it as a hominin as long as a few key bones are recovered that provide evidence of bipedal locomotion.

As important as bipedal locomotion is to the human condition, there is some debate about the timing of and reasons for the beginnings of bipedalism. For many years, the fossils of *Australopithecus afarensis* (aka Lucy) provided the earliest evidence of bipedalism among the hominins. The context of those fossils suggested that bipedal locomotion first occurred in a savannah grassland environment, and at least half a dozen hypotheses were developed to explain the beginnings of bipedalism (Feder and Park Park 2007, 242; Larsen 2017, 219).

The hunting hypothesis suggested that upright walking freed the hands to use tools to hunt. The vigilance model suggests that hominins would benefit from being able to see over the savannah grassland vegetation to see danger coming from long distances. It has also been suggested that an upright stance would make hominins look taller and more intimidating to predators. Others have suggested potential benefits such as being able to reach higher into trees and bushes to harvest foods; reducing the amount of sunlight hitting the body, allowing for better cooling; and the greater efficiency of bipedal walking when compared to knuckle-walking. As long as Lucy was considered to be the earliest hominin, most of these ideas could be considered to be plausible explanations for the beginnings of bipedalism. That changed with the discovery of *Ardipithecus ramidus* (aka Ardi). See the links provided below for an introduction to the Ardi fossils and their implications for the beginnings of upright walking.

The Analysis of *Ardipithecus ramidus*

https://www.youtube.com/watch?v=tcrywnrwMyl

How Ardi Walked

https://www.youtube.com/watch?v=Pw_J6jV02eU

To summarize, Ardi dates to about 4.4 million years ago, or a million years earlier than Lucy. Ardi seems to be an evolutionary mosaic, containing an unexpected combination of traits. She has a small brain and prehensile feet like the apes. But the shape of her pelvis and the presence of an anterior inferior iliac spine on the front of the pelvis suggest that she walked upright, although not as well as Lucy. Her arms were long, but her fingers lack the strong metacarpals that would be expected in a knuckle-walker. She had reduced, non-honing canines. The fossils of plants and other animal species found in the layers in which her bones were recovered clearly indicate she lived in a heavily wooded environment, not a savannah grassland.

So, what does all that mean for the potential reasons for the evolution of bipedal locomotion? If Ardi lived in a dense woodland, as appears to be the case, then her upright stance would probably not result in being able to see danger coming from a long distance. It also would not reduce the amount of sunlight heating the body if Ardi was in shade a lot anyway. Given that she had prehensile feet, Ardi would have been able to easily climb trees to obtain food, so being able to stand up and reach the lower branches would seem to be of little additional use. What does seem likely is that bipedalism would allow Ardi to carry things in the hand, although hunting tools are not known among hominins until a couple million years later. However, it would be useful to carry food, a possibility that the discoverers of Ardi have suggested as an additional potential explanation: male provisioning. It has been suggested that because the species has reduced, non-honing canines, it could mean that a shift in mating behavior is indicated. In this scenario, males would be able to efficiently travel longer distances, bringing food to their mates, and thereby improve the chances of successfully raising offspring to maturity. Although this idea is by no means fully accepted, it does account for the evidence, and it raises the provocative idea that hominin reproductive success (as compared to nonhuman primates) may be at least partly due to the development of pair bonding and sexual division of labor.

Hominin Taxonomy

The diagram presented in Figure 8.6 is a simplified presentation of inferred hominin taxonomic relationships. It is simplified because the specific relationships and evolutionary connections among species are still being debated, and because many of the details of that debate are beyond the scope of an introductory text. The earliest fossils presently classified as hominins, *Sahelanthropus tchadensis* and *Orrorin tugenensis*, are not linked with any of the other groups. This is because there are so few fossils of these species that it is difficult to say much about their relationships to other species. *Sahelanthropus* consists only of cranial elements, and the specimen is interpreted as bipedal (and therefore hominin) on the basis of the placement of the *foramen magnum*. The *Orrorin* fossils do include femurs, and on that basis, it has been determined that the species was bipedal and probably more closely related to *Australopithecus* than to genus *Homo* (Richmond and Jungers 2008).

The classification scheme summarized in Figure 8.6 has the advantage of focusing on the placement of the better-known species within each of the four main lineages or genera: *Ardipithecus, Australopithecus, Paranthropus, and Homo*. Although the identity of specific ancestor(s) of humans is still a matter of debate, it is widely accepted that species within the genus *Australopithecus* gave rise to both the genus *Paranthropus* and the genus *Homo*.

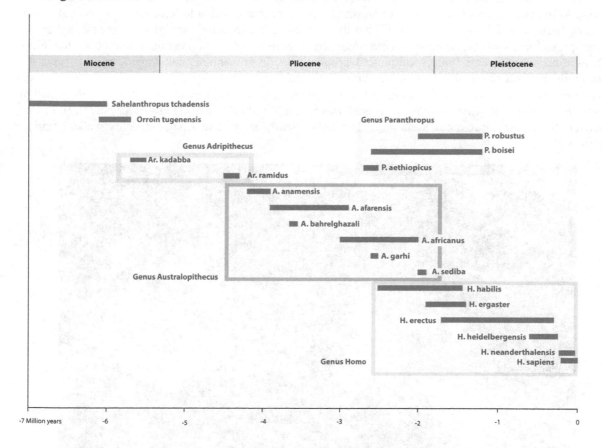

Figure 8.6: Taxonomic diagram of hominin species

What does it mean to assign species to different genera or lineages? The short answer is that researchers have made inferences about the meaning of the differences between the species and genera and have concluded that the *genera* represent hominins with fundamentally different adaptations. Such analyses depend on the age of the fossils as well as the identification of ancestral versus derived traits.

Ancestral traits are characteristics possessed by organisms due to shared ancestry. *Derived traits* are characteristics that did not exist in ancestral populations but are instead a result of an organism's more recent adaptation. For example, humans and monkeys both have five digits on each hand and foot. However, this particular trait is not indicative of a close relationship because both humans and monkeys have retained the ancestral trait of five digits, the general, ancient mammalian condition. In contrast, horses and zebras share the derived trait of a single digit (a hoof), relatively rare in mammals and occurring as a specialized adaptation to running on the open plains. Sharing of such derived traits is indicative of close evolutionary relationships. Regarding the hominid traits mentioned above, the chimpanzee and other great apes have retained the ancestral condition of a rectangular dental arch, inherited from ancestral populations of Miocene apes (Stringer and Andrews 2005, 120). This ancestral tooth arrangement is also seen in the hominin *Australopithecus anamensis,* but humans show the derived trait of a parabolic dental arch, the loss of honing canines, and the shift to a balanced dentition.

One can also think of ancestral traits as representing a more generalized condition and derived traits as those resulting from more specialized adaptations. These terms refer to adaptive potential, because evolution is irreversible. A generalized form will have more potential for adaptive flexibility than a specialized one. While the specialized form may be more efficient in the specific contexts for which it evolved, if conditions change, the specialization may not be useful, and the adaptive potential needed to respond to the changes may have been diminished. Such a scenario seems to have been played out among the three best-studied hominin genera. Within the hominins, the ancestral condition is represented by the australopithecines, such as *Australopithecus africanus* (Figure 8.7). *A. africanus* retains some apelike traits, such as a relatively small brain, pronounced prognathism, large canines, and long forelimbs. Yet the australopithecines also exhibit certain key humanlike traits related to bipedalism, such as a short, wide pelvis; upright spine; locking knee joint; and realigned and arched foot. Such details are best illustrated by the fossils attributed to *Australopithecus afarensis*, often referred to as *Lucy* (Figures 8.8 and 8.9). In fact, fossilized footprints discovered at Laetoli, Tanzania, clearly show that Lucy's species walked upright (Figure 8.10).

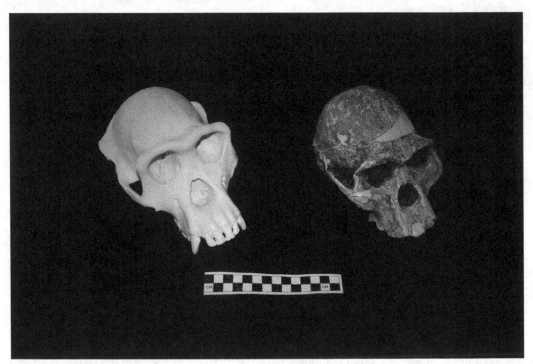

Figure 8.7: Comparison of fossil cast of *Australopithecus africanus* (STS 5) with that of a modern chimpanzee (*Pan troglodytes*)

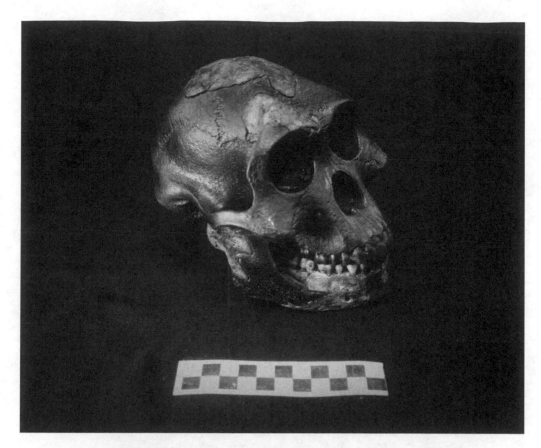

Figure 8.8: Fossil cast of *Australopithecus afarensis* (aka Lucy)

Figure 8.9: Artist's reconstruction of female *Australopithecus afarensis*

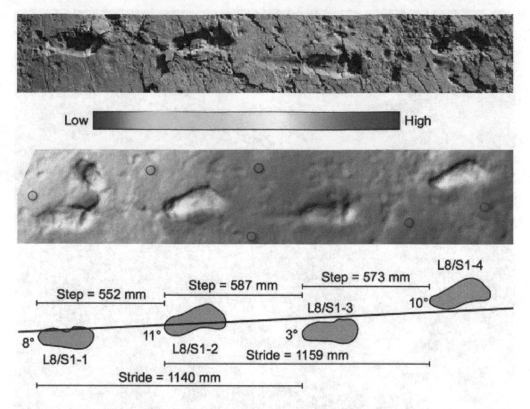

Figure 8.10: Laetoli footprints attributed to *Australopithecus afarensis*

From the combination of traits found in the australopithecines, two different sorts of specializations seem to have developed. The first of these is represented by the genus *Paranthropus*. The species in this genus all retained the ancestral condition (among hominins) of bipedal locomotion. But they developed a specialized dietary adaptation, the consumption of small, hard food items, such as nuts, roots, and seeds. These were evidently processed by simply crushing and grinding them with the teeth, especially the very large molars. As the molars became ever more massive, corresponding changes can be seen in the rest of the skull. *Paranthropus* forms exhibit prominent sagittal crests, nuchal crests, and massive, wide zygomatic bones to accommodate the large chewing muscles (Figure 8.11). These skeletal traits, while resembling those of gorillas, were not inherited from a common ancestor with gorillas. Instead, both gorillas and *Paranthropus* developed massive jaw muscles as part of their feeding adaptations. That the adaptations were very distinct is indicated by the differences in dentition. While gorilla dentition retains the ancestral ape pattern with larger front teeth and honing canines, the *Paranthropus* teeth are reorganized, with reduced canines and much larger molars. The enamel on the molars is thickened, and evidence of heavy pitting and crushing wear has been observed under the microscope. The *Paranthropus* species were specialized vegetarians and eventually became extinct. Basic characteristics of the early hominin fossils are summarized in Table 8.1.

The second kind of adaptation involved the continuation of generalized dentition, use of stone tools, and consumption of protein in the form of bone marrow and meat scavenged from carcasses of animals probably killed by carnivores.

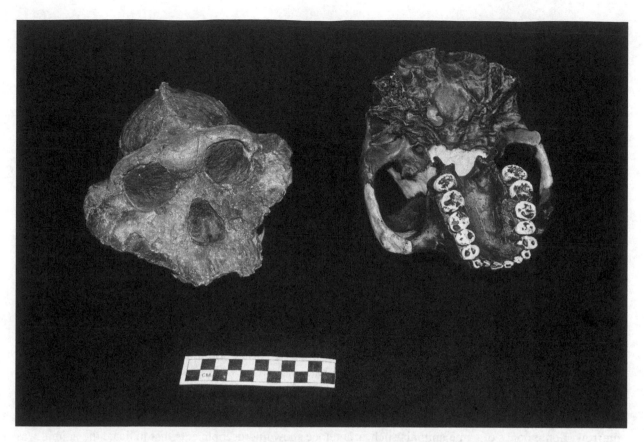

Figure 8.11: Fossil casts of *Paranthropus boisei* skulls showing (left) broad face, large supraorbital ridge, and sagittal crest (right). large spaces behind the zygomatic arches to accommodate jaw muscles and large molar teeth.

Table 8.1: Summary of Early Hominin Fossil Traits

Species	Dates	Size	Brain Size	Skull	Notes
Ard. ramidus	4.4 mya	no data	no data	non-honing canines	Woodland setting
A. anamensis	4 mya	114 lb	no data	large canines	Woodland setting
A. afarensis	3.6–3.0 mya	110 lb	430 cc	small canines parabolic arch	grasslands stone tools
A. africanus	3.0–2.0 mya	100 lb	450 cc	teeth larger than Lucy's	apelike ratio; open grasslands
A. garhi	2.5 mya	80 lb	450 cc		toolmaker; grasslands
A. sediba	2.0 mya	no data	420 cc	gracile with small teeth, slight chin	long arms, humanlike pelvis
P. robustus	2.0–1.5 mya	105 lb	510 cc	robust with sagittal crest	Grasslands

Species	Dates	Size	Brain Size	Skull	Notes
P. boisei	2.3–1.2 mya	101 lb	510 cc	robust with sagittal crest	Grasslands
P. aethiopicus	2.5 mya	no data	410 cc	robust with sagittal crest	Grasslands

cc: cubic centimeter; lb: pound; mya: million years ago

Hominin Brain Size

The human lineage represented by the genus *Homo* took an evolutionary track different from that of *Paranthropus*. Evolving from either *Australopithecus afarensis*, *A. africanus,* or possibly *A. garhi*, *Homo habilis* ("handy man") is the earliest fossil assigned to our genus (Figure 8.12). The earliest indirect evidence of stone tool use is found at the site of Dikika, in the Lower Awash Valley in Ethiopia. Fossil ungulate bones dating to about 3.4 mya show cut marks and percussion impacts made by stone tools, providing the earliest evidence for meat and marrow consumption by hominins (McPherron et al. 2010). Given the age of the site, this meat-scavenging behavior can be attributed to *Australopithecus afarensis*, the only hominin species known from that region at that time.

This pattern of behavior becomes more common at later sites which are attributed to *Homo habilis,* a species that exhibits a significant increase in brain size over earlier hominins and is believed to have been a consistent maker and user of simple stone tools. Whatever foods *H. habilis* was eating, they were processed partly with stone tools, eliminating the need for the development of large jaws and massive teeth. It seems the stone tools were used to assist early members of the genus *Homo* in their scavenging of meat and bone marrow. Animal bones at *H. habilis* sites are often crushed and split, apparently for the extraction of bone marrow. Some bones of game animals such as antelope show microscopic cuts that indicate the animal was first gnawed by a large carnivore such as a hyena and then processed by a hominin with a stone tool. Thus, the evidence suggests that the human lineage reflects a specialization involving increasingly large brains and increasing use of stone tools. Recent research indicates that these two developments are closely interconnected.

Figure 8.12: Fossil casts of *Homo habilis* skulls (KNM-ER 1470 and 1813)

Our ancestors have been consuming increasing quantities of meat for at least the last two million years (Mann 2000). The shift to the consumption of meat, (densely concentrated sources of calories and energy), is understood to have been a key element in the evolution of the genus *Homo* (Kaplan et al. 2000, 161), especially changes in the brain that led to what we identify as intelligence. The results of this shift to meat consumption on brain size are illustrated in the graph reproduced below. All but one of the members of the genus *Homo* have larger brain volumes than the australopithecines, and this distinction increases over time. It seems that the increasing consumption of lean meat by our hominin ancestors was both necessitated by and allowed for the increase in brain size that has been the hallmark of our lineage (Figure 8.13).

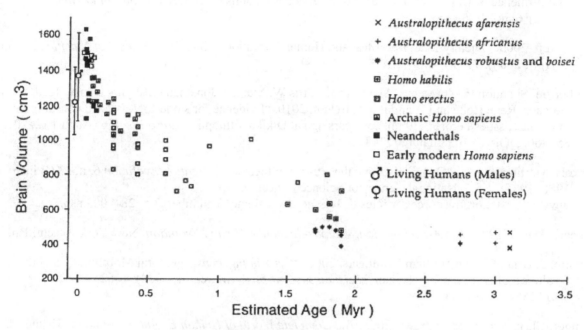

Figure 8.13: Change in Hominin brain sizes over time

References and Further Reading

Campbell, Bernard. 1974. *Human Evolution: An Introduction to Man's Adaptations.* 2nd ed. Chicago: Aldine.

Conroy, Glenn C., and Herman Pontzer. 2012. *Reconstructing Human Origins: A Modern Synthesis.* 3rd ed. New York: W. W. Norton & Company.

Clark, Wilfred E. Le Gros. 1967. *Man-Apes or Ape-Men? The Story of Discoveries in Africa.* New York: Holt, Rinehart and Winston.

Darwiniana and Evolution. n.d. "Transitional Human Fossils: Six Million Years of Human Ancestry." Darwinia.org. Accessed August 30, 2017. http://darwiniana.org/hominid.htm.

Eckhardt, Robert B. 2000. *Human Paleobiology.* Cambridge, UK: Cambridge University Press.

Feder, Kenneth L. and Michael Alan Park. 2007. *Human Antiquity: An Introduction to Physical Anthropology and Archaeology.* 5th ed. New York: McGraw Hill.

Hooper, Rowan. 2007. "Our Upright Walking Started in the Trees." New Scientist, May 31, 2007. www.newscientist.com/article.ns?id=dn11965.

Institute of Human Origins, Arizona State University, *Becoming Human.* www.becominghuman.org/.

Kaplan, Hillard, Kim Hill, Jane Lancaster, and A. Magdalena Hurtado. 2000. "A Theory of Human Life History Evolution: Diet, Intelligence, and Longevity." *Evolutionary Anthropology* 9, no. 4 (August 16, 2000: 156–85.

Larsen, Clark Spencer. 2017. *Our Origins: Discovering Physical Anthropology.* 4th ed. New York: W. W. Norton & Company.

Leonard, William R., and Marcia L. Robertson. 1994. "Evolutionary Perspectives on Human Nutrition: The Influence of Brain and Body Size on Diet and Metabolism." *American Journal of Human Biology* 6, no. 1: 77–88.

Mann, Neil. 2000. "Dietary Lean Red Meat and Human Evolution." *European Journal of Nutrition* 39, no. 2 (April 2000): 71–9.

McPherron, Shannon P., Zeresenay Alemseged, Curtis W. Marean, Jonathan G. Wynn, Denne Reed, Denis Geraads, Rene Bobe and Hamdalla A. Bearat. 2010. "Evidence for stone-tool-assisted consumption of animal tissues before 3.39 million years ago at Dikika, Ethiopia. *Nature Bol* 466 (August 12, 2010: 857–60. DOI: 10.1038/nature09248.

Nickels, Martin K. 1986. "Creationists and the Australopithecines." *Creation/Evolution* 6, no. 3 (Winter 1986–1987): 1–15. National Center for Science Education. www.ncseweb.org/resources/articles/623_issue_19_volume_6_number_3_5_28_2003.asp.

Pilbeam, David. 1972. *The Ascent of Man: An Introduction to Human Evolution.* New York: Macmillan.

Richmond, Brian G., and William L. Jungers. 2008. "*Orrorin tugenensis* Femoral Morphology and the Evolution of Hominin Bipedalism." *Science* 319, no. 5870 (March 21, 2008): 1662–5. DOI: 10.1126/science.1154197.

Stringer, Chris, and Peter Andrews. 2005. *The Complete World of Human Evolution.* London: Thames & Hudson.

Talk Origins Archive. 2016. www.talkorigins.org/faqs/homs/index.html.

Thorpe, S. K. S., R. L. Holder, and R. H. Crompton. 2007. "Origin of Human Bipedalism As an Adaptation for Locomotion on Flexible Branches." *Science* 316, no. 5829 (June 2007): 1328–31. www.sciencemag.org/cgi/content/full/sci;316/5829/1328.

Varki, Ajit. 2018. "How Are Humans Different from Other Great Apes?" American Academy of Arts and Sciences. https://www.amacad.org/news/how-are-humans-different-other-great-apes.

Chapter 9: The Emergence of Biologically Modern Humans

Surprises and Revisions

Q&A: Are we related to Neanderthals?

Yes, some of us are. DNA evidence demonstrates that Neanderthals interbred with the ancestors of modern European and East Asian populations.

By now you should be aware that the discovery of the fossil evidence for our common ancestry with apes came with a surprise. The human lineage has been characterized by increasing brain size and a dependence on tools, so scientists had expected our earliest ancestor would be a large-brained ape. Instead, *Australopithecus afarensis* was small-brained but bipedal. The recent discovery of a three-year-old *A. afarensis* girl suggests that she and her species retained an ancestral ability to climb and swing through trees like our nearest ape relatives (Wilford 2006). New research on fossils assigned to the species *Orrorin tugenensis* has pushed back the date of the evolution of bipedalism to about 6 million years ago (mya; Richmond and Jungers 2008). The surprises have continued.

For a time, some researchers suggested that the "robust" australopithecines (classified as *A. robustus A. boisei*) with their larger skulls might represent the males of the same species as the smaller, "gracile" australopithecines (*A. africanus*), mirroring the gorilla pattern of extreme sexual dimorphism. Further research has shown this not to be the case, and the robust forms have been reclassified by many as a new genus, *Paranthropus*. As new fossils continue to be discovered and new dates become available, existing interpretations are reconsidered and alternative views are evaluated. While details are still being debated, most researchers agree on the broad outlines of human evolution, from *H. habilis* to *H. erectus* (and/or *H. ergaster*) to *H. sapiens*. Most of the debates about the fossil evidence for this evolutionary sequence involve different interpretations of the relationships and interactions among the various species. This section will mainly provide a summary of some of the most important traits and behaviors attributed to different species, as well as some interpretations based on recent research.

While a detailed consideration of all these issues is beyond the scope of this introductory text, students should be able to describe the general evolutionary trend of the genus *Homo* and discuss the adaptations of the various species. You should also be able to discuss the traits scientists use to define modern humans. Finally, you should be able to discuss the recent African origin of modern humans and our relationship to the Neanderthals.

Homo Habilis

When the Leakeys discovered some of the earliest stone tools at Olduvai Gorge, they first suggested *Zinjanthropus (Paranthropus boisei)* as the toolmaker. Shortly thereafter however, they discovered a different hominid, *Homo habilis,* with a proportionately larger brain and lacking the massive chewing apparatus indicative of a specialized vegetarian diet (Figure 9.1). As a result of those discoveries, for many years it was widely accepted that *H. habilis* and perhaps other "early *Homo*" species were the makers of the first stone tools. Now we know that *Australopithecus afarensis* used stone tools to process the bones of ungulates as far back as 3.4 mya, about 900,000 years before the existence of *H. habilis* (McPherron et al. 2010). Nevertheless, *H. habilis* is identified as the species that marks a turning point in human evolution in which the members of genus *Homo* are consistently associated with stone tools and the dietary changes they indicate. *H. habilis* had a larger brain (680–800 cubic centimeters [cc]) than earlier hominins, and the consistent presence of stone tools implies greater intelligence. Larger brains and habitual tool use become the hallmarks of the human lineage.

The stone tools that are found at sites attributed to *H. habilis* are classified as part of the Olduwan tool tradition, named after Olduvai Gorge, where they were first discovered. Olduwan tools consist of simple, crudely made pebble tools (Figure 9.2) and flakes that would seem to be best suited to scavenging. Most of the bones from these sites are the lower-limb bones of ungulates such as antelopes, body parts that have relatively little meat on them. Additionally, none of the Olduwan tools are suitable as projectiles or other weapons that might be capable of taking down an antelope. The impact fractures and cut marks (some of which occur on top of carnivore tooth marks) are more consistent with hominins scavenging carcasses of animals killed by carnivores and breaking open the leg bones to extract the marrow (Binford 1985).

Figure 9.1: Fossil casts of *Homo habilis* (KNM-ER 1470) and *H. rudolfensis* (KNM-ER 1813)

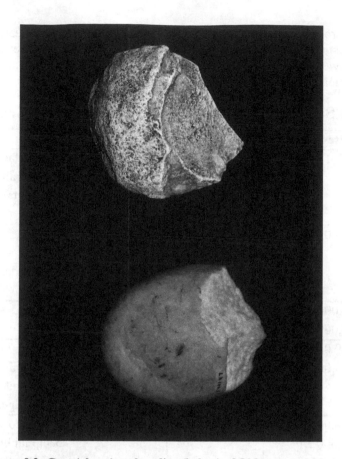

Figure 9.2: Cast (above) and replica (below) of Olduwan pebble tools

More recent research on the eastern shore of Lake Turkana in Kenya has provided evidence that hominins processed a wide range of animal remains as far back as 1.95 mya (Braun et al. 2010). Fractured long bones and bones with cut marks indicate that the carcasses of hippos, rhinos, crocodiles, turtles, and catfish were being processed with stone tools. That these activities predate the existence of *Homo erectus* (including *H. ergaster*) makes *H. habilis* the most likely candidate for the butchering and scavenging behavior exhibited at the site.

While scavenging may not seem very glamorous and may not fulfill our expectations of a powerful and dominant human ancestor, it nevertheless seems that the hominins were, for many millennia, mainly foraging and scavenging for a living. Importantly, this meant they were not competing directly for food with the many carnivores in their environment but were nonetheless benefitting from the addition of meat products that were necessary for brain development. Indeed, scavenging may have been the primary dietary adaptation of hominins well into *Homo erectus* times.

Homo Erectus

H. erectus is the first species for which we find fossil remains outside the continent of Africa. The earliest example of *H. erectus* fossils outside Africa is at the site of Dminisi, Georgia (the former Soviet republic), where the remains date back to 1.75 mya (Figure 9.3). Distinctive anatomical traits exhibited by these fossils include an angular cranium that is widest at the base of the skull and has a keel or ridge along the top centerline. In cross-section, *Homo erectus* skulls have a gabled outline, like the profile of a barn roof. Another characteristic trait shown in this figure is the prominent brow ridges above the eye sockets. It has been suggested that the expansion of *H. erectus* out of Africa was a result of the expansion of their range, following animal herds because of the increased importance of meat in the diet (Wilford 2000). Members of the species were larger than any earlier hominids, with brain sizes averaging nearly 1,000 cc (Table 9.1). They were also tall and strong; the 12-year-old boy from Lake Turkana was 5 feet 10 inches at the time of his death, and his bones were slender but strong, indicating powerful musculature and a very active lifestyle. Increasing amounts of meat in the diet would have been necessary to fuel their larger bodies and brains.

Table 9.1: Summary of Fossil Traits in Members of Genus *Homo*

Species	Dates	Size	Brain Size	Skull	Notes
H. habilis	2.5–1.8 mya	5 ft 0 in	680 cc	smaller face, larger brain than austr. of sim age	associated with simple tools
H. erectus	1.8–0.3 mya	5 ft 10 in	950 cc	keeled cranium skull widest at base	Acheulean technology
H. floresiensis	80,000–18,000 BP	3 ft 4 in	380 cc	skull widest at base	micro-blade technology
H. heidelbergensis	789,000–130,000 BP	5 ft 4 in	1,250 cc	reduced prognathism prominent brow ridges	simple tools, prepared core technology
H. neanderthalensis	350,000–30,000 BP	5 ft 6 in	1,500 cc	elongated with occipital bun, prominent brow ridges	Mousterian tool technology
H. sapiens	195,000 BP–present	5 ft 7 in	1,400 cc	high round cranium, vertical forehead	increased symbolic behavior

Note:

mya : million years ago.

BP : years before present.

cc : cubic centimeters

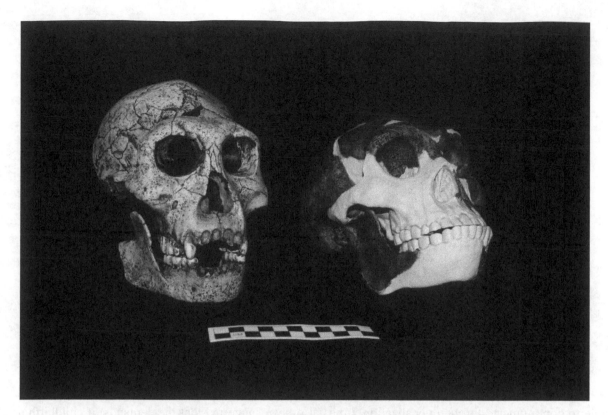

Figure 9.3: Fossil casts of *Homo erectus* skull (KNM-ER 3733) and Dmanisi cranium (D2700)

Yet, the early *H. erectus* populations were still scavengers, armed only with simple pebble tools like those used by *H. habilis*. Some researchers have argued that the sites Ambrona and Torralba in Spain indicate that *H. erectus* populations engaged in cooperative hunting of large game, but this view has been largely discredited. It has also been suggested that *H. erectus* practiced cannibalism, a contention based largely on the discovery of skulls from Zhoukhoudian, China, from which the bases and faces of the skulls were removed. Recent reanalysis of these fossils has indicated that predation by large, extinct hyenas is the most likely explanation for the damage observed on erectus skulls (Boaz and Ciochon 2001). Thus, like their predecessors among the australopithecines and *H. habilis, Homo erectus* individuals were among the prey consumed by large carnivores.

Eventually, by about 1.4 mya, *H. erectus* developed more complex stone tools referred to as *Acheulean*, but this technology was apparently not the cause of or necessary for the migration out of Africa, as the Dmanisi fossils are associated with simpler tools. Even the more advanced Acheulean technology lacks tools that could be construed as hunting weapons. The primary tool type was the hand axe, which could potentially be used for many purposes but probably not as a lethal projectile. Rather, the Acheulean tools (Figure 9.4) seem to have allowed *H. erectus* to be more efficient at scavenging meat and marrow from carcasses they encountered.

Leaving Africa meant moving out of the warm tropics and into temperate zones and a variety of cooler environmental settings. This migration was probably assisted by the ability of *H. erectus* populations to control fire. It is not clear whether they were able to generate fire on their own. It is also unclear how far back in time the control of fire can be unequivocally inferred. Nevertheless, fire would have provided several advantages, such as warmth, protection from predators, and heat for cooking. It would also provide light, a way of extending the day and a place around which social groups could interact during the evenings.

Figure 9.4: Replica of Acheulean Hand axe, length 7 Inches (17.7 cm)

There is some physiological evidence from fossil brain casts that *Homo erectus* would have been able to communicate through vocalization. It has also been suggested that the demands of childbirth and child rearing would imply the existence of sexual division of labor. The brain size of *Homo erectus* individuals was such that the skulls of their infants would have been too large to pass through the birth canal. This suggests that infants were born before their brains were fully developed, as is the case with modern humans. Like modern humans, infants would be almost helpless during the first couple of years of growth, and this implies a division of labor, in which some members of the group cared for the young while others foraged and scavenged for food. In such behaviors, we can infer the beginnings of social behavior that becomes increasingly elaborated in later human species. So, *Homo erectus* seems to have controlled fire, produced complex tools, and used them to become a mobile, efficient scavenger, adapting to regions throughout Africa, Asia, and Europe and possibly benefiting from rudimentary vocal communication and simple social organization. This way of life persisted throughout much of the Old World, largely unchanged for about 1 million years, until the appearance of modern humans.

About 700,000 years ago, after some *Homo erectus* populations had already left Africa, those groups remaining in Africa gave rise to a new species, *Homo heidelbergensis* (Figure 9.5). After evolving in Africa, *H. heidelbergensis* populations also migrated out of Africa, and their fossils have been found in Europe and East Asia. The populations in Europe eventually evolved into the Neanderthals, and those remaining in Africa evolved into *Homo sapiens* (Campbell et al. 2006, 313). Thus, *Homo heidelbergensis* is believed to be the common ancestor of Neanderthals and biologically modern humans. Further evidence for and discussion of this conclusion is presented in the video *Last Human Standing*, which may be viewed at the link below.

Last Human Standing

https://www.dailymotion.com/video/x3oatqe

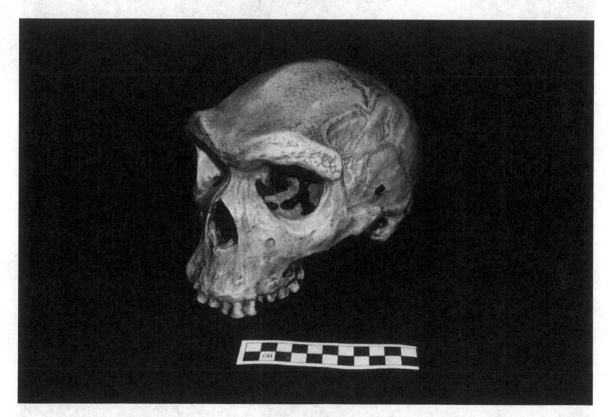

Figure 9.5. Fossil cast of *Homo heidelbergensis* Skull (from Kabwe, Africa). This specimen is characterized by a large brain size and less prominent brow ridge than *H. erectus*, but it is still widest at the base, and very angular, traits shared with *H. erectus*.

Archaic and Modern Humans

Anatomically modern human fossils are defined as such because they exhibit a set of characteristics that sets them off from earlier, "archaic" human populations, such as Neanderthals (Figure 9.6). Neanderthals have a low, elongated skull, with a prominent bulge or bun at the rear and a large brow ridge over the eye sockets. Their average cranial capacity was larger than that of modern humans, although the distribution of brain sizes measured for both species overlap considerably (Figure 8.13).

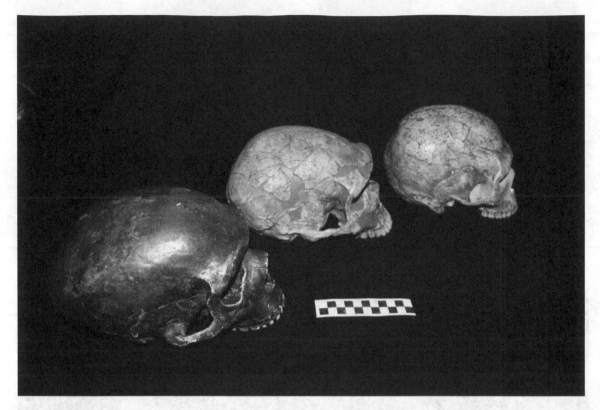

Figure 9.6: Fossil casts of skulls of three Neanderthal specimens, (from left to right) La Ferrassie I, La Chappelle-aux-Saints, and Le Moustier. Note elongated skulls with occipital buns and prominent brow ridges.

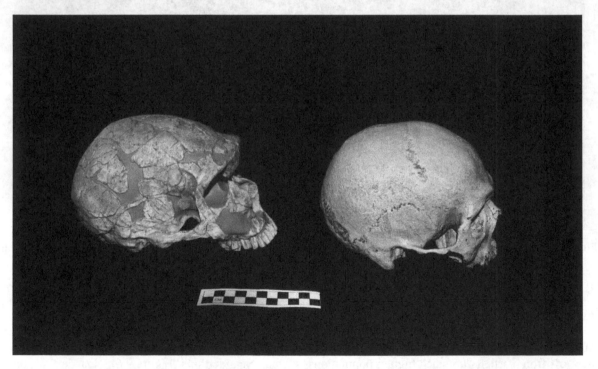

Figure 9.7: Comparison of skull and facial features in Neanderthal (La Ferrassie I; left) and a prehistoric example of *Homo sapiens* (Cro-Magnon I; right) discovered near Les Eyzies, France, and dating to 30,000 years ago

In contrast, modern humans have a flat face, lacking the prognathism characteristic of earlier forms. In addition, the skull is rounded, with a high cranium and vertical forehead. There are no heavy brow ridges, and the face is smaller and lighter, with a protruding chin. There are behavioral differences as well. Modern humans produced more complex and specialized tool kits than *H. erectus* or archaic *H. sapiens* groups, such as *Neanderthals*. Moreover, some researchers suggest that modern humans perceived and adapted to the environment differently from archaic peoples.

For example, archaeologist Ofer Bar-Yosef has compared the artifacts of Neanderthals and modern humans who lived in the same region of what is now Israel. Based on the sources of stone tool raw materials, he concludes that modern humans seem to have been more mobile, exploiting resources that were further away from their home bases and even venturing out into desert areas that may have been avoided by or unknown to the Neanderthals. A similar argument has been made by Paul Bahn, who compared modern human and Neanderthal sites in southern France. Almost all modern sapiens camps were situated on high ridges that offered good views, providing the opportunity to monitor the movement of game herds and to plan their hunting strategies in response. In contrast, Neanderthals lived at lower elevation sites, in caves down in the valleys where they would have had less advanced warning of approaching game animals. It seems their approach to hunting was more opportunistic, involving less logistical planning. The difference may have conferred only a small advantage to *Homo sapiens,* but perhaps that was enough. Over time, the Neanderthal populations were displaced into less desirable regions, such as Britain, northern Spain, and northern Germany, and they disappeared altogether about 27,000 years ago.

Learning and transmitting the more sophisticated environmental knowledge of modern humans may have been facilitated by symbolic communication; prehistoric artwork provides physical evidence of their capacity for symbolic communication. It has been suggested that by adding artistic designs to their environment (in rock art, for example), modern humans were identifying important places and generating mnemonic devices or cognitive maps of the landscape, helping them remember the locations of springs and food sources. The ability to conceive of the known landscape and to imagine an unknown world beyond it was long believed to be a distinctly modern human trait. Why? The earliest hominid fossils in Australia are fully modern humans; it was argued that it must have required more complex conceptualization of the earth to reach such an isolated area. That is, it was necessary to conceive of a land mass that was largely out of view and invent boats to cross the straits between Indonesia and Australia. Modern humans were the only land animals in Southeast Asia to reach Australia; surely it must have required a special kind of human to do so. Or perhaps not.

Homo Floresiensis

Although not directly related to modern humans, the case of *Homo floresiensis* provides an interesting and completely unexpected example of evolutionary diversity within the genus *Homo*. It was long thought that like Australia, the islands east of Java were inaccessible to premodern humans. But in 1998, researchers working on the island of Flores in Indonesia found deposits containing stone tools dated about 800,000 years old, much older than the first modern humans. The form of the stone tools and the dating of the find implied that *Homo erectus* had somehow traveled beyond Java and the Wallace Trench, the deep-sea trench that separates Java from the eastern islands of the Indonesian archipelago. It seemed likely that boats might have been required to accomplish this move. Even more remarkable, however, was the subsequent discovery of skeletons of the humans who made the stone tools.

The diminutive skeletons exhibit an unexpected mixture of characteristics in a body standing only 3.5 feet tall. The brain size is about the same as that of a chimpanzee, and the lower jaw lacks a chin. However, the face is small, delicate, and non-prognathic, like that of modern humans. Although the cranial capacity is little more than a third the size of *H. erectus*, it has a similar shape. The skull is angular, with a prominent keel or ridge along the top of the skull, and the widest part of the skull is at the base (Figure 9.8). The hips resemble those of australopithecines, and it is clear that the species was bipedal (Stringer 2004; Dalton 2005).

Figure 9.8: Rear view of fossil casts of skulls of (left to right) *Homo erectus*, *H. floresiensis*, **and** *H. sapiens*. **Note that the skulls of** *H. erectus* **and** *H. floresiensis* **are keeled or pointed at the top, and the widest part of the skull is at the base, in contrast to the shape of modern human skulls.**

Because of the unique combination of traits, researchers have classified the find as a new species of humans, *Homo floresiensis*; the press has dubbed them the "Hobbits" because of their small size and apparently long arms. It seems the species evolved from an ancestral population of *Homo erectus* that somehow reached the island of Flores during a period of lower sea level, perhaps by boat. Isolated from the mainland, over time, the body size was reduced by a process called *island dwarfing*; the same process seems to have affected the *Stegodon*, the tiny extinct elephants the Hobbits hunted. The latest dates for the Hobbit skeletons are only 18,000 years ago, which means this small, isolated species persisted until well after the time modern humans entered the region (Stringer 2004). *Homo floresiensis* is not part of the lineage of modern humans, but the discovery of the species illustrates at least two significant points: humans did not need to be modern in order to build boats and cross water barriers, and unexpected evolutionary twists and turns are still being discovered.

Out of Africa Certainly, But When?

The main question regarding the relationship between modern humans and Neanderthals is the nature of their interactions. How different were they? If they were in competition, did it involve warfare? What was the Neanderthals' contribution to the genetic makeup of modern humans? Most simply, were they capable of interbreeding? This question is central to the well-researched novels in the *Clan of the Cave Bear* series by Jean Auel. The question of the potential for interbreeding was traditionally viewed as central to the debate about which model of modern human evolution is correct.

The two main competing hypotheses or models for the evolution of modern humans are referred to as *multiregional evolution* (MRE) and *recent African origin* (RAO). The multiregional model recognizes that *Homo erectus* left Africa about 2 million years ago, spreading throughout Asia and Europe. Then, erectus populations evolved first into archaic sapiens and eventually *Homo sapiens,* in many regions throughout their range. Therefore, archaic sapiens populations such as Neanderthals would have contributed to the wide range of diversity in modern humans. The retention of some regional clusters of traits could yield what we might today call *races*.

The RAO model is a bit more complicated, as two or more migrations out of Africa are identified. Clearly, *H. erectus* populations left Africa about 2 mya (based on the fossils from Dmanisi), and the erectus populations did evolve into other species after leaving Africa (archaic sapiens as well as *Homo floresiensis*). However, fully modern sapiens first evolved in East Africa between 150,000 and 200,000 years ago, not throughout Eurasia. After their evolution in East Africa, modern sapiens also left the continent to occupy other environments in what was the second "out of Africa" migration. As modern sapiens groups moved into areas already occupied by archaic sapiens forms, they out competed the earlier forms, first pushing them into marginal habitats and eventually overwhelming them entirely.

The two models have different implications for the fossil record. If MRE is correct, we should expect to see sequences of transitional fossils in many parts of the Old World, with some very ancient traits retained in modern populations. If RAO is correct, transitional fossils (between *erectus* and modern *sapiens*) should occur only in Africa, where modern *sapiens* evolved. In addition, there should be a suite of characteristics that distinguishes all modern humans from all premodern forms. The fossil record is somewhat equivocal on these points, with much debate focused on how to interpret the details of key fossil specimens. Perhaps the most promising area of study for providing a definitive answer is the comparison of mitochondrial DNA.

Unfortunately for proponents of the MRE model, several kinds of recent evidence have converged to offer convincing support for the RAO model (Shipman 2003). Genetic research on modern East African populations has documented the oldest and most diverse lineages known so far. We would expect modern humans to have evolved in the region where the most genetic diversity is present (because the mitochondrial DNA has had the longest time to accumulate mutations in that region), and the researchers estimated that the oldest lineages dated back to about 170,000 years ago. This estimate fits well with age and location of the modern human fossils recently discovered at Herto, Ethiopia, which are dated from 154,000 to 160,000 years ago. Moreover, the fossils accepted as being transitional between archaic and modern *sapiens* are from Africa, not other parts of the Old World.

The other sort of evidence that undermines the MRE model comes from the comparison of Neanderthal DNA with that of modern humans. In 1999, Svante Pääbo and a team from the Max Planck Institute for Evolutionary Anthropology in Germany made a dramatic breakthrough in the recovery of DNA from Neanderthal fossils. Several studies of Neanderthal DNA done about that time reached the same conclusion: that Neanderthals did not contribute to the genetics of modern sapiens in Europe (Wilford 2000; Harrington 2000; Wade 2006; Shipman 2003). However, only a few years later, Pääbo's team found evidence that Neanderthals share between 1 and 4 percent of their DNA with non-African populations of modern *Homo sapiens.* In other words, there is now strong evidence for small-scale interbreeding between modern humans and Neanderthals that most likely occurred in southwest Asia or Eastern Europe after modern humans left Africa (Sankararaman et al. 2012; 2014). There is even some indication that certain characteristics in modern humans can be traced to Neanderthal genes, such as red hair, prominent brow ridges, rosy cheeks, thick straight hair, fair skin and freckles, and the propensity for autoimmune diseases, among others.

So as is often the case in science, answering one question leads to many more, and the picture of our prehistoric past is more complicated than ever. Certainly, we are all of African origin, but there seem to have been several out-of-Africa events, followed by subsequent mixing among the populations (Figure 9.9). Modern humans left Africa and replaced the archaic human populations that had preceded them, but they also interbred with them to some small degree. One might consider this the Mostly Out of Africa model. Moreover, the interbreeding now documented among Neanderthal, Denisovan, and modern human groups argues against the MRO expectation that there should be distinct regionally isolated populations analogous to races.

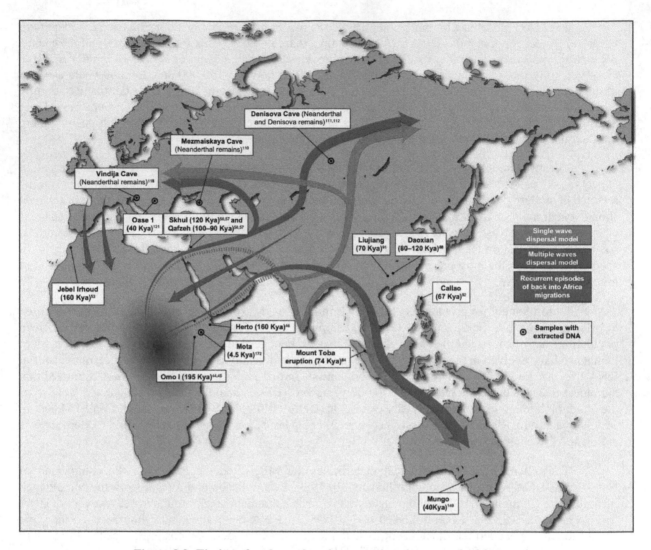

Figure 9.9: Timing of early modern human migrations out of Africa

It is now estimated that the Neanderthal and ancestral human lineages split about 500,000 years ago, before modern sapiens had evolved. According to Pääbo, the mitochondrial DNA differences between Neanderthals and modern humans suggest they separated from a common ancestor about 400,000 years ago. The estimated timing of the split implies that the common ancestor could be *Homo heidlebergensis*. It is also estimated that both the Neanderthal and modern human populations in Europe were very small in number, perhaps fewer than 10,000 individuals. Apparently, all populations of early humans were rather small, and their numbers grew significantly only after the end of the Ice Age (Wade 2006, 4).

References and Further Reading

Alper, Joe. 2003. "Rethinking Neanderthals." *Smithsonian* (June 2003): 83–7.

Binford, Lewis. 1985. "Ancestral Life Ways: The Faunal Record." *Anthroquest* 32, no. 1: 15–20.

Boaz, Noel T., and Russell L. Ciochon. 2001. "The Scavenging of 'Peking Man.'" *Natural History* (March 2001): 46–51.

Braun, David R., Jown W. K. Harris, Naomi E. Levin, Jack T. McCoy, Andy I. R. Herries, Marion K. Bamford, Laura C. Bishop, Brian G. Richmond, and Mzalendo Kibunjia. 2010. "Early Hominin Diet

Included Dirverse Terrestrial and Aquatic Animals 1.95 Ma in East Turkana, Kenya." *PNAS* 107, no. 22: 10002–7. DOI: 10.1073/pnas.1002181107.

Brown, P., T. Sutikna, M. J. Morwood, R. P. Soejono, Jatmiko, E. Wayhu Saptomo, and Rokus Awe Due. 2004. "A New Small-Bodied Hominin from the Late Pleistocene of Flores, Indonesia." *Nature* 431 (October 28, 2004): 1055–61.

Campbell, Bernard G., James D. Loy, and Kathryn Cruz-Uribe. 2006. *Humankind Emerging.* 9th ed. Boston: Pearson Education, Inc.

Carretero, Jose-Miguel, Laura Rodriguez, Rebeca Garcia-Gonzalez, Juan-Luis Arsuaga, Asier Gomez-Olivencia, Carlos Lorenzo, Alejandro Bonmati, Ana Gracia, Ignacio Martinez and Rolf Quam. 2012. "Stature Estimation from Complete Long Bones in the Middle Pleistocene Humans from the Sima de lose Huesos, Sierra de Atapuerca (Spain)." *Journal of Human Evolution* 62, no. 2 (February 2012): 242–55. DOI: 10.1016/j.jhevol.2011.11.004. Epub December 22, 2011.

Dalton, Rex. 2005. "Looking for the Ancestors." *Nature* 434 (March 24, 2005): 432–4. www.nature.com/nature.

Harrington, Spencer P. M. 2000. "DNA Study: Neanderthals Played Little Part in Evolution of Modern Humans." *Archaeology* (April 5, 2000). https://archive.archaeology.org/online/news/neanderdna.html.

Knight, Will, and Rachel Nowak. 2004. "Tiny New Species of Human Unearthed." New Scientist, October 27, 2004. https://www.newscientist.com/article/dn6588-tiny-new-species-of-human-unearthed/.

McDougall, I., F. H. Brown, and J. G. Fleagle. 2005. "Stratigraphic Placement and Age of Modern Humans from Kibish, Ethiopia." *Nature* 433 (February 17, 2005): 733–6.

Richmond, Brian G., and William L. Jungers. 2008. "*Orrorin tugenensis* Femoral Morphology and the Evolution of Hominin Bipedalism." *Science* 319, no. 5870 (March 21, 2008): 1662–5. https://pubmed.ncbi.nlm.nih.gov/18356526/.

Shipman, Pat. 2003. "We Are All Africans." *American Scientist* 91, no. 6 (November–December 2003): 496–9.

Sankararaman, Sriram, Swapan Mallick, Michael Dannemann, Kay Prufer, Janet Kelso, Svante Paabo, Nick Patterson, and David Reich. 2014. "The Genomic Landscape of Neanderthal Ancestry in Present-Day Humans." *Nature* 507 (March 20, 2014): 354–7. https://doi.org/10.1038/nature12961.

Sankararaman, Sriram, Nick Patterson, Heng Li, Svante Pääbo, and David Reich. 2012. "The Date of Interbreeding Between Neanderthals and Modern Humans." *PLOS Genetics*, October 4, 2012. https://doi.org/10.1371/journal.pgen.1002947.

Stringer, Chris. 2004. "A Stranger from Flores." *Nature (October 27, 2004).* https://www.nature.com/articles/news041025-3.

Wade, Nicholas. 2006. "New DNA Test Is Yielding Clues to Neanderthals." *New York Times,* November 16, 2006. http://www.nytimes.com/2006/11/16/science/16neanderthal.html.

Wilford, John Noble. 2000. "Tests Suggest Neanderthals Were Hunters, Not Scavengers." *New York Times,* June 13, 2000. http://www.nytimes.com/library/national/science/061300sci-anthro-neanderthal.html.

Wilford, John Noble. 2006. "Little Girl, 3 Million Years Old, Offers New Hints on Evolution." *New York Times,* September 21, 2006. http://www.nytimes.com/2006/09/21/science/21child.html?ei=5070&en=c1843fc5064123.

Wilford, John Noble. 2000. "Fossil Signs of First Human Migration Are Found." *New York Times,* May 12, 2000. http://www.nytimes.com/library/national/science/051200sci-ancient-skull.html.

Wong, Kate. 2005. "The Littlest Human: A Spectacular Find in Indonesia Reveals That a Strikingly Different Hominid Shared the Earth with Our Kind in the Not So Distant Past." *Scientific American,* February 2005, 58–65.

Chapter 10: Cultural Evolution in Modern Humans

In previous chapters, we have focused mainly on the philosophical arguments and genetic and fossil evidence for human biological evolution. However, in the period since the evolution of fully modern humans, most of the changes in our species have been the result of *cultural* evolution. The beginnings of agriculture, the expansion of humans into the New World, the rise and fall of civilizations; all of these developments and more were accomplished only after humans became fully modern. It is these sorts of changes and the archaeological evidence for them that we will examine during the latter parts of the book. The human species is a product of both biological and cultural evolution, but biological changes played a more prominent role in the early evolution of humans, while cultural changes have dominated the more recent developments that characterize our species.

Q&A: How is it possible to know where and how prehistoric people lived?

The cultural changes in human lifeways are documented almost entirely by the material byproducts of human behavior that comprise the archaeological record.

Culture as Human Adaptation

Culture can be defined as the complete set of knowledge, belief, and rules of behavior that are learned by members of a society (Tylor 1871). Culture is also our extrasomatic means of adaptation. In other words, culture exists outside of or beyond the body; it is intellectual rather than biological, and it is the way we make sense of and interface with the physical and social environments within which we live. It is the primary means for nongenetic adaptation (Ashmore and Sharer 2010, 18). The material byproducts of hominin behavior reflect culture at some level, and some archaic human populations, especially Neanderthals, even generated rock art. But it is during the Upper Paleolithic period that archeologists see a significant increase in artwork and other activities that seem to indicate a leap forward in the complexity of human culture. There are sites in South Africa that have yielded Upper Paleolithic–style stone tools and perhaps representational art dating as far back as 70,000 years. In Europe, this cultural evolution occurred about 40,000 years ago.

Randall White (1982; 1993) has identified a series of eight major behavioral developments that are evident in the Late Paleolithic period. A brief consideration of just a few of these cultural innovations is sufficient to illustrate the degree to which material remains can help us identify cultural behaviors that changed the ways modern humans adapt.

Manufacture of Nonutilitarian Objects

Nonutilitarian artifacts are those that don't serve any obvious necessary practical function. They include such things as jewelry, body art, and tools that are unnecessarily fancy or too fragile to actually be used. Nonutilitarian objects are generally inferred to have had symbolic meanings rather than practical value. So, for example, personal adornment like tattoos might serve to identify an individual, communicate their role in society, or document their relationship to a particular social group. Jewelry may indicate social status, the accumulation of wealth, or participation in a social network that provides access to high-value resources.

Movement of Raw Materials over Long Distances

The movement of raw materials from a distant source to a place where tools made from those materials are manufactured, used, and discarded indicates several sorts of sophisticated thinking. The fact that a certain raw material was recognized as appropriate and preferred for a particular task and that it was collected and brought to a location where the raw material doesn't occur naturally indicates an awareness of spatial distributions. It also reflects the ability to plan ahead and take the raw material to the places where it will be used in the future. Gaining access to the raw material suggests the people involved had social relationships with the intervening groups that would allow for visiting the raw material source or trading for the material.

Elaborate Burials Containing Grave Goods

Burials with grave goods are generally taken as an indication of a sense of belonging to a social group and the care that is given to a deceased member of the group. Grave goods also imply that people recognize that certain personal items belong to the deceased or are part of that person's identity. The inclusion of grave goods might also reflect a belief in an afterlife, where such things as weapons and containers might be needed by the deceased, either in the afterlife or during the deceased's journey to the spirit world.

Production of Works of Art

It is likely that much or most artwork is a form of symbolic communication. Finding prehistoric art means that someone felt it was important to take the time to create it. It is reasonable to expect that there was a cultural reason to create the art and a reason that it was produced or deposited in a particular location. For example, many examples of rock art occur in caves, and that is often taken to indicate the artists had a sense of entering the underworld; producing the art was part of a spiritual journey. Other designs depicting hunting scenes might be commemorating past hunts or might be attempts to capture the animals' spirits so as to be successful in upcoming hunts. In any event, the production of art is presumed to have intellectual meaning to those who create it.

Of course, it is impossible to directly observe the behavior of humans who lived in prehistoric times, so it is necessary to make inferences about their behavior from the material culture they left behind. Archaeological sites usually do not contain fossils, because most sites are too young for fossilization to have occurred during the time since they were deposited. So rather than yielding fossils, most archaeological sites are made up of artifacts, features, and ecofacts. *Artifacts* are any portable item that has been manufactured, used, modified, or moved by humans. They include things as mundane as waste flakes generated during the manufacture of stone tools and a pebble picked up and used as a hammerstone, as well as items such as food remains, milling stones, elaborate jewelry, ceramic vessels, glass bottles, and papyrus scrolls. *Features* are also made by humans, but they are things that may be thought of as fixtures or facilities within a site, which are not usually portable. Examples include such things as building walls, campfires, irrigation canals, pyramids, and rock art. *Ecofacts* are natural materials that are recovered within archaeological sites that are indicative of things such as the depositional conditions that produced the soil layers, insects that may indicate the season the site was occupied, and pollen that provides information on the vegetation at the site during the time of occupation. All of these contents of archaeological sites and the relationships among the sites themselves are used to make inferences about the behaviors that produced the material remains.

Artifacts and Technology

Most people probably give little or no thought to stone tool manufacture. Nevertheless, stone tool technology is important for understanding our past because it represents a huge part of the archeological record. Stone tools and the byproducts of their manufacture are virtually ubiquitous on archaeological sites from most time periods, including well into the Neolithic. The earliest stone tools date back to about 3.3 million years ago and are believed to have been made by *Australopithecus ramidus*. The earliest stone tools made by members of genus *Homo* were the Olduwan tools made by *Homo habilis* about 2.4 million years ago. The oldest pottery vessels seem to be those made by the Jomon culture in Japan about 12,000 years ago. That means that 99.5 percent of the archaeological record of tool use consists almost entirely of stone tools (and some of the bones on which they were used). If we are to understand much at all about human cultural behavior prior to the past 12,000 years, we need to pay attention to stone tools and the byproducts of their manufacture.

Lithic artifacts (stone tools and their byproducts) are useful indicators of human behavior for several reasons. First, they are essentially nonperishable. It is logical to assume that early humans were using other kinds of materials, such as plants and animal hides, but those types of organics do not preserve readily for long periods of time. The further back in time one is working, the more likely it is that lithics will dominate the archaeological record. In addition, stone tool manufacturing is a reductive technology. Most of the tools used today are built with additive technologies—that is, several kinds of materials are combined or assembled to make the final tool. Reductive technologies work differently and are less common today than in ancient times. In making a stone tool, such as a spear point, one chips away all the stone material that is not a spear point. Conceptually, this is something like a sculptor chipping away all the marble that is not the image of Venus de Milo, without the benefit of a chisel. Instead, stone tools are manufactured by using hammers made of stone, bone, antler, or hardwood to remove material from a core, or chunk of raw material.

This chipping or flaking (aka. flint knapping) is actually fairly complicated. One cannot simply smash two rocks together and obtain a useful tool. Even when making a relatively simple stone tool, such as an Olduwan pebble tool (Figure 10.1), one must control the amount of force applied to the stone, the angle at which the force is applied, and the precise location on the rock to which the force is applied. And the same thing must be done, in the proper sequence, for each chip removed from the raw material. In the case of an artifact like an early hand axe made by *Homo erectus,* a single tool requires the systematic removal of hundreds or even thousands of chips or flakes (Figure 10.2). I constantly marvel that our prehistoric ancestors figured out the physics of sending force through a viscous solid (in modern scientific terms), which is the way chipping acts on cryptocrystalline rocks, such as flint and volcanic glass.

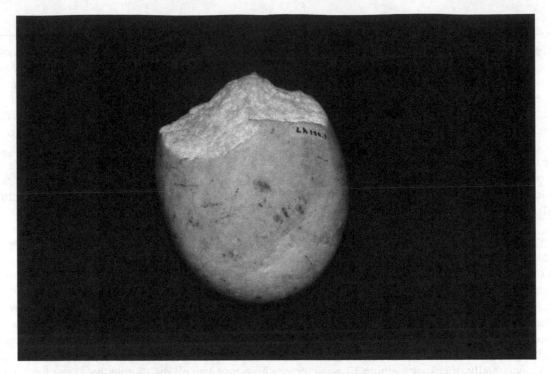

Figure 10.1: Olduwan pebble tool replica, showing the simple design with only a few flakes removed from the smooth pebble.

Figure 10.2: Lower Abbevillian hand axe replica, showing that flakes have been removed from the entire tool, reshaping the stone and producing multiple working edges in the process

Another important aspect of flint knapping as a reductive technology is that flaking produces byproducts at each stage of tool manufacture. These byproducts are mostly discarded, but they can be used to infer what parts of the manufacturing sequence took place at which locations, as well as telling us what specifically the toolmaker was trying to do at each step along the way. And to the extent that we can identify and distinguish different sources of raw material, we can often determine where different parts of the manufacturing sequence took place. Consider the following example.

I've had the good fortune to be able to analyze an artifact collection from the Fillmore Pass site, a 10,000-year-old campsite at Fort Bliss, Texas. The collection contains several dozen Folsom points, along with a number of preforms representing the earlier stages in the spear point manufacturing sequence. Although all of the preforms were made of chert from local sources in the Franklin Mountains, none of the completed Folsom points were of those materials. All of the finished points were made of materials from other parts of the Southwest, some from as far away as Amarillo, Texas, and they were all broken during use. What we can infer from this pattern is that Folsom points were being made at the Fillmore Pass site using local materials, but many attempts were unsuccessful, and the broken preforms were discarded on the site. Any completed points made of Franklin Mountains chert were carried away to be used and were eventually broken and discarded somewhere else. The completed points discarded at Fillmore Pass consist entirely of points made elsewhere; they were broken during use and replaced with new points at the Fillmore Pass site, and the discarded bases leave a record of the distant raw material sources that were used by the site's occupants. Some of the raw materials are very distinctive, so it has been possible to show that the site's occupants traveled at least 250 miles to the north and east of El Paso. So even if tools look really crude (like some of the Olduwan tools made by *H. habilis*), we can be confident that they reflect human activity when they occur miles away from the sources of raw material from which they were made. Remember the lengthy discussion in Chapter 3 regarding the interpretation of indirect evidence? It's very relevant to the study of stone tool manufacture.

Aside from the things we can infer from the technological details of the manufacturing process, we can make inferences about culture change. If we compare the tools from different time periods, it is possible to see some general trends in biological and cultural change (Table 10.1). The simplest technologies involving simple pebble tools and flakes are earliest, and they are associated with the earliest hominin forms (Figure 10.1). Increasingly more sophisticated tools are invented by successively more evolved species. The tools created by *Homo erectus* populations, often assigned to the Acheulean tradition (Figure 10.3), require more control and planning to execute. The hand axe, for example, requires the removal of hundreds of flakes in a particular sequence in order to thin and shape the tool into its final form. It also requires the toolmaker to have an idea of what the final form is before starting the manufacturing process, and the ability to plan how to move through the steps needed to reach the final form. This is a level of sophistication not evidenced by the earliest stone tools.

Table 10.1: Summary of Stone Tool Traditions, Dates, and Associated Species (Adapted from Stringer and Andrews, 2005, 215)

Tool technology	Time range	Population
Olduwan	2.5 mya	*H. habilis*
Acheulean	1.8 mya–300,000 BP	*H. erectus*
Mousterian (Levallois cores)	300,000–40,000 BP	Neanderthal
Upper Paleolithic (blades)		
Châtelperronian	38,000–33,000 BP	*H. sapiens*
Aurignacian	35,000–29,000 BP	
Gravitation	29,000–22,000 BP	
Solutrean	22,000–17,000 BP	
Magdalenian	17,000–11,000 BP	

mya: million years ago; BP: years before present

Figure 10.3: Acheulean hand axe replica. Note the refined shape and numerous flake scars indicating the large number of flake removals needed to thin and shape the tool.

As impressive as a ate Acheulean hand axe is, in some ways it is not a very efficient tool. It could have been used for a few different tasks, but it is bulky and heavy, and the working edges are very similar, limiting the number of functions. Additionally, the production of a single tool requires a large piece of raw material, which yields only a single tool.

Later tool manufacturing techniques, such as the Levallois core method developed by Neanderthals, are more efficient (Figure 10.4). In the Levallois technique, the knapper produces a conical core of a more or less standardized size and shape. The top, or widest part, of the core is shaped so that a blow struck on the side will remove a wide, flat flake of predictable size, which is then further modified into various sorts of tools (Figure 10.5). The core can be reshaped and used to generate a whole series of Levallois flakes of similar size and shape, making more efficient use of the available raw materials. The flakes can be modified into a variety of tools for carrying out tasks that require a variety of shapes, types of working edges, etc. So even as far back as Neanderthal times, we see evidence for increasing efficiency in manufacture and diversification of tool function. These patterns continue and are intensified by *Homo sapiens* populations living during the Upper Paleolithic period.

Figure 10.4: Replica of Levallois core and corresponding Levallois flake. The core (top) has a groove, or flake scar, running from left to right. The scar shows where the corresponding flake (bottom) was removed.

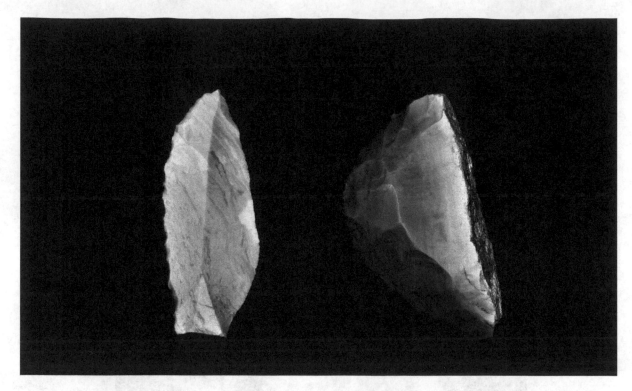

Figure 10.5: Replicas of a Mousterian backed knife (left) and side scraper (right)

Over time, the number of regional variants of tool technologies increases, as does the number of different kinds of tools, with the maximum range of complexity being developed by modern humans during the Upper Paleolithic period with the invention of prismatic blade technology (Figure 10.6). The technique used to produce prismatic blades involves the use of indirect percussion on a prepared core. That is, an antler, bone, or wood punch is held on a specially prepared spot on the core, and when the punch is struck by a hammer, the force is directed down the core in a precise alignment with the ridges on the core. The result is the production of long, thin blades that are triangular in cross-section and taper to a razor-sharp edge along both sides. By moving from ridge to ridge around the core, many blades can be detached from a single core, and the length of cutting edges produced far exceeds what could be made with earlier techniques. However, not only did the prepared blade technology utilize raw materials efficiently, it also permitted Upper Paleolithic peoples to make a wide variety of tools with specialized functional edges and forms (Figure 10.7).

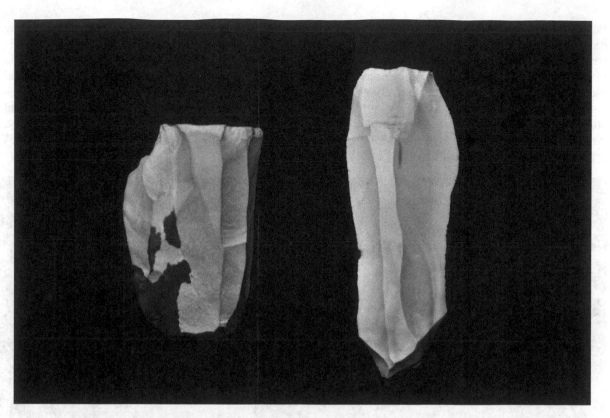

Figure 10.6: Replicas of a percussion blade core of tan chert and prismatic blade from a larger core of gray chert material

Figure 10.7: Replicas of Upper Paleolithic tools made by modifying the edges of percussion blades; left to right: projectile point, drill, graver, burin, and scraper

Late in the Upper Paleolithic period, *Homo sapiens* toolmakers invented another kind of technology involving the use of soft-hammer percussion. In this technique, cores are struck with hammers made of antler, bone, or wood. Soft hammers apply force to the stone differently, causing the removal of thin, broad, flat flakes from the surface of the core and resulting in the thinning of the core, or biface in the process (Figure 10.8). The core can be chipped into very thin and sharp projectile points and knives, some of the best-known examples of which were produced by Solutrean groups in Europe during the late Upper

Paleolithic period (Table 10.1). Some of the Solutrean bifaces are so well made and fragile that they may have functioned as art or ceremonial items (Whittaker 1994, 33). But soft-percussion biface technology is very functional and efficient in several ways. Bifaces such as the larger ones in Figure 10.8 could be manufactured at raw material source areas, thus removing the weathered outer surface of the stone and making them more portable. Large, very sharp flakes can be removed from the core as needed, serving as something of a prehistoric Swiss Army knife. Eventually, after the removal of many flakes for tools, it would still be possible to produce the spear point or knife that was the ultimate objective of the biface technology. And when a knife or point is broken, a biface is easier to resharpen than a blade tool. A different sort of efficiency, but efficient nonetheless.

Figure 10.8: Replicas of Soft-Hammer Percussion Bifaces and Bifacial Cores. The two long and narrow artifacts at top right and bottom center are completed knives, and the others are thin bifacial cores that have not yet been flaked into finished tools.

Following the Upper Paleolithic in many parts of the world, another change in stone tool technology is evident: a shift toward smaller tools made by a technique called *pressure flaking*. Pressure flaking involves pressing a flaking tool, such as an antler tip, against the edge of the stone tool and pushing to remove a flake. The removal of a pressure flake involves less force and produces smaller flakes that does percussion flaking, but that is part of the advantage of the technique. Pressure flaking is used to make very small or very finely finished edges on tools (Figure 10.9) that would not be possible with percussion flaking. The shift to small tools was probably influence by several factors, but those influences likely included a change in the size of the game animals being hunted, the range at which they were hunted, and the increasing scarcity of high-quality stone tool raw materials. Thus, pressure flaking is often used to make tools out of very small pieces of raw material, especially where high-quality stone such as obsidian and chert is scarce in the local environment. This is another example of a different sort of technological efficiency.

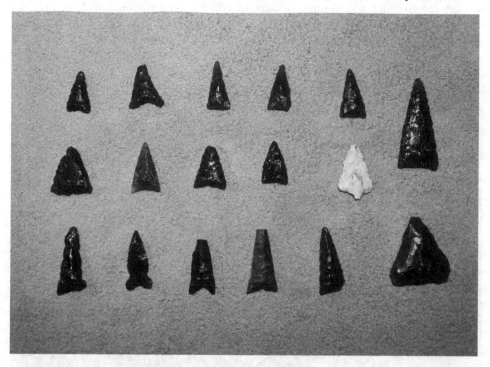

Figure 10.9: Small projectile (arrow) points of obsidian and chert made by pressure flaking. length of specimen at lower right is 1.9 centimeters.

The long-term patterns reflected in stone tool technology indicate that tool manufacture has become more efficient and specialized over time. This shouldn't be very surprising, as we are still witnessing an intensification and speeding up of that pattern. The rates of change and innovation has increased markedly through time. With our computers that become obsolete in a few years and phones that people want to replace nearly every year, we are still living out the general pattern that began millions of years ago. Not only does our technology change ever more rapidly, but the changes include a proliferation in the variety of tool types, many of them specialized for very specific tasks.

In contrast to stone tool manufacture, ceramic technology, or the production of pottery, is an additive technology. In most cases, prehistoric pottery manufacture involves the collection and processing of clay, and the addition of a nonplastic tempering material such as grass, crushed shell, crushed pottery, crushed rock, or sand. The temper is mixed in with the clay to prevent shrinkage and cracking during firing. The firing may or may not involve the use of a formal kiln feature that would be recognizable as such within an archaeological site. Although not as impervious as stone artifacts, ceramic vessels, or at least fragments of broken vessels (known as *sherds*), are readily preserved and common parts of the artifact collections from many sites. Due to their common occurrence and the tendency for humans to decorate their pottery, both complete vessels and fragmentary sherds may yield a variety of kinds of information about the people who made them.

The form and the details of manufacturing techniques may indicate where the pottery was made, how old it is, and what it was used for. Chemical analysis of the clay, temper, and paint may provide information on where those raw materials were obtained and, by extension, on how far they were moved across the landscape before the pottery was broken or discarded. Residues on the interior of vessels may reveal what was cooked or stored in the vessels. The occurrence of nonlocal pottery styles on sites help define the trade relationships among groups living in different regions. And the painted designs often depict animals or aspects of nature that are important in a group's ideology.

In southern New Mexico and west Texas, the earliest pottery dates to about A. D. 250. The vessels are made of clay that fires brown (thus brown wares), and most are undecorated or minimally embellished utility wares used for cooking and storage (Figure 10.10). In some regions, such as the Mimbres River drainage, later populations made pottery that was much more elaborate, such as the bowls illustrated in Figure 10.11. Vessels with extensive decorative designs such as these were often not used for domestic functions, but interred with the deceased as burial goods. The designs are highly stylized depictions of subjects like wind, water, insects, feathers, etc., and sometimes they were purposely broken after being placed in the grave (Figure 10.11, bowl on right). Thus, an entirely different level of abstract or esoteric meaning is embodied in these vessels.

Figure 10.10: Early brownware utility ceramics from the Gila mountains region in southwestern New Mexico

Figure 10.11: Late-Style Mimbres Black-on-white pottery bowls showing fine line work and highly stylized design elements; Southwestern New Mexico, approximately AD 1100

The vessels in Figure 10.12 all come from northern Chihuahua, Mexico, within the region often referred to as the *Casas Grandes interaction sphere*, but they were made at different sites (Paquime, Carretas, and Villa Ahumada) that served as regional centers within the larger regional sociopolitical system. Interestingly, one of them is an example of an effigy pot, a vessel that is constructed in the form of a macaw. Such vessels have sometimes been interpreted as having special spiritual meaning in the context of shamanic practices (VanPool and VanPool 2007).

Figure 10.12: Polychrome pottery from the Casas Grandes Region of northern Chihuahua, Mexico, approximately AD 1300

Figure 10.13: Ginger jars, soy sauce bottle, and assorted porcelain recovered during excavations in the historic Overseas Chinese neighborhood in downtown El Paso, Texas

Even more recent ceramics may be of interest to archaeologists, such as those working on historic period sites. Beneath downtown El Paso lies the remains of an extensive historic occupation of the Overseas Chinese, a neighborhood that was established by and for the laborers who built the Southern Pacific railroad from California to El Paso in 1881. In much of downtown El Paso, the buildings lack basements and elevators, so there is often good preservation of the sediments, building remnants, and artifacts buried under the modern city. Although there has been relatively little excavation of the Chinese community, test excavations have yielded a wide variety of very well-preserved artifacts, including many pieces of pottery that were shipped directly from mainland China (Staski et al. 1985). The collection includes such items as ginger jars, soy sauce jars, rice bowls, spoons, and medicine bottles, all of which reflect a concerted effort on the part of the Overseas Chinese to maintain contacts with their home cultures in China (Figure 10.13).

Just as there is a record of changing technology recorded in the artifacts contained in a site, so, too, do the features provide evidence of cultural change. Figure 10.14 shows a prehistoric pithouse in the final stages of excavation. Although it measures about 4 meters in diameter and a meter deep (involving significant labor to construct), such dwellings are generally associated with populations who derive the majority of the subsistence from hunting and gathering. The semisubterranean construction takes advantage of the thermal properties of the soil layers, suggesting it is probably a fall and winter season residence. Storage pits around the outside and under the floor support the idea that the village was occupied for weeks or months.

Figure 10.14: Excavation of a 1,200-year-old pithouse at the Three Rivers Site (LA 4921), Otero County, New Mexico

In much of the southwestern United States, the shift to above ground structures occurred about A.D. 1100. Figure 10.15 shows a small area of stabilized wall remnants in the much larger pueblo complex at Pecos Pueblo National Monument a few miles east of Santa Fe, New Mexico. Dating to about A.D. 1300–1400, these features indicate a community organization that is larger and more complex than that of a pithouse village. There are many more rooms, but they are smaller, and perhaps half of them are for storage of agricultural produce. Neighboring families share walls, and relatively large numbers of people live in close proximity. This implies the existence of social mechanisms that serve to ameliorate interpersonal stress and unite community members for the purposes of construction projects and other community-wide activities. The reconstructed kiva, or ceremonial chamber, in Figure 10.16 is visual evidence of ritual activities that would help serve to foster intracommunity cooperation.

Figure 10.15: Stabilized wall remnants of a pueblo room block at Pecos Pueblo National Monument, New Mexico

Figure 10.16: Reconstructed prehistoric kiva, or underground ceremonial chamber, Pecos Pueblo National Monument, New Mexico

In other areas of the Southwest, we see architecture that suggests the sites were constructed in defensive settings, in response to regional stress and competition over natural resources. The ruins in the

Gila Cliff Dwellings National Monument (Figure 10.17) were built in the late 1200s AD. They were occupied for only about 20 years, during a time of environmental instability and population movement. One can imagine the challenge of collecting and shaping the rocks, carrying the stones up into the caves, and building irregularly shaped masonry rooms to fit that unique location. The difficulties inherent in this sort of construction effort supports the idea that regional unrest was an important factor in choosing to live in a defendable location, despite the logistical challenges of construction.

Figure 10.17: Masonry houses built into caves at the Gila Cliff Dwellings National Monument, New Mexico

Imparting Meaning to the Landscape

Many of us may not give much thought to the nature of art or what it might say about our species. Of course, examples of art are all around us every day, and even if we notice it, we may still take it for granted, for that very reason . . . because we've always known art, and it's ever-present. Art is such a basic part of our daily lives that it's hard to imagine life without art. And that's really the point; art is a basic trait of modern humans. The ability to make and interpret art is so basic to the human condition that it can be considered part of the "psychic unity of humankind." What that means is that all biologically modern humans have the same basic needs, desires, abilities, and thought processes. Even though prehistoric populations didn't drive cars or use computers, we can still identify them as fully modern by their use of artwork. Not only did prehistoric people make designs, but the designs held meaning, and some of the images were used in ways that we still use imagery today. Artwork is not simply about making pleasing designs; it is about symbolic communication. Let's consider some examples of how indigenous peoples communicate through artwork and how those examples relate to the archaeological record.

One of the most well-known and accessible sorts of art in the archaeological record is rock art. Even though many people have seen or at least know about the existence of rock art, a surprising number of people have misunderstandings about the nature of the designs and the significance of the places where they were created. There is a place I sometimes go fishing on the Mescalero Apache reservation in southern New Mexico. Once, while obtaining my tribal fishing permit, I overheard a local non-Indian rancher commenting on the photographs of local rock art designs displayed in the office. I was amazed to hear him say that the rock art was no big deal, dismissing the designs as "just a bunch of old Indian graffiti." I could understand that he might have a political reason for resenting the presence of Native Americans on land he would like to control, but he was not only angry; he was simply ignorant about Native American rock art sites. They are not graffiti; rock art sites are profoundly sacred places to all the Native American groups with whom I've worked.

For example, consider the rock art panel illustrated in Figure 10.18. This design is near my summer archaeological field school site in southern New Mexico. It is part of a collection of more than 21,000 petroglyphs at the Three Rivers site (Duran and 1999). When I first saw this particular panel, I was in the company of the Governor of the Tigua tribe of the Ysleta del Sur Pueblo. The designs extend an impressive 15 feet up the imposing basalt column. We looked up, stopped in our tracks, and were transfixed by the power of the image. My companion was speechless for a moment, and then he exhaled slowly and said, "There is the whole world, the entire cosmos of my people." It was the first time he had seen that particular prehistoric rock art panel, but the images are the same as those still used by his people today. There is a corn plant growing out of a crack in the rock at the base of the design. The ears of maize, the subsistence base of the pueblo peoples, are clearly indicated at the joints of the stalk. The top of the plant reaches up to the image of a cloud, the details of which include rain coming off the bottom, the arc of a rainbow curving over a lightning bolt, and wisps of clouds extending into the sky above the stepped design. There is a thunderbird perched atop the cloud, and above it all are the eyes of the "One Who Watches." The entire panel relates to the connection of earth and sky, the water cycle, fertility, renewal, and the place of the pueblo peoples in the universe. The image is a metaphor for the tribe's authority to exist as a people, and for their belonging to that part of the landscape. This is not graffiti, or even merely an outdoor art gallery. It is a place to teach and remind people who they are and what their priorities should be—living in harmony and balance with nature. These holy sites also serve as mnemonic devices for groups who lack a writing system and who know about the past through oral history. Sacred sites like these are places of power.

Figure 10.18: Summary of Puebloan cosmology recorded at the Three Rivers Petroglyph site, Otero County, New Mexico

The concept of power is difficult to express simply in English. Power is a spiritual energy or life force that enables an individual to interact with the forces of the natural and supernatural worlds. Supernatural power derives from a variety of plants, animals, and meteorological phenomena. Once obtained, power gives one the ability to influence certain aspects of nature by virtue of a special relationship with the spirits responsible for them. Different kinds and degrees of power may be bestowed on different individuals, depending on which spirits are involved. Powers accepted and used on behalf of the entire tribe are more potent than those used by individuals for the benefit of their family, such as healing ceremonies. Powerful places are locations where spiritual power is received or where its use is needed for protection from spiritual danger (Carmichael 1998, 91).

In my ethnographic research on sacred sites, I have classified powerful places into three different sorts of sites: natural areas of intersection, places of transformation, and resource areas (Carmichael 1998, 92–94). The physical and spirit worlds intersect at several kinds of places. Among the most important of these are sacred mountains. There are several sacred mountain peaks within the traditional range of the Mescalero Apaches. Not only do these peaks define the geographical core of their territory, but they are also important in tribal cosmology. The mountain peaks correspond to the foundational tipi poles that make up the holy lodge used in their most sacred ceremonies. The holy lodge and its support posts correspond, in turn, to the mountains, which "hold up" the "tipi cover" that is the sky. Because the mountain peak is where the earth touches the sky, it is a place of intersection, an axis of spiritual power in the fabric of the cosmos. Sierra Blanca (Figure 10.19) is a sacred place because it touches the sky and has been a source of spiritual power. It has also been the focus of many ceremonial activities over the generations, and it becomes more sacred with each additional religious observance. The entire mountain is a sacred landscape, even though there is almost nothing manmade to be found there. Other such places include caves, where it is possible to enter the earth (the spirit dimension), and springs, where water has just issued forth from that spiritual dimension.

Figure 10.19: Sierra Blanca, sacred peak on the Mescalero Apache reservation, southern New Mexico

Another major category of sacred sites consists of places of transformation, where journeys to the spirit world are undertaken. The most sacred of these are burials. At death, individuals are transformed, and their spirits make a four-day journey back to the spiritual world. Funeral rites are intended to expedite the journey and prevent the spirits of the deceased from attempting to stay in this physical dimension. The sweat lodge is another kind of transformation site, as are places where shamans make contact with the spirit world. In many indigenous societies, shamans use prayer, divination, and healing to attend to the needs of their people. In each of these activities, the shaman can make a ritual transformation, traveling to the spirit dimension to obtain assistance in making diagnoses, etc. Figure 10.20 is an example of a directional shrine associated with a prehistoric pueblo village site in northern New Mexico. We know about the use of these features because they are still in use among contemporary Puebloan peoples. This feature measures only about 1 meter by 0.5 meters and consists of an arrangement of four rocks, but it is as sacred as the altar in a Christian church.

Figure 10.20: Directional shrine on an ancestral Pueblo residential site in the Jemez Mountains, near Los Alamos, New Mexico

Another transformation place is shown below in Figure 10.21. This cluster of rock art designs at the Three Rivers Petroglyph site includes a rare depiction of a full anthropomorphic figure at the left center of the photograph. The figure is bent over in a posture that has been interpreted as representing the feelings experienced during shamanic trances. The figure is grimacing, showing teeth, and wearing a feathered headdress or hair ornament. It is likely that this panel is describing and/or commemorating a ritual transformation experienced by a shaman who chose this site because of its spiritual power.

Figure 10.21: Place of ritual transformation, Three Rivers Petroglyph site, Otero County, New Mexico

Once such places become imbued with sacred power, they become memorable. They become part of the way we experience and remember the details of the landscape, how we connect to and "know" the land (Tuan 1977). Especially for preliterate cultures, knowing the earth in this way, through the sacred details and the stories that accompany the artwork, allowed people to remember an enormous amount of detailed knowledge that would help them survive and adapt. Being able to walk across 20 miles of open desert and go right to the only spring in the area would be facilitated by naming and imparting meaning to the mountains and the landscape through art. The art is symbolic communication, instrumental to the survival of our ancestors and characteristic of our species as a whole.

References and Further Reading

Ashmore, Wendy, and Robert J. Sharer. 2000. *Discovering Our Past: A Brief Introduction to Archaeology.* 3rd ed. New York: McGraw Hill.

Basso, Keith. 1996. *Wisdom Sits in Places: Landscape and Language Among the Western Apache.* Albuquerque: University of New Mexico Press.

Carmichael, David. 1998. "Places of Power: Mescalero Apache Sacred Sites and Sensitive Areas." In *Sacred Sites, Sacred Places*, edited by David Carmichael, Jane Hubert, Brian Reeves, and Audhild Schanche. London: Routledge Press.

Duran, Meliha S., and Helen K. Crotty. 1999. *Three Rivers Petroglyph Site: Results of the ASNM Rock Art Recording Field School. The Artifact* 37, no. 2. El Paso, TX: El Paso Archaeological Society, Inc.

Fagan, Brian. 1998. *From Black Land to Fifth Sun: The Science of Sacred Sites.* Reading, MA: Helix Books, Addison Wesley.

Larsen, Clark Spencer. 2017. *Our Origins: Discovering Physical Anthropology.* New York: Norton.

Sewall, Laura. 1999. *Sight and Sensibility: The Ecopsychology of Perception.* New York: Jeremy P. Tarcher/Putnam.

Staski, Edward, Deborah Sick-Connelley, Bonnie G. McEwan, Pauline M. Darcy-Staski, and Karen Fourdurean. 1985. *Beneath the Border City, Volume 2: The Overseas Chinese in El Paso.* New Mexico State University, University Museum Occasional Papers, No. 13, Las Cruces, NM.

Stringer, Chris, and Peter Andrews. 2005. *The Complete World of Human Evolution.* London: Natural History Museum, Thames & Hudson.

Tuan, Yi-Fu. 1974. *Topophilia: A Study of Environmental Perception, Attitudes, and Values.* New York: Columbia University Press.

Tuan, Yi-Fu. 1977. *Space and Place: The Perspective of Experience.* Minneapolis: University of Minnesota Press.

Tylor, Edward B. 1871. *Primitive Culture.* London: Murray Publishing.

VanPool, Christine S. and Todd L. VanPool. 2007. *Signs of the Casas Grandes Shamans.* Salt Lake City: University of Utah Press.

White, Randall. 1982. "Rethinking the Middle-Upper Paleolithic Transition." *Current Anthropology* 23, no. 2 (April 1982): 169–92.

White, Randall. 1993. "Technological and Social Dimensions of 'Aurignacian-Age' Body Ornaments across Europe." In *Before Lascaux: The Complex Record of the Early Upper Paleolithic,* edited by H. Knecht, A. Pike-Tay, and R. White, 277–99. Boca Raton, FL: CRC Press.

Whittaker, John C. 1994. *Flintknapping: Making & Understanding Stone Tools.* Austin: University of Texas Press.

Chapter 11: Peopling of the New World

Q&A. Why is the New World called the New World?

The continents of the so-called New World are just as old geologically as those of the Old World. The western hemisphere is referred to as "New" because humans inhabited it much later than they did the Old World, where we evolved. Pretty anthropocentric of us, don't you think?

The interpretation of the details involved in the migration of modern humans to the New World is one of the two or three most contentious issues in all of American archaeology. (The others would probably be the origins of agriculture and the collapse of civilizations.) It has long been widely accepted that the first Americans (probably ancestors of today's Native Americans) arrived from Asia by way of the Bering land bridge connecting Siberia and Alaska during the last ice age (Figure 11.1). However, the timing of the migrations and the nature of the human adaptive strategy employed by the first American populations have been debated for many years. In this chapter, we will examine the traditional view of the peopling of the New World, often referred to as the *Clovis-First model*. We will also consider the corollary idea that the extinction of the Pleistocene fauna was caused by the killing efficiency of Clovis hunters. This view is often referred to as the *Overkill model of Pleistocene extinctions*, and it is a key aspect of the Clovis-First model because it purports to explain the rapid spread of Clovis peoples upon their arrival in North America. We will then address some of the sorts of criticisms that have been directed at the Clovis-First model and consider an alternative, the Pre-Clovis model. Students should be able to summarize the two basic models and identify and evaluate the evidence that has been used to support them. In the process, the discussion will also touch on issues such as the technological abilities of Late Paleolithic hunter-gatherer populations and the evidence for climate and sea-level changes of the type being debated in today's discussions of global warming.

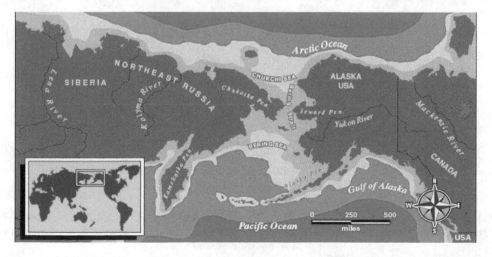

Figure 11.1: The extent of the Bering Land Bridge (Beringia) during the Late Pleistocene

The Clovis-First and Overkill Models

The western hemisphere is often referred to as the New World, not because it is geologically any younger than the Old World, but because humans who evolved very early in Africa, Asia, and Europe did not occupy the Americas until much later. Franz Boaz and Aleš Hrdlička, two prominent anthropologists working in the early twentieth century, were skeptical of suggestions that the Americas had been occupied for more than a few thousand years. Their views were so influential that most archeologists didn't give serious consideration to the idea until stone tools were found in association with the bones of extinct Pleistocene fauna in the late 1930s and 1940s. Once this association was well established, it became widely accepted that the *Paleo-Indians* who made these tools were the earliest occupants of the New World.

The traditional view holds that the first people entered the New World relatively late, about 12,000 years ago. These groups are identified by the presence of distinctive fluted spear points, the earliest of which are *Clovis points*, first discovered at Blackwater Draw near Clovis, New Mexico. Clovis artifacts have traditionally been dated to between 11,500 and 10,900 years ago (Waters and Stafford 2007). It was argued that Clovis populations brought the fluted point technology with them from Siberia during the Two Creeks interval. The major ice sheets of North America are known to have increased and decreased in extent over time, and during the Two Creeks interval, there was an ice-free corridor between the ice masses centered over the Rocky Mountains and the Laurentian Shield (Figure 11.2). Presumably, the Clovis people followed herds of game, such as wooly mammoth, musk oxen, and bison, across the Bering land bridge, down through the ice-free corridor, and into what are now the lower 48 states of the United States.

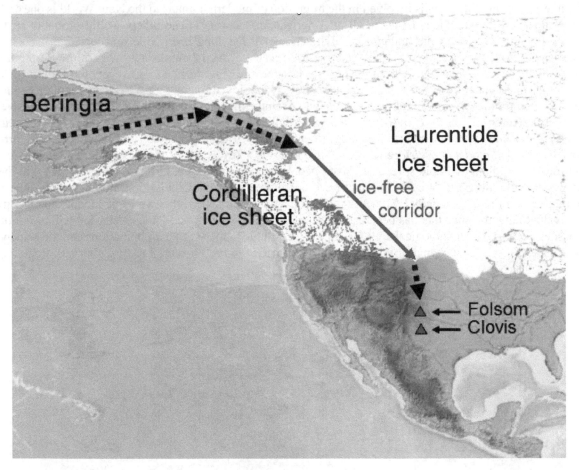

Figure 11.2: Proposed route of entry into the New World from Beringia via an ice-free corridor between the Cordilleran and Laurentide ice sheets. note that movement along the west coast of North America may have been possible as well.

Archaeological finds in Fells Cave near the southern tip of South America indicated that people were living there by 10,000 to 11,000 years ago. This means that Paleo-Indian groups would have had to move very quickly, essentially spreading through and filling up North, Central, and South America in about 1,000 years. The corollary model proposed to account for such a rapid spread has been referred to as *the Overkill model*. This model stipulates that the specialized big-game hunting technology (i.e., Clovis points hafted on spears propelled by spear throwers) brought from the Old World was so efficient that the hunters caused the extinction of a behaviorally unprepared fauna in the New World. Moreover, the hunters killed off more than 120 species of animals representing 32 genera, and as the animals were wiped out, the hunting populations spread rapidly south in search of new populations of game animals. While this model is logically a separate issue from the Clovis-First model, it has generally been considered its corollary because it links the notion of a late entry into the New World with the Pleistocene dates of occupation in South America. The argument has been supported by such evidence as the timing of the Two Creeks interval and the common association of fluted spear points with the bones of herd animals throughout the Americas: mammoth, horse, and bison in North America and guanaco in South America.

Until quite recently, the combination of these two models was the standard textbook explanation for the peopling of the New World. In the last few decades, archeologists have found significant evidence that undermines the Clovis-First scenario. Before examining that evidence however, let's consider the main alternative view, the Pre-Clovis entry model.

Pre-Clovis Entry Model

The Pre-Clovis module postulates an earlier entry into the New World, perhaps even as early as 40,000 years ago. There were four major periods of glacier growth in the Pleistocene during which Siberia and Alaska would have been connected by a land bridge, and smaller fluctuations in the extent of ice fields would have opened the ice-free corridor at various times, not just during the Two Creeks interval. It is also possible that early populations could have traveled over or gone around the glaciers by boat, through the Alaskan archipelago and coastal British Columbia. The initial entry is suggested to have been made by groups who had a generalized adaptation, not specialized big-game hunters. Therefore, they would have lacked the distinctive spear points characteristic of Clovis peoples, and their sites would be more difficult to identify. Furthermore, coastlines exposed during glacial periods would be under water today, making many of their sites difficult to find (thereby explaining the rarity of pre-Clovis sites).

With their generalized adaptation, the pre-Clovis groups would have gradually filled the continents with earlier sites lacking Clovis technology but containing other tools similar to those found in northeast Asia. Only later did the specialized big-game hunting technology develop and spread into areas of plains environments. The Pre-Clovis model has been supported by reference to sites dating prior to Clovis, but until very recently, most archaeologists dismissed the evidence of earlier sites as problematical.

Figure 11.3: Lateral glacial moraines deposited along the valley margins of the Diablo Creek drainage in the Cruces Basin Wilderness Area, northern New Mexico. the moraines were formed of gravels left behind when the glacier melted, indicating the extent of the ice during the Pleistocene.

Climate Change and Glaciation

Both models involve the migration of people from Siberia to Alaska at times of lowered sea level, but how do we know the continents were connected? There are several kinds of evidence that indicate the former presence of vast continental ice masses, especially in the northern hemisphere and the higher mountains of the world. One of the most important such indicators is glacial moraines. Moraines are piles of rocks, gravel, and soil that have been moved by and deposited in front of or alongside glaciers (Figure 11.3). Moraines have been studied extensively (as part of mapping agricultural soils and aggregate sources in the Midwest) and mapped in detail, so we know with some degree of confidence the extent of the ice sheets at different times in the prehistoric past. The periods of growth are named for the places where the moraines record the maximum extent of ice at different times. During the Late Pleistocene, there were four major cycles of glacier growth. In the United States, the cycles are named Nebraskan, Kansan, Illinois, and Wisconsin, after the location of the moraines, indicating the maximum extent of ice. These periods correspond to the Gunz, Mindel, Riss, and Wurm in Europe. The natural climatic cycles are reflected in cycles of glacier expansion and contraction (Figure 11.4).

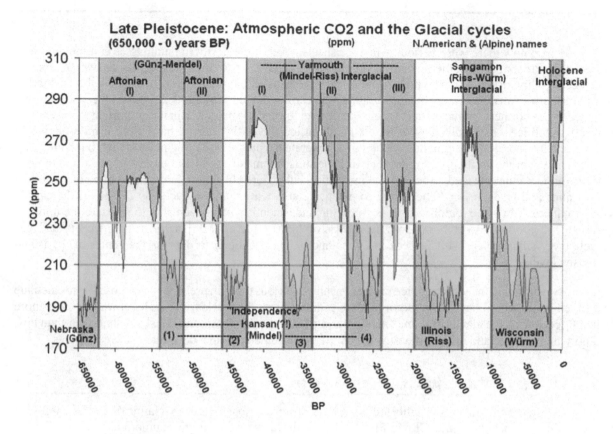

Figure 11.4: Glacial and interglacial cycles of the Late Pleistocene as revealed in Antarctic ice cores

In Figure 11.4, the major periods of glacier growth are indicated in blue, and the warmer interglacial periods are shown in yellow. Within each major glacial cycle, there are number of smaller fluctuations of the sort identified as the Two Creeks interval. The patterns of climate cycles are the result of the *Milankovitch cycles*, named for the Serbian astronomer who calculated their effects. The cycles refer to variations in the earth's orbit, tilt, and spin. The shape of the earth's orbit is more or less elliptical but varies by up to 5 percent on a 100,000-year cycle. The tilt of the earth's axis varies from 21.5 to 24.5 degrees on a cycle of 41,000 years. The third cycle involves precession, the wobbling of the earth on its axis that can be likened to the wobble that occurs as a toy top slows down. The wobble takes 23,000 years to complete one cycle. The combination of the three cycles working together has significant effects on the earth's climate. When the earth's orbit is most elliptical, axial tilt is less (leading to cooler summers), and precession situates the northern hemisphere further from the sun in the winter, the earth experiences glacial cycles.

Pleistocene Ice Ages and Milankovitch Cycles

https://vimeopro.com/huce/spu29/video/104003877

If we know there were periods when ice sheets covered the northern landmasses and the moraines indicate the extent of the ice, then where did all the water come from to form the ice? The answer, of course, is the ocean. Climatic conditions were several degrees (Celsius) cooler than today (because of the orientation of the northern hemisphere away from the sun as the earth wobbled around its axis), and the snowfall that occurred in the northern latitudes didn't melt, but instead formed glacial ice. But it is important to understand just how much ice was involved. We're talking about ice sheets that would have been a mile or two in thickness, with enormous weight, heavy enough to generate the pressure melting point at their base, allowing them to slide over the earth, grinding up rock into the soils that make our "bread basket" agricultural regions so fertile and leveling the landscape like a slow-motion bulldozer. They were large enough to gouge out the Great Lakes and Hudson Bay. They were so extensive and heavy that they actually depressed the earth's continental crust. In some regions, such as New England, scientists have been able to measure the uplift of the crust as it continues to rebound from the release of the pressure after the melting of the ice sheets. Even the relatively small glacier still present in Greenland is heavy enough to depress the center of the island below sea level.

By estimating the volume of ice present on land at various times in prehistory, it is possible to calculate how much water would have been required. It is estimated that the worldwide sea level was lowered more than 400 feet during the glacial maxima. As the Bering Sea between Siberia and Alaska is shallower than this, we know there was a land bridge, measuring some 1,500 kilometers wide, connecting the continents.

Evaluation of the Clovis-First Model

The Clovis-First model has been criticized on several grounds, most clearly by claims of earlier sites. One of the main weaknesses of the Clovis-First model is the fact that a single counter-case, a single well-supported site dating prior to Clovis times, would negate the model. Perhaps for this reason, proponents of the Clovis-First model have been intensely skeptical of any claims for pre-Clovis sites and until very recently have dismissed all such claims more or less out of hand. The site that changed this was Monte Verde, Chile (Dillehay 1997). The Monte Verde site dates back to about 12,500 years ago, predating Clovis by 1,000 to 1,200 years. Because of the distance between Monte Verde and the Bering land bridge, some researchers feel these dates might indicate an initial entry into the New World sometime before 20,000 years ago. The general acceptance of the validity of Monte Verde has led to greater acceptance of some other proposed pre-Clovis sites, such as Meadowcroft Rockshelter in Pennsylvania, the Topper Site in South Carolina, and Cactus Hill in Virginia.

Another site that bears on this debate is Pendejo Cave, located on Fort Bliss about 50 miles northeast of El Paso. The site (named for a nearby drainage) was excavated by my late colleague Richard MacNeishe from 1990 to 1993. MacNeishe was initially searching for caves containing evidence of early maize, but near the bottom of the cave, he encountered the bones of extinct fauna and some associated crude stone tools (MacNeishe and Libby 2004). Although some archaeologists are still skeptical of the findings, leading biologists have characterized the deposits as one of the best Late Pleistocene paleontological sites in the country. It also contains one of the longest sequences of radiocarbon dates in the New World, with 52 dates extending from more than 55,000 years ago at the bottom to 350 years ago at the top.

The oldest dates are not in association with stone tools, but strata dating in the range of 13,000 to 34,000 years ago may very well contain human artifacts. For example, Zone H contained 16 stone tools, 19 waste flakes, two areas of burned soil, and one rock-lined hearth. Seven radiocarbon dates from the stratum range in age from 28,500 to 33,830 years ago. A summary of the pre-Clovis evidence from the site comprises an impressive array of artifacts, including 43 specimens of human hair. A total of 27 hearth features or fire pits have been identified, several of which have yielded radiocarbon samples. Fourteen of the fire pits contain human fingerprints and palm prints left behind in the clay linings of the hearths and hardened by the fires. The oldest of these prints dates 35,900 years ago; not surprisingly, its validity has been questioned by some of the site's detractors. However, other examples of prints found in younger hearths from the Archaic period (ca. 2000–8000 BP) have not been questioned by these same detractors. Isn't that a violation of the principle of uniformitarianism?

A variety of stone tools have been recovered from several pre-Clovis strata. The artifacts are admittedly crude, so crude that detractors have argued they are not tools at all, but pieces of rock that broke when they fell from the roof and impacted other rocks on the floor. Roof fall is an improbable way to produce things that appear to be purposefully chipped, but there is even more support for the legitimacy of the tools. About 52 percent of the artifacts are made of nonlocal raw materials that were carried several kilometers from the source to the cave. As more researchers evaluate the details of the collection from Pendejo Cave, I expect the discipline will eventually validate the suggestion that the site provides evidence for a pre-Clovis occupation in the range of 25,000 to more than 30,000 years ago.

Perhaps the most convincing evidence for a pre-Clovis occupation of North America is presented by artifacts assigned to the Buttermilk Creek complex near Austin. The Gault site and the Debra L. Friedkin site have both yielded artifact assemblages that predate Clovis technology by about 2,500 years. At the Debra L. Friedkin site, more than 15,000 artifacts were contained in a 20-centimeter thick layer of soil dating between 13,200 and 15,500 years old (Waters et al. 2018). Not only are these sites clear evidence of a pre-Clovis presence in the New World, they also suggest that the earlier inhabitants also used a somewhat different technology. Additional finds of pre-Clovis materials have been made in the Pacific Northwest.

Recent research has produced some interesting evidence for pre-Clovis occupations in unexpected locations. More than simply acknowledging the possibility of submerged sites, tantalizing evidence of actual sites is emerging. In 1998, archaeologist Daryl Fedje recovered a 4-inch-long flaked stone blade in sediments dredged up from the ocean off Queen Charlotte Islands along the coast of British Columbia at a depth of more than 120 meters (400 feet; Fiedel 2000). This would seem to suggest that at least a narrow coastal plain was ice-free at the time and could have allowed people to enter North America by traveling along the coast and bypassing any ice sheets that existed further inland. In another study, researchers have identified ancient preserved human coprolites (feces) at the site of Paisley Caves, Oregon. The excreta were identified as human by their DNA, and the radiocarbon dates indicate they were deposited between 13,000 and 14,340 years ago, or about 1,000 years before Clovis (Gilbert et al. 2008; Wolman 2008). Artifacts associated with those early deposits fit within what has been called the *Early Stemmed Tradition*, a technology that doesn't include fluted points and that had previously been believed to be post-Clovis.

Aside from the discovery of specific sites dating to pre-Clovis times, there are other sorts of evidence that can be marshaled against the Clovis-First model. Douglas Wallace (1997) has used mitochondrial DNA analysis to study the global migration patterns of modern humans. The evidence suggests that there were four separate migrations of people into the New World, the earliest occurring about 34,000 years ago. This initial movement was followed by a second wave of immigrants about 15,000 years ago, which may have bypassed the interior of Siberia, perhaps following the Alaskan coastline instead. Next were peoples from Siberia who arrived about 9,500 years ago and became the founders of the Na-Dene language group, which includes Athabascans such as the Navajos and Apaches. Finally, the Inuits and Aleuts arrived in the Arctic in the past 4,000 to 5,000 years.

Evaluation of the Overkill Model

Other details that seem to contradict the pre-Clovis model are related to critiques of the corollary *Overkill model* of Pleistocene extinctions. The idea that prehistoric humans had the capability to kill large numbers of animals and even cause their extinction may seem intuitively appealing because it conforms to a common perception that humans are powerful, violent, and the masters of nature. But the evidence that humans killed a sufficient number of animals to cause the extinction of more than 100 species is equivocal. When I was an undergraduate student at the University of New Mexico (UNM), two of my professors commented on this issue by discussing details of modern elephant behavior. Lewis Binford noted that there are some tribal peoples in Africa who do (or did in historic times) regularly kill elephants, usually because they are damaging their agricultural fields. These groups usually use one of three techniques, all of which are cruel by our standards and require Iron Age technology: 1) using a boat to approach an elephant while it is swimming and using an axe to cut off the trunk, causing it to drown; 2) thrusting a spear with a long iron blade through the belly of the animal, thereby avoiding the thickest skin and reaching the vital organs in the chest cavity; and 3) pounding a metal stake between the toes of an elephant, to which is attached a rope and log, acting as a drag, slowing the animal down, eventually leading to its starvation. Any of these approaches are likely to be more effective than a wooden spear with a 6-inch stone point on the end (Figure 11.5). If Iron Age technology hasn't endangered modern (smaller) elephants, it seems unlikely that Stone Age technology would have endangered their larger Ice Age cousins.

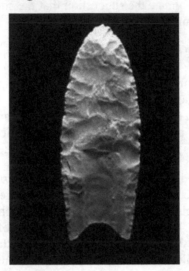

Figure 11.5: Clovis point that would have been hafted onto a spear propelled by a spear thrower

Binford also noted that when Europeans were regularly hunting elephants with large-caliber rifles in the nineteenth century, it was common for local tribal groups to butcher the carcasses for the meat. In the process, multiple iron tools were often found embedded in the chest of the elephant that had never killed it—tools like axes, machetes, and spears. Again, it seems that Stone Age technology might have been even less effective (Figure 11.6).

Figure 11.6: Artist's impression of what a hypothetical mammoth hunt might have looked like

It also turns out that when elephants are wounded, they often make their way into a shallow water body such as a pond or lake. Apparently, the buoyancy provided by the water helps them stay upright, at least for a time. If the wounded animal does die in the pond, what will the resulting archaeological site look like? One might find an elephant skeleton within or along the shore of the pond, with some artifacts or weapons associated with the bones. Another former UNM professor, Jim Judge, noted that such a pattern describes many of the so-called Clovis elephant kill sites in the Southwest: bones associated with one or a few spear points, deposited in a small lake or pond. Both Judge and Gorman (1972) have argued that such finds represent *unsuccessful* hunting sites, in which the animal died much later and was never butchered for consumption. The few prehistoric elephant sites that do have evidence of butchering (dismemberment, cut marks on the bones, etc.) are mostly juvenile animals. This would seem to indicate that even the Clovis hunters understood they weren't able to regularly dispatch adults.

Another interesting argument involves the pattern of extinction at the end of the Ice Age. Donald Grayson (1977; Schwarz 2001) reasoned that if Paleo-Indian hunters were the cause of the extinctions, there should be a different pattern of extinctions in the megafauna (large game animals) for which there is direct evidence of human hunting and the avifauna (birds) for which there is not. He examined the *avifauna from the La Brea tar pits* near Los Angeles and found that the Late Pleistocene birds (including species such as songbirds for which there is no evidence of human predation) experienced the same pattern of extinction as the large game animals. This suggests a larger cause of the extinctions, probably some aspect of major climatic change. Furthermore, Grayson noted that the two species for which there is the most evidence of large numbers of kills (bison in North America and guanaco in South America) are species that survived the Late Pleistocene extinctions. Even the common Paleo-Indian hunting technique of driving entire herds of bison over cliffs didn't threaten the population. Instead, both bison and guanaco seem to have adapted to predation and/or climate change by evolving a smaller body size, but neither were in danger of extinction until European firearms were introduced to the New World. This would also support the view that some more complex ecological factors were involved instead of over hunting.

Finally, new studies have reported research results that may finally refute the Clovis-first model once and for all. Waters and Stafford (2007) recently reexamined the dating of Clovis using the new, more accurate accelerated mass spectrometer method of radiocarbon dating. They dated 43 samples, including bone, charcoal, and seeds from well-documented Clovis sites. The new dates fall within a minimum range of 13,125 to 12,925 calibrated years before present (CALBP) and a maximum range of 13,250 to 12,800 CALBP. This means the duration of Clovis culture spanned only about 200 to 450 years. Even for the most ardent supporters of the Clovis-First model, 200 years isn't enough time for the Clovis peoples to have migrated and/or spread their technology across North and South America. The implication is that Clovis technology was an idea that was introduced to and spread rapidly among pre-Clovis groups already living throughout the hemisphere, not the spread of a small group of immigrants in 200 years.

References and Further Reading

Dillehay, Tom. 1997. *Monte Verde: A Late Pleistocene Settlement in Chile (Vol. 2).* Smithsonian Series in Archaeological Inquiry, Smithsonian Institution.

Fiedel, Stuart J. 2000. "The Peopling of the New World: Present Evidence, New Theories, and Future Directions." *Journal of Archaeological Research* 8, no. 1 (March 2000): 39–103.

Gilbert, M. Thomas P., Dennis L. Jenkins, Anders Gotherstrom, Nuria Neveran, et al. 2008. "DNA from Pre-Clovis Human Coprolites in Oregon, North America." *Science* 320, no. 5877 (May 9, 2008): 786–9. https://doi.org/10.1126/science.1154116.

Gorman, Frederick. 1972. "The Clovis Hunters: An Alternate View of Their Environment and Ecology." In *Contemporary Archaeology: A Guide to Theory and Contributions,* edited by Mark P. Leone, 206–21. Southern Illinois University Press.

Grayson, Donald K. 1977. "Pleistocene Avifaunas and the Overkill Hypothesis." *Science* 18, vol. 195, no. 4279 (February 1977): 691–3.

Holen, Steve, and Dennis Stanford. 2008. "Early Mammoth Bone Flaking on the Great Plains." *Mammoth Trumpet* 23, no. 1 (January 2008): 12–4.

Lovgren, Stefan. 2007. "Clovis People Not First Americans, Study Shows." *National Geographic News,* February 23, 2007. https://www.nationalgeographic.com/science/article/native-people-americans-clovis-news

MacNeishe, Richard S., and Jane G. Libby. 2004. *Pendejo Cave.* Albuquerque: University of New Mexico Press.

Schwarz, Joel. 2001. "Blame North America Megafauna Extinction on Climate Change, Not Human Ancestors." University of Washington. http://www.washington.edu/news/2001/10/24/blame-north-america-megafauna-extinction-on-climate-change-not-human-ancestors/ .

Wallace, Douglas C. 1997. "What Mitochondrial DNA Says about Human Migrations." *Scientific American* (August 1997): 46–7.

Waters, Michael R., Joshua L. Keene, Steven L. Forman, Elton R. Prewitt, David L. Carlson and James E. Widerhold. 2018. "Pre-Clovis Projectile Points at the Debra L. Friedkin Site, Texas—Implications for the Late Pleistocene Peopling of the Americas." *Science Advances* 4, no. 10 (October 24, 2018): eaat4505. DOI: 10.1126/sciadv.aat4505.

Waters, Michael, and Thomas Stafford. 2007. "Redefining the Age of Clovis: Implications for the Peopling of the Americas." *Science* 315, no. 5815 (February 2007): 1122–6.

Waters, Michael, and Thomas Stafford. 2007. "Clovis Dethroned: A New Perspective on the First Americans, Part 2 of 2." *Mammoth Trumpet* 22, no. 4 (October 2007): 1–2, 13.

Wolman, David. 2008. "Fossil Feces Is Earliest Evidence of North American Humans." *National Geographic News,* April 3, 2008. https://news.nationalgeographic.com/news/2008/04/080403-first-americans.html.

Chapter 12: Origins and Consequences of Food Production

Q&A: What was the most important human invention of all time?

The origin of food production is arguably the most important development in human prehistory.

The beginnings of agriculture and animal husbandry mark the most fundamental shift in human adaptation ever recorded. Moreover, it seems to be the only time a species has made such a significant adaptive change without undergoing speciation. In other words, rather than our species evolving a new adaptive form in response to environmental changes, we altered the environment to accommodate our changing needs. Not surprisingly, a development of this magnitude has been the subject of a great deal of research in archaeology; many scholars have contributed to our current understanding of where food production was developed, when it happened, and why it happened at all. More recently, in light of the challenges currently facing our species, researchers have also examined the consequences of food production. This chapter provides a brief introduction to each of these various and complex topics.

Students should gain a basic understanding of what food production is and what its consequences are, both positive and negative. You should also become aware of where and when different sorts of plants and animals were domesticated. And you will be introduced to the various explanations proposed for the beginnings of food production, as well as the evidence and arguments that have been used to evaluate those explanations.

Domestication

Food production involves manipulating nature to generate food supplies in greater quantities and/or in different locations than would occur naturally in the wild. Although the process is accompanied by various technological developments, at the most basic level, food production is based on the domestication of plants and animals. Domestication is the process of changing plants and animals in ways that bring them under humans' control. Humans control the breeding and distribution of plants and animals, selecting for certain traits that we find useful. This process is commonly referred to by the term Darwin gave it: *artificial selection*. Plant and animal species are changed by the selective pressures imposed by humans, to favor the traits desired by farmers and breeders. The traits humans find useful often vary widely from one species to the next. For cattle, we might select for greater hardiness or increased milk production. For sheep, greater docility and wool production are often the desired traits. Some varieties of plants have been bred for their larger fruit or for seeds that stay attached to the plant until they are harvested by humans (as in the case of corn). Other plants have been selected for their ability to thrive at high altitudes, in colder climates, or in marginal soils.

Each case of domestication and each variety developed from an ancestor species constitutes a separate sequence of genetic experiments undertaken over a long period of time, spanning many generations. Thus, domestication is a process, not an event. Different species of plants and animals were domesticated at different times and in different places. Most instances of domestication probably resulted from long-term interactions between humans and the individual species involved, including repeated attempts to change specific traits or expand the region in which a species could exist. Traditional classifications of prehistory identify food production as the hallmark of the Neolithic period. But we know that humans didn't reach the beginning of the Neolithic and suddenly decide it was time to begin farming. Instead, they had been experimenting with plant and animal manipulation for thousands of years; archaeological evidence now shows that the beginnings of domestication go back at least 10,000 years in some parts of the world.

The main reason to undertake domestication appears to have been to increase the food supply. The main benefit would be that more people could be supported by increasing the productivity of the land through the use of new (farming and husbandry) technologies. As we will see, this didn't solve all of humanity's problems, and it actually caused some new ones. But first, let's consider some of the traditional attitudes about agriculture and how new data required their reconsideration.

In the early days of archaeology, it was widely believed that humanity was generally uninventive and that only certain cultures had attained the highest levels of sophistication. It was presumed that the few highly developed cultures were the donors of knowledge that was passed along, somewhat imperfectly, to the surrounding, less developed recipient cultures. In historic times, people of Euro-American heritage identified their own ancestral cultures as being the more highly developed, and as they became aware of prehistoric cultures in other parts of the world, they brought that attitude to the study of those cultures as well. So as Europeans learned about the ancient Greeks and Romans, they identified those cultures as the sources of prehistoric knowledge; after the discovery of even earlier Egyptian dynasties, Egypt came to be viewed as the center of prehistoric learning and sophistication. This belief became formalized as the heliocentric school of thought; scholars believed that other prehistoric cultures were imperfect copies of dynastic Egyptian culture. It was as if Egypt was at the center of the prehistoric world, influencing all other cultures. Like the concentric ripples caused by a pebble thrown into a pond, Egyptian influences would be felt by all the surrounding cultures, but in an increasingly attenuated and imperfect form as the distance from Egypt increased.

With the acceptance of evolutionary thought in anthropology, the heliocentric view became discredited. Individual cultures are not viewed as more or less perfect copies of a single culture that happened to reach a high level of sophistication. Rather, all cultures came to be viewed as adaptations to the different local and regional environments within which they were situated. Much of the evidence for this idea that cultures adapt comes from the study of plant and animal domestication. Consider the following scenario proposed by Thor Heyerdahl in 1969: he proposed that Egyptians could have traveled to Central or South America by building reed boats and following the Canary Current from east to west across the central Atlantic Ocean. In order to test the seaworthiness of the Egyptian crafts, he built such a boat and sailed across the Atlantic to Barbados. Does this mean that Dynastic Egyptian culture influenced prehistoric cultures in the Americas? No, it doesn't. In fact, when one examines the evidence for plant and animal domestication in the two regions, it becomes clear there was no prehistoric contact. As discussed below, different crops were grown in Egypt and Mexico. These crops involved different farming techniques, harvesting methods, and processing and storage technologies. The foods and their preparation methods are entirely different in the two areas. In short, the data on food production are some of the most important pieces of evidence in support of the conclusion that food production was independently invented in six or seven different parts of the world (Figure 12.1). Let's consider some of this evidence.

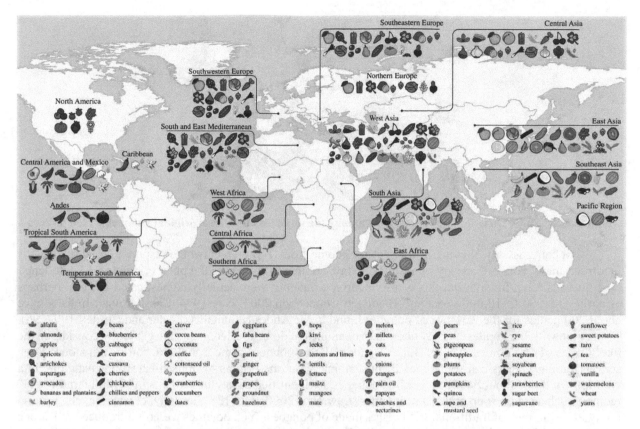

Figure 12.1: Agricultural crops and their regions of origin

Multiple Centers of Domestication

"What would the food of India be without curry—or curry powder without peppers? Indonesia's sambals without their distinctive fire? Hungary's goulash without paprika? Italy's antipasto without pepperoni? Five hundred years ago, none of the people in these countries had ever seen or heard of a chili pepper. No Old World language had a word for chili peppers before 1492" (Andrews 1992, 81).

Most Americans have only a vague sense of where our food comes from, other than knowing that they purchase it at a supermarket. I am not referring to the fact that the supermarket chains buy and ship food from many parts of the globe. Rather, I mean that most people don't know where the crops were originally domesticated. We may have some ideas about the nature of various regional and ethnic cuisines, based on our experiences in the foreign foods aisle at the grocery or our occasional visit to an ethnic restaurant, but even many of those ideas are incorrect. Consider potatoes, for instance (Figure 12.2).

Figure 12.2: Three varieties of potatoes from among the hundreds that were originally domesticated in Peru

When I ask my students where potatoes come from, I often receive the response, "Idaho!" That is incorrect; many potatoes are grown in Idaho today, but that is not where the plant originated. My students' next guess is often Ireland, but this is also incorrect; potatoes were actually domesticated in Peru, perhaps as early as 8,000 to 10,000 years ago (Peruvian Connection 2005; Coe 1994, 21). Peruvian Indians have about 200 names for the varieties of potatoes found in the Andes Mountains (Foster and Cordell 1992, 96). The region with the greatest variety and oldest examples of domesticated plants are generally considered the likely areas of first domestication. But if you didn't know potatoes came from Peru, you are not alone. Even serious culinary books can sometimes be misleading about the origins of domesticates. For example, in a well-known book about Scottish cooking, potatoes are identified as key ingredients in several "traditional" recipes, such as tattie soup and champit tatties (Lawrence 2000, 34, 112). Similarly, colcannon, champ, and boxty are examples of traditional Irish dishes made of potatoes. Yet, potatoes weren't introduced to Europe until the late 1500s and weren't widely used in England until the late eighteenth century (Segan 2003, 98).

Italian food is another traditional ethnic cuisine that is at least somewhat familiar to most Americans. Or is it? In the World Cook's collection of cookbooks, Whiteman et al. claim, "[I]f there is one ingredient that sums up the essence of Italian cooking, it must surely be pasta . . . In Italy, pasta is an essential part of every full meal . . ." (2002, 12). Yet, as the authors go on to admit, pasta, which is made from wheat (Figure 12.3), was originally developed in Asia and brought to Italy by Marco Polo. A quick look at the menu of most good Italian restaurants will reveal additional "traditional" dishes whose ingredients did not originate in Italy or the Mediterranean region. When looking at the menu for one of El Paso's best Italian restaurants (which shall remain nameless), one finds numerous references to tomatoes, but tomatoes were domesticated in South America (Coe 1994, 47). Minestrone is a favorite traditional soup, usually containing zucchini, which was domesticated in Mexico. Linguini grilled chicken Milano (in the style of Milan) obviously contains chicken, but chicken was domesticated in Southeast Asia. Polenta is a "traditional" staple food from northern Italy, but it is made from boiled cornmeal, and corn was domesticated in Mexico. To round out our Italian feast, let's finish up with tiramisu, the traditional Italian dessert containing cocoa, which is also from Mexico, and coffee, which is thought to have originated in Ethiopia.

Figure 12.3: Closeup view of wheat ripening in the fields. Compare these grains with the shape and appearance of sorghum in Figure 12.6.

To demonstrate that long-distance borrowing has occurred in several directions, let us briefly consider some traditional dishes from the cookbooks of the famous Chinese culinary artist Fu Pei-Mei: shrimp with cashew nuts, Kung Pao chicken, and sautéed prawns with tomato sauce. The shrimp and chicken are certainly indigenous to China, but cashew nuts and tomatoes originated in South America. The peanuts used in Kung Pao chicken were from South America, and the chili peppers originated in South America and/or Mexico (Coe 1994, 61). In fact, all of the hot peppers used in Southeast Asian cuisines are descended from stocks that originated in the New World (Andrews 1992).

So where does this leave us? By examining the seeds, bones, and other food remains preserved in archaeological deposits (Figure 12.4), it is now possible to identify the areas where many or most of our foods were first domesticated. For plants, we look to the regions that have the wild ancestors, the most varieties, and the earliest examples. Domesticates are often recognizable by increased seed size or expanded range relative to the wild ancestors. For animals, archaeologists examine the bone refuse for changes in the sex ratios and age distribution within the animal populations. It has been possible to identify at least a half-dozen regions in which domestication was invented independently, at somewhat different times and involving different species (Figure 12.1).

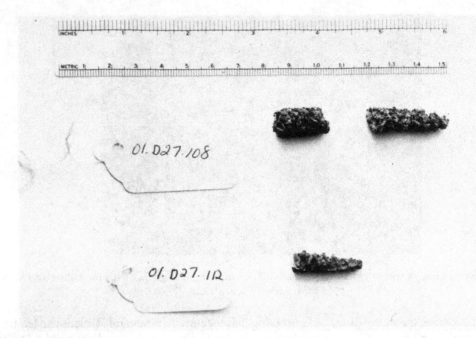

Figure 12.4. Early Chapalote corn (*Zea mais*) from Fresnal Shelter, an Archaic Site in southern New Mexico. Although several varieties of corn were identified from different time periods, the Chapalote dates to approximately 3,500 years ago.

The earliest evidence of domestication comes from southwest Asia, or the area of Mesopotamia often referred to as the Fertile Crescent (largely within present-day Turkey and Iraq). Beginning as early as 9,000 to 10,000 years ago, populations domesticated cereal grains such as rye, wheat, and barley (Larsen 2008, 386). They also cultivated figs and raised animals such as sheep, goats, cattle, and dogs. Food production in Mexico also began about 9,000 to 10,000 years ago with the domestication of squash (including pumpkin, acorn, Hubbard, zucchini, and crookneck), maize (Figure 12.5), and various kinds of beans. In addition, avocados, cocoa, and vanilla originated in Mexico. Domesticated animals were limited to dogs, turkey, and macaws. Also dating as far back as 9,000 to 10,000 years, South American cultigens include tomatoes, moschata squash, potatoes, sweet potatoes, cotton, lima beans, peanuts, and chili peppers. Andean natives also domesticated llamas, alpacas, guinea pigs, and dogs.

Figure 12.5: Varieties of corn, beans, and squash that represent the diversity of the three most important cultigens originating in Mexico

Figure 12.6: Sorghum, one of the grains originating in central and southern Africa

East and southeast Asian food production begins about 7,000 to 8,000 years ago. Plants from those regions include rice, several types of millet, bananas, taro, yam, and mung bean. Domesticated animals include chicken, pig, and dog. Farming developed still later in Africa, about 4,000 years ago; the main crops were sorghum (Figure 12.6), pearl millet, and African rice. Finally, archaeological evidence has documented an interesting case of independent invention of agriculture in eastern North America about 3,000 to 4,000 years ago. A series of indigenous plants, some of which are today considered undesirable weed species, were domesticated by Native Americans in the Illinois and Ohio River drainages. The plants included marsh elder, sunflower (Figure 12.7), and cheno-ams such as sump weed, goosefoot, and pigweed. Their larger seeds and wider geographical distribution relative to the wild ancestral forms identified the domesticated forms. By 2,000 years ago, these local crops were replaced by Mexican agricultural species (corn, beans, and squash) and technology.

Figure 12.7: Domesticated sunflower

A comparison of domestication in the Old World versus New World yields several patterns. Throughout most of the New World, food production began later than in the Old World, by perhaps 500 to 1,000 years later in Mexico and even later in other parts of the hemisphere. In addition to the use of different species, there are differences in emphasis between the Old and New worlds. In the Old World, we see a greater use of domesticated animals, not only for food, but also as beasts of burden, a use that was not widespread in the New World. In the New World, there is a greater emphasis on the use of domesticated plants; moreover, there were more radical changes in plant form, such as the development of the cob in an ear of maize. In the New World, we see more diversity in the kinds of plants used and a wider range of new technologies developed to process and consume them. Examples include the development of potatoes specifically intended for freeze-drying, pottery vessels that served as popcorn poppers, and manioc graters consisting of planks with rows of razor-sharp obsidian blades embedded in the surface.

It should be clear by now that the onset of agriculture was a very, very big deal that affected most of the globe; it spread into nearly all the environments that would support it within about 6,000 years of its invention. Why might this be the case? What is it about agriculture that led most populations on the planet to embrace it?

If You Can Hunt and Gather, Why Farm?

For roughly 95 percent of our time as a species, humans lived as hunter-gatherers, deriving the bulk of our diet from wild plant and animal resources. Yet, for many years, it was assumed that farming must be better. Hunter-gatherers were often portrayed as unsophisticated, warlike peoples barely able to eke out a meager existence. And, after all, the great civilizations of the world are all agrarian-based, so it must be the best thing to do, right? Well, perhaps not . . . it seems this is another example of *hindsight bias*. Contrary to popular belief, hunting and gathering is a healthy, more or less sustainable, and relatively easy way of life. In 1966, the Man the Hunter Symposium, which convened at the University of Chicago, ushered in an era during which anthropologists have closely studied and reported many details of hunter-gatherer lifeways, and the results have revised traditional stereotypes (Lee and DeVore 1968; Bicchieri 1972; Jochim 1976; Gould 1980; Dahlberg 1981).

The Hunter-Gatherer Diet

In most regions of the world, the tropics and temperate zones, hunter-gatherer diets are comprised primarily of gathered foods. Hunted game makes up a relatively small proportion of the diet, perhaps 15 percent, while the rest consists of gathered plant foods and small animals such as insects, reptiles, and mice. Hunter-gatherers usually have to rely on a wide variety of food sources because wild plants and animals are often widely dispersed across the landscape, and most resources are not highly concentrated. As a result, the most common hunter-gatherer diet is what we refer to as *broad-spectrum*. Hunter-gatherer groups in the Great Basin epitomized this pattern; subsistence activities were dominated by plant gathering, and individual bands identified between 29 and 81 different plant species that were used for food (Steward 1938, 19). The main exceptions to this pattern occur in groups adapted to the Arctic (where there are few plants) and the boreal forests, where diets are often focused on fish, sea mammals, or large herd animals.

Hunter-gatherers exhibit an intimate and amazingly detailed knowledge of the environments to which they are adapted. Some of the food sources they used, items that would be overlooked by our society, made it possible to survive in environments that were not suitable for other adaptations. For example, some bands of aborigines traveled long distances to the Australian Alps in order to "hunt" moths as they gathered in narrow canyons and crevices (Flood 1980). Insects were also seasonally important foods in the Great Basin:

> During the autumn, grasshoppers are very abundant. When cold weather sets in, these insects are numbed and can easily be gathered by the bushel. At such times, they dig a hole in the sand, heat stones in a fire nearby, put some hot stones in the bottom of the hole, put on a layer of grasshoppers, then a layer of hot stones, and continue this, until they put bushels on to roast. They are left until cool, when they are taken out, thoroughly dried, and ground into meal. Grasshopper gruel or grasshopper cake is a great treat (Powell 1895, 316).

Perhaps one of the most fascinating and efficient uses of plant resources by hunter-gatherers is the "second harvest" of the pitahaya practiced by the Cochimi Indians of Baja California and recorded by Jesuit missionaries. Pitahaya is a cactus with large edible fruits containing many small black seeds distributed throughout the flesh (Figure 12.8). During the short season when the fresh fruits are available, the Cochimi would eat great quantities, seeds and all, a behavior the missionaries decried as gluttonous. The Cochimi established an area, on a large flat boulder, where everyone would defecate. Then later in the year, during the dry season when fewer foods were available, they would return to the rock, winnow the pitahaya seeds out of the dried feces, and grind them into flour or meal, which could be made into a gruel (Aschmann 1966, 63). The second harvest reflects a truly remarkable understanding of the ecological details and food potential of the environment.

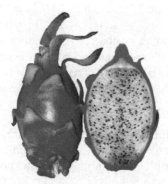

Figure 12.8: Fruit of the pitahaya cactus (*Hylocereus undatus*), like those harvested by the Cochimi hunter-gatherers of Baja California

Hunter-Gatherer Society

Hunter-gatherer populations are generally small, with local *bands* consisting of 25 to 50 individuals. Larger seasonal concentrations of several bands sometimes numbered up to 250 people or so, but they are short-lived because most food sources are not concentrated enough to support such large groups. There is commonly a division of labor within bands based on gender and age, with men doing most of the hunting and women and children doing most of the gathering. It is often necessary for members of the same band to be in more than one place at the same time, because the ripening of different plant foods and the opportunities for encountering game often occur in different locations. When required by these scheduling challenges, the band is split into smaller *task groups* that are focused on a particular set of resources, and the foods obtained by each task group is returned to a base camp to be shared with other members of the band.

Sharing is absolutely essential to the hunter-gatherer adaptation, because when anyone is successful in acquiring resources, the entire group benefits. *Sharing* is required within at least the extended family and often with the entire band. This reality is exemplified in the sharing of hunted game, such as deer or elk. In many groups, the successful hunter is required to share the game so completely that he and his family might get to keep only the hide; all of the meat may be distributed among extended family members or the entire band. In some cases, sharing of this sort is formalized, with each portion or cut of the carcass being designated for a specific relative. I documented this firsthand among the Mescalero Apaches when I attended the funeral for Bernard Second, my adopted Apache brother. Two deer were shot to contribute to the dinner prepared for Bernard's close relatives, and the carcasses were hung on poles lashed between trees behind the house. Our nephew, Medicine Bird, was visiting from Oklahoma, where he was attending college at the time, and when he was preparing to leave for the drive back, my Apache sister handed me a butcher knife and asked me to go out and cut off Medicine Bird's portion. She didn't ask me merely to cut a piece of meat for him; she asked me to cut *his piece,* the piece that was designated as his by virtue of his being Bernard's nephew. As Bernard's brother, I received a different portion. The entire carcass was butchered that way, with the pieces apportioned according to the recipient's relationship to the deceased. In aboriginal times, such arrangements meant that the successful hunter's family might not get any meat, but when others were successful, he would receive his designated portion of their kills. The overall effect is that the band as a whole is fed no matter who makes a kill, and no one accumulates very much more than anyone else (this is considered a good thing in hunter-gatherer societies).

Hunter-Gatherer Residential Mobility

For our purposes in examining the beginnings of agriculture, perhaps the most salient characteristic of hunter-gatherer adaptations is their high degree of *mobility*. Because many wild plant and animal resources are widely dispersed, of low density, and incongruent (different resources are not all in the same places), hunter-gatherer adaptations generally require very large territories. The Kalahari Bushmen, for example, might travel as far as 1,500 kilometers per year, relocating their camps every few weeks in order to take advantage of the key resources available in different portions of their territory. Yet, territoriality is generally loosely organized. Band membership is fluid, with families coming and going, and territories are usually not physically defended. When times are tough in one region, band members may temporarily move to other areas where they have relatives, and that relationship provides access to neighboring territories. Hunter-gatherers have few material possessions because they are constantly on the move. So, the maintenance of social networks upon which one can rely during times of hardship, rather than the accumulation of material goods, is the measure of success.

So how are hunter-gatherer adaptations relevant to understanding the beginnings of agriculture? We now know that many, perhaps most, domesticates were developed by hunter-gatherer populations. But we also know that even though hunting peoples knew about domesticates and agricultural techniques, they did not commit to them right away. In the Southwestern U. S., about 2,000 years passed between the introduction of corn and the shift to farming adaptations based on corn agriculture (Wills 1995, 217).

We also know that hunter-gatherers added more and more species of plants to their diets over time, apparently in response to increases in local and regional population density. In the Tehuacan Valley of Mexico, some domesticates (such as chili and avocado) appear in the archaeological record by 8,000 or 9,000 years ago, but they represent only a few of the 20 or so food plants identified at that time (MacNeish et al. 1967, 301). A variety of agricultural plants were added to the diet over time, but most were added fairly late, after 1,000 BC. In other words, most of the agricultural plants were among the later additions to the hunter-gatherer diet. This lag time in the switch to an emphasis on domesticates suggests that agriculture was not the first choice of responses to resource stress even among peoples who already knew how to farm. Indeed, it seems they first sought other ways to intensify or increase their gathered food sources, by adding more species to the diet, shifting to smaller game such as rodents, and intensifying use of wild species such as *agave*. The shift to reliance on agriculture seems to have been their choice of last resort.

Figure 12.9: Ancestral Pueblo milling bins in a specialized corn processing room at Gran Quivira, Salinas Pueblo National Monument, New Mexico. the three adjacent bins contained milling stones (manos and metates) varying from coarse to fine grit, allowing for the production of a range of corn meal and corn flour products.

The idea that populations shifted to agriculture only when they had no other options makes sense when we look at the consequences of domestication. Agricultural technology changes the carrying capacity of the land, supporting a larger number of people than hunting and gathering would in the same area. Therefore, agriculture makes sense as a response to population growth. Agriculture also provides a way to deal with natural fluctuations in climate and the availability of wild foods. If surplus agricultural products are stored, they can be relied upon during times of hardship (Figures 12.10 and 12.11). A commitment to farming usually means that populations reduce their mobility, staying closer to the agricultural lands that must be tended. Thus, agriculture leads to increased sedentism, the development of more settled communities. Additionally, surplus agricultural products can be used as capital, for trade, to invest in public works, or to support individuals who don't have to work in food production, such as artisans and soldiers.

Figure 12.10: Ancestral Pueblo granaries in Grand Canyon National Park, Arizona

Figure 12.11: Granary in Cueva de la Olla, a Casas Grandes archaeological site in the northwest portion of the state of Chihuahua, Mexico

Unintended Consequences of Food Production

Unfortunately, when populations shift to a reliance on agriculture, the disadvantages outnumber the advantages. Agriculture is more labor-intensive than hunting and gathering. Hunter-gatherers can often feed their families with about two to three days' worth of work per week; such is not the case for farmers and pastoralists. Any of you who were raised on farms or ranches will know that you had little or no leisure time, especially during planting, cultivation, and harvest. Farming is so labor-intensive that the labor needs of farmers heavily influenced the way we structure the academic year in the United States. We have a summer "vacation" mainly because in generations past, the children of farm families were needed as laborers during the growing season. As the use of new agricultural technologies increased (such as clearing forests for farmland, constructing irrigation ditches, excavating, or drilling water wells), so did the demand for labor.

The switch to agricultural production also leads to several kinds of environmental degradation. There is often a loss of wild animal species because of overhunting in the vicinity of sedentary communities. Clearing the land by cutting forests or burning off brush further reduces the biodiversity of the region by removing or altering plant and animal habitat. And when populations rely on a single or a few crops (instead of the many wild species that used to be available), they become more susceptible to crop failure due to severe weather, plant diseases, and insect depredations. The removal of the mature natural vegetation also exposes the soils to increased erosion.

It may surprise you to learn that the diet of subsistence farmers is actually often nutritionally inferior to that of hunter-gatherers. Agricultural diets are higher in carbohydrates and lower in proteins and minerals such as iron. As a result, farming populations have higher incidences of iron deficiency, tooth enamel defects, dental cavities, and degenerative joint disease than hunting populations. Children in agricultural groups mature more slowly, are more likely to experience malnutrition, and are more likely to have intestinal parasites, and as adults, their bodies are smaller and shorter than hunters (Larsen 2008, 395–414). Due to population increases, crowding, and sharing their living space with livestock, agricultural groups are more likely to live in conditions of pollution and have higher incidences of infectious diseases. And as if this weren't bad enough, it was the competition to control productive farmland that led to the development of human warfare (e.g., Haas 1999).

So the shift to an agricultural lifestyle has had mainly negative consequences for humanity. If farming is so bad, then why would anyone do it? The short answer is because our ancestors had no other choice. Researchers have proposed a variety of explanations for the beginnings of agriculture, extending back to V. Gordon Childe's oasis model. Several early explanations were based on the premise that the adoption of agriculture was better, has obvious advantages, or was predestined, but we now know this is not the case. Today, most researchers would argue that some version of a population pressure model (e.g., the views of Binford, Flannery, Boserup, and Rindos) is a better explanation. There appears to have been slow but persistent growth in human populations throughout the Pleistocene, leading to crowding in some regions by the end of the Ice Age. The populations were not large by modern standards, but they were large enough to generate crowding and competition in the context of hunter-gatherer adaptations. (For example, what happened when one hunting band moved its village to the next valley and for the first time found another band already living there?) Archaeological sites have yielded evidence of skeletal stress, suggesting decreased quality of food supplies. Diets were broadened by the addition of insects, mice, and less desirable plant foods (the ones harder to produce and process). Only after these steps were taken did prehistoric populations turn to a reliance on agricultural crops. People didn't choose the path of domestication until they had to, and it was probably not a conscious choice, at least initially. But it seems to have occurred first in the marginal areas where food stress was most acute, and it quickly spread to other regions as populations continued to grow.

The Agricultural Trap

Human populations have continued to grow, and grow, and grow. Once a population has committed to agriculture as a response to population growth, it sets up a positive feedback loop. It is possible to increase productivity, to produce more food, by using the new technology associated with a shift to agriculture. Producing more food, perhaps even generating a surplus, will permit further population growth, which will require increased agricultural production, which in turn leads to more population growth . . . You see where this is going. Some researchers refer to this vicious cycle as the *agricultural trap*, and I would argue that we are still caught in it.

The process of increasing agricultural productivity through the investment of increased technology and labor resources is referred to as *intensification*. Let's consider a hypothetical but realistic sequence of changes in agricultural production that might occur in a given region over a long period of time: 1) A population that has been farming the river bottoms finds that population growth has outstripped the food supply. 2) They open up new fields in the upland areas away from the river, using swidden (slash-and -burn) techniques, in which the trees are chopped down and burned. After one or a few seasons, the cleared fields are allowed to lie fallow so that the soil nutrients can be replaced, but as population continues to grow, there is pressure to shorten the fallow period. 3) The society shifts to a "brush fallow" approach, which means swidden fields are not allowed to sit idle long enough for trees to regrow. Instead, they are cleared again as soon as shrubs have grown up, and clearing such fields is more labor-intensive than simply cutting and burning trees. 4) Cultivation is a logical next step, in which fields are cleared of weeds and other plants that compete with the cultigens for water. Entire families are out in the fields using hoes to chop the weeds. And someone needed to invent the hoes. 5) People living in some environments learn to do crop rotation, and they can now produce two or three crops per year, as long as they plant in the correct sequence that allows one crop to replenish the soil with the nutrients needed by the following crop. 6) Fertilization is another way to increase productivity. The farmers carry the feces of domesticated animals to the agricultural fields and mix them into the soil. They learn to bury fish in the holes they dig for planting seeds, but obtaining the fish is a lot of work, and using the fish as fertilizer means people aren't consuming them directly. 7) In dry years, some fields fail, so the people learn to design, construct, and maintain irrigation ditches to bring water to the fields. Special community groups and leadership roles have to be created to organize and oversee the labor needed to build and operate the irrigation system. 8) The society learns that a neighboring population is also looking to expand its agricultural production, but all of the good farmlands are already being used. So the leaders organize the population and make war on their neighbors in order to take control of their farmlands. 9) Following the Industrial Revolution, it becomes possible to greatly expand the areas farmed by using machines to do most of the farm labor, such as plowing, cultivating, harvesting, hauling the produce to market, and drilling deep wells. With each level of intensification, there are increased costs, and the ability to accommodate additional population growth sets up another cycle of growth and stress, requiring still more intensification.

The costs associated with the last level of intensification are precisely those with which we are still trying to cope. There are the costs of making steel for the machines and rubber for their tires, the gasoline or diesel fuel that powers the equipment, and the oils and grease lubricants they require. There are the chemical fertilizers sprayed from behind a tractor or a low-flying airplane. There are the highways and railroads needed to deliver the food products to the distributors and markets, as well as the trucks, trains, and ships needed to transport them. There are the freezers, refrigerators, and other storage facilities, as well as the coolants and electrical power needed to operate them . . .

Today's agriculture is enormously expensive, and it generates a larger environmental impact than most people seem to realize. Let's examine a few statistics regarding the costs of technology in general and consider that proportional changes apply to the agricultural portion. Prehistoric global energy use prior to the beginnings of food production has been estimated at .001 to .002 terawatts (TW) for a population of 5 to 10 million people (1 TW = 1 trillion watts). World consumption in 1990 was 13 TW, or 7,000 to 13,000 times higher (Whole Systems 2007, 2). The overall rate of technological change continues to increase rapidly (witness how quickly our computers become obsolete). The cost of such rapid technological change is illustrated by the oil demands of the US military. It is estimated that the average soldier in Iraq used about seven times more oil per day than was the case in the first Gulf War (Klare 2008). Because our agriculture production is mechanized, and because our distribution system is dependent on oil, it now takes about 10 fossil fuel calories to produce one food calorie for the American diet (Starrs 2005). About 15 percent of US energy is consumed in supplying the country with food, with about half used in production and half going to food processing and packaging. Food items in US grocery stores have traveled an average of 1,500 miles to get there, and one study in the United Kingdom indicated that distances involved in global food transportation have risen by 50 percent over the past 20 years (Church 2005, 4).

The international food system is amazingly complicated and inefficient, at least in terms of transportation costs. Researchers at the Swedish Institute for Food and Biotechnology studied the steps involved in growing the tomatoes, converting them to paste, making tomato ketchup, and packaging and storing the ketchup for distribution. It is distressing to learn that the manufacture of something as mundane as a bottle of ketchup includes more than 52 processing and transportation steps, many involving international shipments (Church 2005, 3). The tomatoes were grown in Italy and converted there into tomato paste. Bags used to package the tomato paste were made in the Netherlands, shipped to Italy to be filled, and then shipped to Sweden where the ketchup was produced. The plastic bottles were made in the United Kingdom or Sweden out of materials from Japan, Italy, Belgium, the United States, and Denmark. The screw cap was made in Denmark and shipped to Sweden.

Still other processes include transportation of fertilizers, pesticides, and the operation of farm equipment and processing machinery. Now think about the effects of a more or less similar level of complexity being embedded in the production of many other foods we consume. Even when processing costs are minimal, transportation can still be very costly. "Because they travel by air instead of ship, Hawaiian pineapples are among the most carbon intensive of foods, contributing about 40 pounds of CO_2 [carbon dioxide] per pound of pineapple. That is about 10 times the next highest figure among the foods studied" (Starrs 2005). David Pimentel, professor of agricultural science at Cornell University, has estimated that if the rest of the world ate the way Americans do, all known fossil fuel reserves would be exhausted in just seven years (Starrs 2005). The cost and inefficiency of the world food system, or at least that of developed countries, does not seem to be sustainable, but we have yet to figure a way out of the agricultural trap.

References and Further Reading

Andrews, Jean. 1992. "The Peripatetic Chili Pepper: Diffusion of the Domesticated Capsicums Since Columbus." In *Chilies to Chocolate: Food the Americas Gave the World,* edited by Nelson Foster and Linda Cordell, 81–93. Tuscon, AZ: University of Arizona Press.

Aschmann, Homer. 1959. *The Central Desert of Baja California: Demography and Ecology. Iberoamericana* no. 42. Berkeley: University of California Press.

Aschmann, Homer, trans. and ed. 1966. *The Natural & Human History of Baja California (From Manuscripts by Jesuit Missionaries).* Los Angeles: Dawson's Book Shop.

Bicchieri, M. G., ed. 1972. *Hunters and Gatherers Today: A Socioeconomic Study of Eleven Such Cultures in the Twentieth Century.* New York: Holt, Rinehart and Winston, Inc.

Binford, Lewis R. 1983. *In Pursuit of the Past: Decoding the Archaeological Record.* London: Thames and Hudson.

Binford, Lewis R., ed. 1977. *For Theory Building in Archaeology: Essays on Faunal Remains, Aquatic Resources, Spatial Analysis, and Systemic Modeling.* Cambridge, MA: Academic Press.

Church, Norman. 2005. "Why Our Food Is So Dependent on Oil." *Countercurrents,* April 7, 2005. www.countercurrents.org/po-church0700405.htm.

Coe, Sophie D. 1994. *America's First Cuisines.* Austin: University of Texas Press.

Dahlberg, Frances, ed. 1981. *Woman the Gatherer.* New Haven, CT: Yale University Press.

Flood, Josephine. 1980. *The Moth Hunters: Aboriginal Prehistory of the Australian Alps.* Australian Institute of Aboriginal Studies, New Series, no. 14. Humanities Press.

Foster, Nelson, and Linda Cordell, eds. 1992. *Chilies to Chocolate: Foods the Americas Gave the World.* Tuscon, AZ: University of Arizona Press.

Fox, Michael W. 1991. "Animal Agriculture: Human and Animal Well-Being." *HSUS News* 36, no. 3 (Summer 1991). Humane Society of the United States.

Gould, Richard A. 1980. *Living Archaeology.* Cambridge, UK: Cambridge University Press.

Haas, Jonathan. 1999. "The Origins of War and Ethnic Violence." In *Ancient Warfare,* edited by John Carman and Anthony Harding, 11–24. Gloucestershire: Sutton Publishers.

Jochim, Michael A. 1976. *Hunter-Gatherer Subsistence and Settlement: A Predictive Model.* Cambridge, MA: Academic Press.

Kipple, Kenneth F., and Kriemhild Conee Ornelas, eds. 2000. *The Cambridge World History of Foods.* Cambridge, UK: Cambridge University Press.

Klare, Michael T. 2008. "Portrait of an Oil-Addicted Former Superpower: Rising Oil Prices Undermine Status of the U.S." Obliterating America's Superpower Status." *European Energy Review,* July/August 2008, 100–103.

Larsen, Clark Spencer. 2008. *Our Origins: Discovering Physical Anthropology.* New York: W. W. Norton & Company.

Lawrence, Sue. 2000. *Scots Cooking: The Best Traditional and Contemporary Scottish Recipes.* London: Headline Book Publishing.

Lee, Richard B., and Irven DeVore, eds. 1968. *Man the Hunter (The First Intensive Survey of a Single, Crucial Stage of Human Development—Man's Once Universal Hunting Way of Life).* Chicago: Aldine Publishing Co.

MacNeish, Richard S., Douglas Byers et al. 1967. *The Prehistory of the Tehuacan Valley, Volume One, Environment and Subsistence. Douglas Byers, General Editor.* Published for the Robert S. Peabody Foundation, Philips Academy, Andover, MA. University of Texas Press.

Mufson, Steven. 2008. "Siphoning Off Corn to Fuel Our Cars." *Washington Post,* April 30, 2008, A01. http://www.washingtonpost.com/wp-dyn/content/article/2008/04/29/AR2008042903092.html.

Peruvian Connection. 2005. "Potatoes: From the Andes to Ireland." *Peruvian Connection, A Newsletter of Andean Art & Culture,* March 2005.

Powell, John Wesley. 1875; 1895. *Canyons of the Colorado.* Reprint of 1875 edition with the addition of six chapters. Meadville, PA: Flood and Vincent.

Rindos, David. 1984. *The Origins of Agriculture: An Evolutionary Perspective. Cambridge, MA:* Academic Press.

Segan, Francine. 2003. *Shakespeare's Kitchen: Renaissance Recipes for the Contemporary Cook.* New York: Random House.

Starrs, Thomas. 2005. "The SUV in the Pantry." *The WASTENOT-gram.* American Solar Energy Society.

Steward, Julian. 1938. "Basin-Plateau Aboriginal Sociopolitical Groups." *Bureau of American Ethnology Bulletin* 120, Smithsonian Institution.

Whiteman, Kate, Jeni Wright, and Angela Boggiano. 2002. *Italian Kitchen.* New York: World Cooks Collection, Barnes & Noble Books.

Whole Systems. 2007. "Species Extinction and Human Population. Whole-Systems.com

Wills, W. H. 1995. "Archaic Foraging and the Beginning of Food Production in the American Southwest." In *Last Hunters, First Farmers,* edited by T. Douglas Price and Anne Birgitte Gebauer, 2115–242. School of American Research Press.

Chapter 13: Evolution of Civilizations

Civilization Defined

What does it mean to be civilized? This is another of those terms that have different meanings as technical terms in anthropology than they do in the common vernacular. In general usage, it might be common to say, after emerging from a weeklong backpacking trip in the wilderness that one has returned to civilization. In this sense, it might simply mean you have cell phone service again, or that your access to Burger King has been restored. Or, we might refer to someone as being civilized if they are polite, cultured, or treat others with respect; that is, if they are civil in their treatment of their fellow humans. While these are laudable traits, this is not what is meant when we talk about the evolution of civilization. For our purposes here, civilization refers to a set of behaviors that reflect a certain level of social-cultural complexity.

Figure 13.1: Panoramic view of the Avenue of the Dead and Pyramid of the Sun, a portion of the ancient city of Teotihuacan near Mexico City

The defining characteristics of *civilization* include populations that are sufficiently large and sedentary that they live in relatively dense concentrations; some of the settlements would be considered cities, even by modern standards (Figure 13.1). The population is organized according to socioeconomic strata, with a majority of the people being workers and an elite class that controls their labor and many other aspects of behavior. Subsistence is based on food production that is efficient enough to generate a surplus. That surplus is controlled by the elite and invested to create social infrastructure that serves the elite and the general public to varying degrees. The workers not involved in food production are freed up to work as craftsmen, merchants, artists, soldiers, construction workers, etc. Monumental public works, such as pyramids, irrigation systems, roads, and monuments, serve vital integrative purposes, both in a practical sense, as with the case of irrigation canals, and at an emotional level, as with public monuments that help establish a sense of nationalism or shared public identity. The organization of the society is accomplished through a system of government, and the important ideologies, laws, and accounting records are maintained using an official form of recordkeeping or writing (Figure 13.2).

Figure 13.2: Egyptian hieroglyphs

In this chapter, students should gain an understanding of the basic components of civilizations. You should also become familiar with the range of explanations or causes that have been proposed to explain their development. You should learn about some of the reasons that prehistoric and historic civilizations have collapsed and how that might relate to observations about the behavior of our own society.

Why Do Civilizations Develop?

The first civilizations rose in the same regions where food production was developed and intensified (Figure 13.3). From this pattern, it is reasonable to infer that food production and therefore larger, more densely concentrated populations were preconditions for the evolution of civilizations. The specific circumstances that led to population concentration, and the particular form taken by agricultural intensification, varies from region to region. Therefore, depending on which regions and which civilizations they study, researchers have proposed somewhat different scenarios for how such stratified societies came about. For the purposes of discussion, the most commonly proposed explanations for the development of civilization can be grouped into environmental and cultural factors. A variety of Old World and New World examples of civilizations illustrate the role of different potential causal factors.

Figure 13.3: Regions where many of the civilizations of the ancient world evolved

In the early years of anthropology, the development of civilization was often viewed as the inevitable result of *unilineal cultural evolution*. It was assumed that cultures evolved through a series of stages involving increasingly complex advances in technology, such as the intensification of agriculture, development of metallurgy, etc. (Morgan 1877). Morgan argued that culture moved forward toward civilization as it developed greater complexity. But the idea is circular because it essentially says that civilization happened because it did. Karl Marx proposed an economics-based version of this idea of increasing complexity. As agricultural production became intensified, there emerged a division between those who owned the means of production, such as farmland and livestock, and those who did not. As surpluses (wealth) accumulated among the former, the need arose for exchange between the different classes. This need was filled by the development of a new class of full-time merchants. As commerce became increasingly important, government structure and policies were needed to solidify the unequal structure of society. In this view, the main function of government would be to protect the interests of those who control wealth while reinforcing their authority (Figure 13.4).

Environmental influences have also been invoked as explanations for the development of particular societies. Karl Wittfogle (1957) suggested that control of water supplies and the need to build water infrastructure such as irrigation systems were the impetus for civilization (Figure 13.5). In this model, known as the *hydraulic hypothesis*, it is the need to control and direct a large labor force in the building, maintenance, and operation of irrigation systems that causes society to be reorganized into a ranked society with different social classes. Whoever controls the water can dictate the activities of others, and their power is reflected in the construction of monumental architecture, such as palaces and pyramids. The lower classes must in some sense accede to control by the elite in order to benefit from the overall productivity of the system.

Figure 13.4: Egyptian pyramids at Gizah. These massive public works probably served various functions, including honoring the pharaohs, establishing a visible monument to a shared national identity, and the redistribution of resources in the form of food supplies distributed to workers.

Figure 13.5: Modern use of chinampa (floating garden) technology in Xochimilco, Mexico

The *circumscription hypothesis* (Carneiro 1970, 734) alleges that only coercive force can account for the development of civilization, not enlightened self-interest. Carneiro argues that in areas where resources are limited and populations are bounded or hemmed in by their neighbors, social responses to population growth are limited. Eventually such populations, if they are to continue to grow, will expand into neighboring territories and seize land by force. In other words, competition among neighboring groups resulted in military growth and organization. As civilizations expanded, they absorbed defeated enemy populations, thus accelerating the rate of population growth and the need for further expansion.

It should be apparent that the potential causes or traits of civilizations don't occur in the same sequence or in the same combinations in all places where civilizations developed. For example, population growth and trade may have been the early catalysts in Egypt, whereas flood control was most important in the Indus Valley, and defensive fortifications were more initially more important in China. The overall constellation of traits end up being similar in different regions, but the history of their development differs from place to place, making it difficult to identify a single cause. Trigger (2003) identifies two key developments that must occur for civilizations to evolve: increasing social complexity and the growth of cultural institutions that manage that complexity. Some of the institutions that appear in most or all civilizations to accomplish the management tasks include kingships, class systems, religion, support of the upper classes through the use of force, and control of economic production.

I am personally drawn to Jonathon Haas's (1982) idea of *social integration* as a useful way to discuss these various social mechanisms. The social integration model recognizes that different combinations of trade, warfare, irrigation, and population control needs led to the formation of complex societies in different places. The key common element was the need to develop large-scale mechanisms of social integration—that is, ways to control and mobilize large labor forces operating on behalf the entire society and ways to build the social infrastructure necessary to operate a complex system. The social structural changes involved, placing some people in charge of the labor of others, led to the formation of social hierarchies, differential access to goods and services, and, eventually, the accumulation of what we would call wealth. One of the attractive aspects of the social integration model is that it doesn't much matter which driver to integration is most characteristic in a particular culture or specific place or time. The pressures on a cultural system to grow and expand include several factors working together and in different combinations in different places. But, in the end, the results are more or less the same. Large populations need complex social structures to manage all the parts of society so that the system as a whole can function.

Social integration as a route to the evolution of civilization can be viewed as one permutation, or variety of culture change that is predicted by a *world systems* model. The world systems concept is an approach to studying cultural change in complex social systems (Chase-Dunn and Hall 1977). It extends the Marxist emphasis on materialism to a consideration of international relations. In its original configuration, the world systems model was intended to apply to modern market economies (Wallerstein 1974). However, if one shifts the focus from modern countries in a global economy to prehistoric societies in regional economies, a "world economy" perspective can be a useful way to examine prehistoric complex societies (Upham 1982).

A world systems model envisions an economic system in which some players benefit while others are exploited. If we consider this on a regional, prehistoric scale, it could be argued that there will be core societies that constitute the center or hub of regional economic systems, which exploit surrounding peripheral societies for things such as raw materials and exotic artifacts that identify or reinforce elite status in the core societies. Peripheral societies in these regional systems would be dependent on the core societies for capital, organizational knowledge, and perhaps protection from other core societies.

Part of the structure of the core society consists of a set of mechanisms that redistribute resources from the undeveloped, raw material exporting periphery to the developed, industrialized (or at least civilized) core of the system. So, the general scenario in the context of a world systems perspective might be something like this: Population growth leads to agricultural intensification, the investment of more soil, water or energy per unit of time or area (Harris 1977, 5). Intensification leads to additional population growth, environmental degradation, and increased production costs. Rising costs lead to population pressure, leading in turn back to the next cycle in the agricultural trap discussed in the previous chapter. As long as there are suitable lands into which the society can expand, migration will be the result. When that is not an option, warfare is a likely outcome. So the major internal, external, and managerial challenges involved in several of the regional examples of civilizations are all accommodated in the world systems view, albeit in different combinations and sequences.

Let's consider one additional idea: societies as systems of energy capture and use. This model, developed by archaeologists working on the rise and fall of prehistoric societies in New Mexico, explicitly accounts for not only the rise of complexity, but also cyclic changes and even collapse of complex systems (Stuart and Gauthier 1981). The possible adaptive approaches are conceived of as occurring in two dichotomous evolutionary modes or adaptive strategies. Power strategies are characterized by increasing rates of population growth, high levels of overall productivity, and high rates of energy expenditure. Growth in these aspects of society is supported by intensification within the subsistence strategy. In contrast, efficiency strategies exhibit low rates of population growth, production, or energy expenditure. They reflect extensive, broad-spectrum adaptations that tend toward the maintenance of homeostasis. This dichotomy is probably overly simplistic in the real world, as most cultural systems fall somewhere along a continuum between the extremes.

In this model, hunter-gatherers and other small-scale societies would be at low energy use end of the spectrum. They have relatively small populations, relatively small energy requirements, and large per capita areas of the landscape. Moving toward the other end of the spectrum is representative of a power drive; population growth is rapid, leading to the formation of large social groups. The labor input devoted to production increases, as does the emphasis on agriculture and the overall amount of energy consumed per capita. Smaller and smaller areas of land are needed per capita because increases in productivity support larger populations in smaller portions of the landscape. What is perhaps most interesting about this model is that it provides a way to think about individual societies or regional populations moving from one part of the continuum to another. In other words, individual systems have the potential to oscillate between power and efficiency drives or poses, depending on the circumstances at hand. Intermittent periods of growth, or power drives, may be interspersed with periods of decline or homeostasis (Carmichael 1985, 29).

Patterns like this have been documented for a number of prehistoric groups, such as the Maya (Diamond 2005). Periods of growth occurred at some Mayan cities at the expense of their neighbors in the periphery, but during periods of decline, cities in the periphery sometimes entered power phases, thereby overtaking the earlier core settlements in the system. When the system overshoots the carrying capacity of the environment in which it is situated, the entire system may collapse, as in the case of the Mayan empire. However, in this model, it is possible to conceive of the collapse referring to the world (i.e., regional) system, not the biological population. Overpopulation, environmental degradation, and warfare all result in real hardships and losses to real human populations. Yet, there still are many indigenous Mayans in Mesoamerica. The structure of the Mayan world system collapsed, but the biological population survived, most notably those at the bottom of the social hierarchy, not the elite.

Resource-Intensive Adaptation and Modern Oil Dependency

Societies involved in a power strategy are well known to us today. The United States has been in such a growth mode for the past century, and the rates of growth and change are accelerating. From a world systems perspective, much of the cost of our system is in acquiring natural resources and transporting them to the system core, the United States. Or if the consumer goods are manufactured elsewhere, the natural resources will go there, and the finished goods are then transported to the system core. As indicated in Chapter 12, the cost of transporting food over long distances is one example of this. Another example is the ongoing quest for oil. Most geologists believe we have already reached or will soon reach the moment of peak oil, the point at which we have already found and extracted half of all the available oil supplies. After that point, significant new discoveries will be few, and the remaining oil will be harder to extract and be in greater demand, thereby raising prices. Worldwide oil production is apparently now at or near its peak, and we can expect a downturn in the global availability of oil in the not-so-distant future (Klare 2007).

We live in a highly stratified, hierarchical world in which 1,000 people at the top control assets worth twice that of those held by the bottom 2.5 billion people. The top 10 percent own 85 percent of everything. Much of that wealth relates to the control, distribution, and use of oil resources. It is already the case that wars are being fought about who will have control over the dwindling supply. If our society and/or other societies around world make poor choices about how to address future energy needs, it is possible that we might exceed the carrying capacity of the environment within which we operate. Yes, technological advances might forestall the large fluctuations at least for a time, but many analysts view our present course of action as unsustainable.

Shermer (2008) argues that in all of human history, there have only been about 60 civilizations. The average longevity of those civilizations has been 420 years. Among the civilizations that have developed since the time of Christ, the average longevity has been 304 years (Shermer 2008, 30). The United States has been a system for about 240 years; is a system collapse really on the horizon? We shall see.

We do not mean to imply that ecological or nuclear dooms are inevitable. But we do think they are unacceptably probable. Because of the immense human tragedy that is likely to accompany future core wars or global ecological disaster we must educate the citizens of the world about how the forces of social evolution work, and we must organize the political forces that will try to reform the capitalist world-system in order to prevent these outcomes. But we should also prepare for the possibility that partial dooms may indeed occur, and be ready to reshape the system of survivors into a democratic and collectively rational global commonwealth that will eliminate warfare and poverty, protect the global ecosystem, and regulate population growth at a sustainable level (Chase-Dunn and Hall 1997, 8).

We will consider a major potential impetus for systemic collapse—global climate change—in the final chapter. For now, think about what it would mean to return to an economy without oil . . . to cycle back to an efficiency trajectory in our adaptive strategy. Author Charles Sullivan (2007) has written the essay *Uncommon Grace: Biology and Economic Theory* as a way to think about the alternatives—the way it was before and how it could be again.

References and Further Reading

Carmichael, David L. 1985. "Archeological Excavations at Two Prehistoric Campsites Near Keystone Dam, El Paso, Texas." University Museum Occasional Papers, No. 14. Las Cruces, NM: New Mexico State University.

Carneiro, Robert. 1970. "A Theory of the Origin of the State." *Science* 169: 733–38.

Chase-Dunn, Christopher, and Thomas D. Hall. 1997. Paradigms Bridged: Institutional Materialism and World-Systemic Evolution. Paper presented at the annual meeting of the Social Science History Association, Washington, DC, October 18, 1997.

Church, Norman. 2005. "Why Our Food Is So Dependent On Oil." Countercurrents.org, April 7, 2005. www.countercurrents.org/po-church0700405.htm.

Conner, Steve. 2007. "World's Most Important Crops Hit by Global Warming Effects." *The Independent UK,* March 19, 2007.

Diamond, Jared. 2005. *Collapse: How Societies Choose to Fail or Succeed. New York:* Viking Press.

Fox, Michael W. 1991. "Animal Agriculture: Human and Animal Well-Being." *HSUS News* 36, no. 3 (Summer 1991). The Humane Society of the United States.

GRAIN. 2008. "Making a Killing from Hunger." Grain.org, April 28, 2008. https://grain.org/article/entries/178-making-a-killing-from-hunger.

Haas, Jonathon. 1982. *The Evolution of the Prehistoric State. New York:* New York University Press.

Harris, Marvin. 1977. *Cannibals and Kings: The Origins of Cultures. New York:* Random House.

Klare, Michael T. 2008. "Portrait of an Oil-Addicted Former Superpower: How Rising Oil Prices are Obliterating America's Superpower Status." *Tom Dispatch,* May 8, 2008. https://grist.org/article/portrait-of-an-oil-addicted-former-superpower/.

Kunstler, James Howard. 2007a. "Ten Ways to Prepare for a Post-Oil Society." *AlterNet,* February 10, 2007. https://www.permaculturenews.org/2014/03/20/10-ways-prepare-post-oil-society/.

Kunstler, James Howard. 2007b. "We Must Imagine a Future Without Cars." *AlterNet*, April 4, 2007. https://www.alternet.org/2007/04/we_must_imagine_a_future_without_cars/.

Mittelstaedt, Martin. 2007. "How Global Warming Goes Against the Grain." *Saturday's Globe and Mail*, February 23, 2007. How global warming goes against the grain - The Globe and Mail

Morgan, Lewis Henry. 1877; 1964. *Ancient Society.* Cambridge, MA: Belknap Press.

Mufson, Steven. 2008. "Siphoning Off Corn to Fuel Our Cars." *Washington Post,* April 30, 2008, A01. www.washingtonpost.com/wpdyn/content/article/2008/04/29/.

Shermer, Michael. 2008. "The Chain of Accidents and the Rule of Law." *Skeptic* 14, no. 2: 28–36.

Sen, Amartya. 2008. "The Rich Get Hungrier." *New York Times,* May 28, 2008. www.nytimes.com/2008/05/28/opinion/28sen.html?th&emc=th.

Starrs, Thomas. 2005. "The SUV in the Pantry." *The WASTENOT-gram.* Newsletter of the American Solar Energy Society.

Stuart, David, and Rory Gauthier. "1981 Prehistoric New Mexico: Background for Survey." Historic Preservation Bureau, Department of Finance and Administration, Santa Fe, NM.

Sullivan, Charles. 2007. "Uncommon Grace: Biology and Economic Theory." .Uncommon Grace: Biology And Economic Theory By Charles Sullivan (countercurrents.org)

Trigger, Bruce. 2003. *Understanding Early Civilization: A Comparative Study. Cambridge, UK;* Cambridge University Press.

Upham, Steadman. 1982. *Politics and Power: An Economic and Political History of the Western Pueblo.* New York: Academic Press.

Wallerstein, Immanuel. 1974. *The Modern World System*. New York: Academic Press.

Whole Systems. 2007. "Species Extinction and Human Population."

Wittfogel, Karl. 1957. *Oriental Despotism: A Comparative Study of Total Power.* New Haven, CT: Yale University Press.

Chapter 14: Global Warming: Legacy of Human Development?

> This is literally a math test, and it's not being graded on a curve. It only has one correct answer. And if we don't get it right, then all of us– along with our 10,000-year-old experiment in human civilization – will fail. (Bill McKibben 2016).

Several sorts of insights should be obtained from this final chapter. First, you should develop a basic understanding of what global warming is and what scientists understand to be the causes and mechanisms of the processes involved. That is, what is the scientific consensus? Second, you should become familiar with the kinds of evidence that have led an overwhelming majority of scientists to reach consensus on the facts, causes, and implications of global climate change. The webpage built to accompany the film *An Inconvenient Truth* summarizes more than a dozen specific sorts of evidence for global warming and human agency in global warming (https://www.climatecrisis.net). You should be able to discuss that evidence. Third, you should be able to recognize some of the spurious arguments used by those who deny the reality of global warming and identify the faults in such arguments as well as the reasons some people still adhere to those ideas. Fourth, you should be able to show how global warming is part of the evolutionary trajectory of modern humans and how it relates to topics previously discussed in this book. Hopefully, you will be able to discuss what we might do in response, individually and collectively.

Q&A: How is modern climate change related to past human activities?

Continued population growth and the ever-greater intensification of the food production technology needed to feed that population have led to agricultural dependency on fossil fuels. Beginning with the onset of the Industrial Age and accelerating in recent years, the use of fossil fuels is now impacting the climate to which we have adapted.

The Scientific Consensus

By now, most or all of you have at least heard of global warming. If you are like many Americans, however, you may not know much about it, and you might not even believe it's a very important issue. Nearly half the adults in this country either don't believe global warming is real, don't believe human actions are contributing to the problem, or don't believe it will have significant negative effects on our way of life. All these beliefs are scientifically indefensible. There is now an overwhelming scientific consensus that global warming is real, that human actions are making a significant contribution to warming, and that warming will have devastating consequences for all of us. If you still wonder about this or have heard arguments to the contrary to which you'd like to respond, please refer to the Logical Science website for documentation of the consensus (https://www.logicalscience.com). Students are also encouraged to browse the information on these additional webpages, links to which are provided at the end of the chapter: National Snow and Ice Center, World Wildlife Fund, Real Climate, and World View of Global Warming.

So what is the scientific consensus? The sun's energy enters the earth's atmosphere and heats up the planet, after which much of it is radiated back into space in the form of infrared waves. Under normal conditions, some of those waves are trapped by the atmosphere, thereby helping keep the earth's temperature within a habitable range. However, the accumulation of carbon dioxide (CO_2) and other greenhouse gases has led to more and more of the infrared radiation being trapped within the atmosphere, thereby increasing the temperature of the atmosphere and ultimately the earth itself. Human activities have contributed to the increased concentration of greenhouse gases since our prehistoric ancestors first began significant deforestation thousands of years ago (Ruddiman 2003). However, the rate of increase accelerated greatly after the onset of the Industrial Age because recent growth has been powered by the burning of fossil fuels.

The level of CO_2 in the atmosphere is currently about 412 parts per million (ppm; National Oceanic and Atmospheric Administration [NOAA] 2021). This concentration is higher than at any time in the past 3.6 million years. It is higher than at any time since the evolution Australopithecines and higher than anything that has been experienced by modern humans as a species. It is estimated that if current warming trends continue, the level of atmospheric CO_2 could reach 500 to 600 ppm over the next 45 years. These numbers, these facts and estimates, should be a matter of great interest to anyone who cares about the continued health and viability of our species and the other organisms with which we share the planet.

Denial Is Not Just a River in Egypt

There is very little doubt among climate change researchers that global warming is really happening and human actions are contributing significantly to the results. Yes, it is a politically and socially controversial allegation, but the science is not in doubt. Donald Kennedy, editor of *Science* magazine (the journal of the American Association for the Advancement of Science) has remarked that "consensus as strong as the one that has grown around this topic is rare in science" (2001). James Baker, former head of the National Oceanic and Atmospheric Administration (NOAA) , said there is "better scientific consensus on this issue than any other, with the possible exception of Newton's Law of Dynamics" (Warrick 1997). There is always debate in science, so it is true to say there is still debate about climate change. However, the debate has long since moved beyond whether global warming is happening and whether human actions are contributing to topics such as how the details are playing out, their implications for specific regions, and what we might try to do in response.

The operation of the elements that work together to produce weather and climate are complicated and more research needs to be done, but that doesn't mean we should withhold acceptance of, or a response to, the large-scale changes that can already be documented. In April 2006, Dr. Charles Kennel made a presentation as part of the University of Texas at El Paso Millennium Lecture Series entitled *Had We World Enough and Time: Global Earth Science and Sustainability*. Dr. Kennel is director of the Environment and Sustainability Initiative at University of California, San Diego, and former director of the Scripps Institution of Oceanography, where the accumulation of greenhouse gasses was first discovered 50 years ago. He oversees the program that has sensors placed in the oceans all over the world to monitor temperature changes. For him and his staff, the question is not whether climate change is happening or whether human actions are contributing; those issues have been clearly laid to rest. They are now focused on refining our understanding of the details of the changes so that we can minimize the loss of life and property in the most vulnerable regions. Kennel estimates that we have until about 2055 to figure out a global response if we are to prevent truly catastrophic losses. Continued debate over whether global warming is happening or whether humans are to blame will cost many lives.

A fair analogy would be this: global warming is in doubt only in the same way that evolution is in doubt. That is, there is no scientific debate about whether evolution is real, although there is debate about how it happened in specific cases. Like the reality of global warming, the fact of evolution is controversial, but not because of the science is in doubt; it is controversial because the science has implications for people's social, ideological, and economic beliefs and programs. Researchers and teachers who deal with the topic of evolution have been subjected to social (as opposed to scientific) skepticism and derision for years. We recognize the political rhetoric and forms of argument used to fight evolution that are now being used to deny global warming, such as denying the science, mounting *ad hominem* attacks against scientists, and enlisting political operatives to make policy changes that aren't supported by the science. The uproar over climate change research has reached the public's awareness more recently, so the reaction of nonscientists is still cresting, contributing to the perception of great uncertainty where there is little or none.

Evidence for Climate Change

The science behind global warming is not new, and the findings are not controversial for most climate researchers. Why? Because the data have been accumulating for decades, and many scientists conducting research in this area have been watching the patterns in the data become clearer by the decade. When I was in graduate school in the 1970s, I studied climate change; I took a graduate minor in geology, specifically glacial geology and climate change. Archaeology figures into this area of study because archaeological sites provide evidence of both natural changes and human effects on the environment (such as regional vegetation change), and ways of dating the changes documented in the sites. One of my professors was using prehistoric pollen data to reconstruct changes in the locations of winter and summer air masses during and after the late Pleistocene and the effect of those changes on the makeup and distribution of vegetation communities. Of course, back then the research wasn't playing into a public discourse on global warming; it was below the public's radar, so to speak. But the point is, when scientists say they can distinguish natural cycles of climate change from human-induced changes, they have the data to back it up; they've been studying both for more than 40 years, whether the public was aware of their efforts or not.

A couple of years ago, a good friend asked me with some indignation and disbelief how scientists could know that global warming has even occurred. As a devotee of Rush Limbaugh, he was under the impression that scientists are making irrational, politically motivated guesses based on the past 50 years or so of weather records. He asked, "Do you have some sort of prehistoric thermometers out there that you dig up?!!!" Well, actually, yes, we do—at least indirect indices of temperature. Researchers have been analyzing glaciers, ice cores, tree rings, varves (silt layers in northern lakes), prehistoric pollen profiles, prehistoric faunal assemblages, sea floor sediments, and the contents of prehistoric pack rat nests for years. The patterns in all these sorts of data indicate that global warming is real and that human actions are contributing significantly to the observed changes.

Figure 14.1: Photographs documenting the extensive melting of the Muir Glacier, Glacier Bay National Park, Alaska between 1941 and 2004. In the left image, the frame is dominated by the jagged surface of the glacier that is hundreds of feet thick, extending all the way to the mountain in the distance. Sixty-three years later, most of the glacier has melted, leaving a fjord where the ice used to be.

The amplitude of the cyclical changes that can be attributed to natural causes has been well documented, so it is possible to identify the human contribution to current CO_2 levels (see Figure 11.1 in Chapter 11). The fluctuation of atmospheric CO_2 is clearly indicated in ice cores drilled in Greenland and Antarctica. The Antarctic cores go back 650,000 years; one can count the individual layers of ice laid down each year, actually see the increase of airborne particulates resulting from the Industrial Age, and measure the chemical composition of the atmosphere in air bubbles trapped in the ice at the time each layer was deposited. The major periods of glacial growth are indicated in blue, and the intervening warming periods are in yellow (Figure 11.1). In past Pleistocene warming cycles, CO_2 levels have only once risen above 290 ppm (during the middle Yarmouth interstadial about 325,000 years ago) and have never exceeded 300 ppm (Figure 14.2). We are presently in another warming cycle, the Holocene, but human activity has caused the CO_2 concentration to overshoot the natural levels of previous warming cycles. Current levels of atmospheric CO_2 stand at about 412 ppm, higher than at any time in the past 3.6 million years. The last time CO_2 levels were this high, the earth was inhabited by *Australopithecus*.

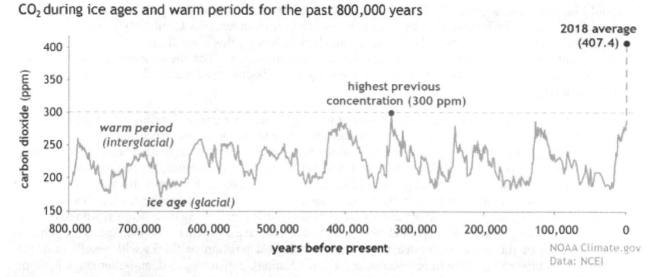

Figure 14.2 Graph showing prehistoric and modern levels of atmospheric carbon dioxide. Note that the current levels of 400 ppm or more are off the chart. Those levels have never before been reached during the time when *Homo sapiens* has existed.

There are some (perhaps many?) citizens and surely several rightwing pundits who reject this information out of hand because it is Al Gore or some university scientists who are presenting the information to the public. But a rejection of the evidence for that reason is illogical—an example of *argumentum ad hominem*. One must evaluate the data rather than dismiss the messenger, and these data are solid. But if the data are solid, then why do so many citizens and even a few scientists still reject the argument of climate change? Some reject the data because the implications challenge what they believe they know or what a trusted pundit has said or because they run counter to their hopes for our country's policies. There seem to be several types of people, or several kinds of groups sharing certain sorts of attitudes or interests, who, intentionally or not, are contributing to the confusion. They include people who just don't understand science, those who are ideologically opposed to science in general or global warming in particular, those skeptical of the idea that humans can alter the earth, and those who continue to benefit (economically, politically, etc.) by maintaining the *status quo*. Let's consider some examples.

As scientists, we shouldn't expect the public to simply "trust us" because we know what we're doing. But the public has (or should have) some responsibility to make an effort to become aware of and understand the scientific information. Herein lays one of the main difficulties in discussing the issue of global warming: our society is largely poorly informed about climate science, and the public has not followed the research that provides the evidence for warming. Therefore, the general public is dependent on journalists, elected officials, and the media to inform them about and explain the findings of science. Unfortunately, surveys have shown that our politicians, political pundits, and newspaper editors, among others, are usually no more knowledgeable about science than other members of the public. Yet, they have far greater access to the public than do scientists. As a result, much of the information on warming that does reach the public is misrepresented, screened, censored, distorted, and misunderstood. It is no wonder that the public is confused.

Biases Contributing to Climate Change Denial

Although climate change denial is not necessarily limited to one particular political party or another, some analysts suggest that political ideology does indeed influence the way the warming issue is presented and discussed. The results of polls conducted by the *National Journal* indicate that although evidence for global warming has been getting stronger, many conservatives have become increasingly skeptical. In other words, skepticism about global warming is becoming political party dogma (Chait 2007). It is not clear why this should be the case; even much of the energy industry has accepted the reality of warming, with some executives asking for increased federal regulation of their own industries. Chait (2007) suggests that the conservative movement seems to be taking its marching orders on this issue from a very small group of ideological leaders who have decided to defy the scientific consensus: "The phenomenon here is that a tiny number of influential conservative figures set the party line; dissenters are marginalized, and the rank and file goes along with it."

A fairly well-known example involves Limbaugh's derisive comments dismissing the reality of global warming. He said, "Even if polar ice caps melted, there would be no rise in ocean levels . . . After all, if you have a glass of water with ice cubes in it, as the ice melts, it simply turns to liquid and the water level in the glass remains the same" (Rendall et al. 1995, 17). Unfortunately, Limbaugh's analogy is inaccurate and faulty. Most of the ice in the world is on land, not already floating in the oceans (the way ice cubes are floating in his drink). When the ice melts it does indeed contribute to ocean level rise, a fact that is already being recorded. I encounter questions every year from students (often quoting their parents) who have been misled by Limbaugh's statement. He and other pundits like him have done enormous damage to the public's understanding of the issue, in service to whatever ideological position he thinks will benefit from the confusion (antiliberal, anti-environmentalist, anti-United Nations, anti-foreign aid, anti-alternative fuels, or whatever).

Another sort of ideological bias, or vested self-interest, is evident in the censoring of government scientists by political appointees (Begley 2007; Clayton 2007). One of the recent administration officials whose actions are most egregious in terms of misrepresenting science was Phillip Cooney. Cooney was an American Petroleum Institute lobbyist who was hired as chief of staff in the White House Environmental Office during the second Bush administration. Even though he had no scientific training, he was authorized by the White House to edit, revise, and censor scientific reports on global warming written by scientists in various government agencies. He would probably have continued doing so for several years if a principled whistleblower had not exposed his intellectual fraud. Cooney resigned and was quickly hired by ExxonMobil. It's not too hard to understand that he had personal ideological and financial reasons for resisting and misrepresenting the scientific evidence for global warming. He is only one of many administration officials who have viewed one of their tasks as denying, censoring, and undermining legitimate scientific findings that would otherwise be communicated more clearly and honestly to the American public. In some agencies, nearly half of the staff scientists have reportedly experienced censorship or pressure to alter their findings from their politically appointed supervisors (Public Employees for Environmental Responsibility n.d.). In recent years, some administration officials have completely removed any mention of climate change from several government agency websites that were formerly used to inform the public about the issue.

False Balance in the Media

The media are also partly to blame, for their ignorance of how science works, for oversimplifying concepts to the point of misrepresenting them, and for a sometimes misguided attempt to create "balance" in their coverage of science topics. Even the way a topic is framed can influence the discussion. For example, the media have often presented global warming as if the entire earth is warming in a uniform way, and when people see evidence to the contrary, they become confused or doubtful. But the scientific understanding of global warming doesn't say this. Scientists recognize that heating is not uniform on all parts of the globe. It is recognized that some parts of the earth might seem to be cooling slightly and others heating, as global air and ocean circulation patterns change. So climate change deniers who point to regional details, such as increased rain in northern Europe or increased snow in eastern Antarctica, for example, have been misled. The recent global warming models have predicted these sorts of regional variations.

It is also sometimes the case that earlier scientific findings have been revised or corrected by more recent research, but the earlier findings are still promoted by the media. For example, one paper from the past decade suggested that high-altitude balloon data indicated atmospheric cooling instead of warming.

Since then, those data have been reexamined, and it has been determined that the sensors used to gather the data didn't function properly when the original study was conducted. Newer data have overturned the older study (thereby supporting the warming predictions), but some of the media and climate change deniers continue to cite the older paper as legitimate counter-evidence. That's simply not an accurate representation of the state of the science.

Another common problem is the media's effort to report or even create "balance" in the news, even when there isn't any. If 98 percent of the scientists in the world accept the evidence for evolution and 2 percent do not, then giving equal time to both positions is not balanced. The same goes for global warming. Imagine if a reporter at a house fire worked very hard to find a view that would "balance" the news of the shock, disorientation, and sorrow of the homeless family. Would we applaud the effort to find someone, anyone, who thought the fire was a good thing? Perhaps a neighbor who observes that at least they won't have to paint the gutters this year? Wouldn't that strike you as trivial or misguided? But that's something like what reporters often do in stories about global warming. For example, we see a story reporting that NASA's Dr. James Hansen has testified about global warming at a congressional hearing, and in an apparent attempt to provide balance, the reporter finds someone, anyone, who might be willing to rebut Dr. Hansen. When the reporter can't readily find a scientist willing to do so (because there are so few), he gets a statement from Oklahoma Senator Jim Inhofe, who has no scientific training whatsoever, earned his college degree in economics, and represents an oil-producing region. Senator Inhofe steadfastly refuses to even consider any of the scientific evidence placed before him and considers global warming a hoax. He is certainly entitled to his opinion, but why should that opinion be represented as equivalent to Dr. Hansen's warranted argument based on scientific evidence? That is not "balance" in any meaningful sense of the word.

The media can sometimes be cavalier about how they represent and compare the various groups who comment on the topic of global warming. The Intergovernmental Panel on Climate Change (IPCC) is a case in point. Created in 1988 under the auspices of the United Nations, the IPCC is not just another organization with an opinion paper. Rather, it is a clearinghouse that reviews, evaluates, and summarizes the work of climate scientists from all over the world. The IPCC reports themselves are then subjected to scientific review. Only the most widely accepted (and therefore, perhaps, most conservative) conclusions are included in the final reports. The counterarguments denying warming issued by political policy groups are not comparable to the IPCC reports, because they aren't based on the sort of comprehensive examination of the science that is undertaken by the IPCC, and the policy statements they produce are not peer-reviewed. Therefore, they should not be interpreted as providing "balance" to the positions articulated by the IPCC.

Additional evidence of the impact of "balance" in the popular media is provided by a study of peer-reviewed science articles on global warming from the past decade (Oreskes 2004). A scientifically selected 10% sample of articles (n=928) was drawn and the articles were analyzed in detail for their findings on the issue of climate change uncertainty. The articles were unanimous in their conclusions; the percentage of articles in which the authors had doubt about humanity's role in warming was exactly zero! In contrast, a similar analysis of the global warming stories published in the four major US print media (*New York Times, Los Angeles Times, Wall Street Journal,* and *Washington Post*) found that 53 percent of the popular articles expressed doubt about the human role in warming. More than half the articles gave equal weight to the scientifically discredited notion that humans play no role in warming. Clearly, some of the most influential media outlets in the country have been complicit in grossly misrepresenting the science of global warming to their readers. There is very little scientific debate about the overall facts of global warming, but this reality has not been clearly communicated to the public.

There are, admittedly, a few scientists who continue to argue against global warming or at least against a significant role for human agency (just as there are a few scientists who continue to argue against evolution). But just because some scientists are climate change skeptics doesn't mean their skepticism is still warranted. A decade or two ago such a position might have been considered cautious or even prudent; today it might be considered irresponsible.

There are several reasons scientists might continue to deny the evidence for global warming. One might be that they don't conduct research on the subject and have not stayed abreast of the recent literature. Another might be a paradigmatic belief that humans are not capable of causing large-scale effects on the earth or the atmosphere. Such an assumption has sometimes been evident in the interpretation of archaeological remains in the Southwest. For example, it has long been known that Chaco Canyon and Mesa Verde were heavily occupied by prehistoric peoples for a time but that both areas were abandoned, perhaps abruptly. For a long time, many researchers were convinced that climate change caused the region to become uninhabitable (at least for pueblo agriculturalists), leading to abandonment. This view was based on data for vegetation change, mainly from pollen studies, which seemed to indicate the loss of pine trees. However, when scientists began comparing prehistoric pack rat nests against the pollen data, a different picture emerged. Pack rats (*Neotoma*) collect local vegetation with which to build their nests. The animals urinate in the nests (thereby fusing and preserving them) and defecate in them, leaving behind pellets that can be dated by radiocarbon. The nests are, effectively, time capsules containing samples of the local vegetation. The pack rat nests in Chaco Canyon showed that only the incidence of trees changed, not the overall vegetation in the vicinity of the nests. The new data showed that the loss of pine trees was not the result of climate change, but of deforestation by prehistoric Puebloan peoples. Human-induced environmental degradation contributed to the changes that forced the people to relocate. It hadn't occurred to many researchers that prehistoric populations could actually alter the environment to that extent. Scientists trained in or influenced by such paradigmatic expectations may well be honestly predisposed against the evidence for phenomena that seem to be beyond the scale of human impacts. Hopefully, such a predisposition would eventually be overcome by paradigm shift in response to new data.

There is another, more troubling reason some scientists might still maintain a position not supported by the evidence: money. There has been an organized effort on the part of companies in the extractive industries to sow doubt about global warming in order to confuse the public and derail action by legislators (Begley 2007). Among other revelations, a conservative think tank funded by ExxonMobil offered scientists $10,000 to write articles undercutting global warming science and climate models. One scientist even admitted receiving $165,000 from the coal industry to trash mainstream environmental science. This is not how academic articles are normally written or how the academic publication process operates. The tactics of the think tanks, public relation firms, and lobbying groups involved in the organized denial of climate change are modeled after the tactics used by the tobacco industry in their denials about the harmful effects of cigarette smoking. Unfortunately, the well-funded lobbying efforts have successfully misled much of the public about the scientific consensus on warming.

Most scientists are not policy wonks; most are nose-to-the-grindstone researchers. Yes, some are occasionally thrust into the policy limelight because of the implications of their research, but most do not have an axe to grind with regard to public policy. They're just doing their work on bugs, worms, sedimentation rates, tree ring width, animal migrations, bark beetle infestation, sun spot activity, Arctic shoreline erosion, coral bleaching, etc. They are usually not trying to attack certain people, agencies, administrations, or programs. Scientists are just trying to make the best sense they can of the natural phenomena they observe in the world around us. Mostly, scientists just do science. And as is the case with evolution, just because the scientific results are unsettling or inscrutable to some members of the public doesn't mean the results are false or uncertain.

Evidence and Decision-Making

In his book *Collapse: How Societies Choose to Fail or Succeed*, Jared Diamond (2005) explores how and why some societies were unable to make decisions or take the actions that would have ensured their survival. One of the cases he considers is the fate of the aboriginal inhabitants of Easter Island. He wonders about the thought process of the person who chopped down the last tree on the island, thereby completing the destruction of the ecosystem to which the islanders' society was adapted. Perhaps we should consider an analogous circumstance that may be faced by our own society. Who will be the one who watches the last mountain glacier melt, and what would they be thinking about that? Is it really possible that enough humans can be blind to the evidence, the effects of climate change, that we can actually stand by while the natural systems that support our societies are altered beyond recognition?

How many of you know someone who has never viewed *An Inconvenient Truth* or *An Inconvenient Sequel*? Why haven't people gone to see them? Have they ignored the documentaries because some political pundit or television personality disapproves of them? Why do we as individuals choose to remain ignorant of or unresponsive to the evidence for climate change? Why do we choose to let others do our thinking for us? Sara Goudarzi, writing for LiveScience (2007), reports on a talk given by Jon Krosnick, professor of communication and political science at Stanford University, in which he addresses the disconnect between what science knows and what the public believes. Krosnick said that in order for the public to embrace an issue like global warming and make behavioral changes, they must believe the problem exists and that the results would be bad for people. Because the public doesn't have absolute certainty about the problem (or certainty about human agency), warming doesn't generate the same sort of concern that scientists have expressed. Furthermore, Krosnick suggested that most people won't acknowledge something is a problem unless they believe it can be fixed; if they believe it can't be fixed, it is simply too upsetting to think about. So the efforts by climate change deniers who suggest there is significant disagreement among scientists are contributing directly to the public's lack of a sense of urgency and will in addressing the problems.

Nevertheless, evidence of climate change is all around us and becoming more obvious with every passing year. The Arctic is warming faster than other parts of the globe, and more than 200 native Inuit and Aleut villages are threatened by climate related erosion and/or flooding. Thirty-one communities are facing immediate threats of destruction and will need to be abandoned or moved (US Government Accountability Office 2009). Glacier National Park in Montana has lost almost all of its ice, and the remaining glaciers will probably be lost over the next few decades. The snows of Kilimanjaro in Africa survived a 300-year period of drought that occurred about 4,200 years ago, but today's climate change is different. If current climate conditions persist, the Kilimanjaro ice fields will probably be gone in the next several decades (Thompson et al. 2009).

Key Indicators of Arctic Climate Change, 1971 to 2017

https://www.youtube.com/watch?v-O9uunW_DBZE

The most potentially damaging loss of mountain glaciers is in the Himalayas. When the fiftieth anniversary celebration of the first summiting of Mount Everest was held a few years ago, the ceremony was held at the site of Edmund Hillary's and Tenzing Norgay's base camp. At the time of their climb, it was at the base of Khumbu Glacier. Today the campsite is 5 kilometers from the base of the glacier; the Khumbu Glacier has melted and receded that much in the past 50 years. The real scary part is this: seven major river systems originate in and are fed by the Himalayan glaciers. They provide half the drinking water for 40 percent of the world's population in parts of China, India, and Southeast Asia. Increased melting will cause flooding in the short term, and over the long term, that fresh water will no longer be held in storage for human consumption.

The effects of climate change are already being felt in terms of human agricultural production. Warming over the past 25 years has led to decreased yields from some of our most important food crops: wheat, rice, corn, soybeans, sorghum, and barley. Researchers found that decreased yields and increased use of chemical fertilizers and pesticides coincided with periods of increasing temperatures. These crops account for more than 40 percent of the production of the world's farmlands, 55 percent of the nonmeat calories we produce, and more than 79 percent of animal feed raised worldwide (Conner 2007).

It is predicted that if global warming continues along its present trajectory, sea level will continue to rise. The conservative estimates speak about something in the range of 3 feet in the next 50 years. More extreme possibilities include an eventual rise in sea level of 18 to 20 feet, if all of the mountain glaciers and most of the Greenland and Antarctic ice fields melt. A 20-foot rise in sea level would displace hundreds of millions of people, especially in low-lying coastal areas of Asia, such as Beijing (20 million), Shanghai (40 million), and Calcutta and Bangladesh (60 million). It is uncertain whether the number of tropical storms will rise, but it is predicted that their intensity will increase, because the intensity of storms is fed largely by the surface water temperatures. The slightly warmer surface temperature in the Gulf of Mexico is why Katrina grew from a Category 1 storm on Florida's east coast to a Category 4 by the time it hit New Orleans. Coastal populations will be increasingly vulnerable to high-intensity storms.

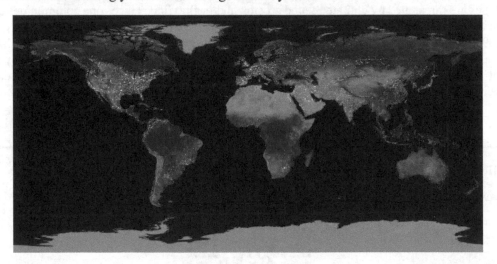

Figure 14.3: Map showing predicted inundation of coastlines associated with a global sea level rise of 6 meters

We are likely to see more fires like the ones that ravaged Europe in 2003. Lowland insects such as mosquitoes, ticks, and tsetse flies are migrating to higher elevations and latitudes, carrying diseases to populations of people who have never experienced them before. Forests are being decimated by bark beetles, whose spread is no longer contained by cold winter temperatures. Areas that are expected to experience reduced rainfall and worse droughts include most of the southwestern United States, the southwest coast of South America, sub-Saharan Africa, much of China and Southeast Asia, and central Russia. Much of North America and northern Europe is predicted to receive more rainfall but less snow. Parts of southern Australia are already being abandoned by farmers because of the extended drought conditions. If these sorts of effects are not enough to inspire action from the public, one wonders what it will take.

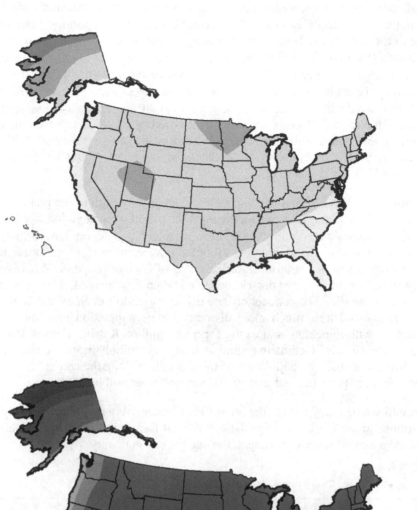

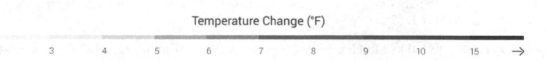

Temperature Change (°F)

Figure 14.4: Predicted average temperature increases related to global warming under two different emissions scenarios. Top: lower emissions, assumes substantial reduction in greenhouse gases. Bottom: higher emissions, assumes continued increase in greenhouse gases. (Fourth National Climate Assessment 2014, US Global Change Research Program)

Denial continues to be something more than a river in Egypt; denial is widespread here in Texas. We are asked not to litter (Don't Mess with Texas), but we're happy to pollute. Texas emits more CO_2 than any other state in the country. If Texas were a country, its emissions would make it the seventh largest CO_2 polluter in the world (Burnett 2007). The state's high level of emissions is mainly a result of large coal-fired power plants and large gas-guzzling vehicles. Thirty-five other states have plans in place to cut CO_2 emissions, but many Texas leaders are global warming skeptics. State Senator Kirk Watson from Austin proposed a bill that would have created a task force to study the effects of climate change in the state; it passed the Senate but died in the House, where it was opposed by lobbyists representing the oil, gas, coal and chemical industries, and state automobile dealers. When Rev. Raymond Bailey asked his Waco congregation to consider reducing the trips they make in their cars, they told him, "Now, Preacher, don't mess with our cars . . ." (Burnett 2007).

The choice between our fossil fuel–powered cars or the health of the planet should not be a tough call. The last time CO_2 and temperature conditions on the planet were anything like today (during the Riss-Wurm interglacial), there weren't anywhere near as many people on the earth (perhaps fewer than 100 million), and none of them lived in cities. All of them were mobile foragers or hunter-gatherers capable of moving at a moment's notice without significant loss of lives or property. Wherever they moved to, the land was likely to be vacant or only sparsely occupied when they arrived. The Western Hemisphere was completely devoid of people. The concept of land ownership didn't even exist. Think about how different our situation is today and how much more disruptive large population movements will be. Recall the problems associated with relocating and caring for a half-million Katrina victims, the 2.5 million refugees of the Iraq war, or the tsunami victims in southeast Asia, and multiply those scenarios by a couple of orders of magnitude. More than half the population of the planet live along the coasts. In 1990, that amounted to about 3.6 billion people; it is estimated that by 2025 that number will be 5.3 billion.

When will we be ready to face the scientific evidence? When will we be ready to make behavioral changes in response to the climate change dangers? What form will those changes take? What will be the outcome of nature's evolutionary experiment, the one we call humanity?

References and Further Reading

Begley, Sharon. 2007. "Global-Warming Deniers: A Well-Funded Machine." *Newsweek,* August 13, 2007. Last updated August 15, 2007. http://www.sharonlbegley.com/global-warming-deniers-a-well-funded-machine.

Bronen, Robin. 2011. "Climate-Induced Community Relocations: Creating an Adaptive Governance Framework Based in Human Rights Doctrine." *New York University Review of Law and Social Change* 35: 356–406.

Burnett, John. 2007. "In Texas, Climate Creeping onto Agenda." *NPR,* December 26, 2007.

Chait, Jonathan. 2007. "Why the Right Goes Nuclear over Global Warming." *Los Angeles Times,* March 25, 2007.

Clayton, Mark. 2007. "Study Finds White House Manipulation on Climate Science." *Christian Science Monitor*, December 12, 2007.

Conner, Steve. 2007. "World's Most Important Crops Hit by Global Warming Effects." *The Independent UK,* March 19, 2007.

Diamond, Jared. 2005. *Collapse: How Societies Choose to Fail or Succeed. New York:* Viking Press.

GAO (United States Government Accountability Office). 2009. Alaska Native Villages: Limited Progress Has Been Made on Relocating Villages Threatened by Flooding and Erosion. Report to Congressional Requesters. GAO-09-551. Washington, D. C.

Gelbspan, Ross. 2005. "Snowed: Though Global Climate Change Is Breaking Out All Around Us, the U.S. News Media Has Remained Silent." *Mother Jones* (May/June 2005).

Gore, Al. 2006. *An Inconvenient Truth: The Planetary Emergency of Global Warming and What We Can Do About It.* Emmaus, PA: Rodale Press.

Goudarzi, Sara. 2007. "Why Americans are Skeptical of Their Role in Global Warming." LiveScience, February 19, 2007. https://www.livescience.com/4384-americans-skeptical-role-global-warming.html.

IPCC. 2007. *Climate Change 2007. Contributions to the Fourth Assessment Report of the Intergovernmental Panel on Climate Change, Volumes 1–3.* Cambridge, UK: Cambridge University Press.

Kennedy, Donald. 2001. An Unfortunate U-Turn on Carbon. *Science* 30 Mar 2001: Vol. 291, Issue 5513, p. 2515. DOI: 10.1126/Science. 1060922

Kennel, Charles F. 2007. "Had We World Enough and Time: Global Earth Science and Sustainability." Millennium Lecture Series, University of Texas at El Paso, April 9, 2007.

Logical Science. 2007. "The Consensus on Global Warming: From Science to Industry and Religion." www.logicalscience.com/consensus/consensusD1.htm.

McKibben, Bill. 2016. "Recalculating the Climate Math." *The New Republic,* September 22, 2016. https://newrepublic.com/article/136987/recalculating-climate-math.

Mooney, Chris. 2005. "Some Like It Hot: Forty Public Policy Groups … Seek to Undermine the Scientific Consensus That Humans Are Causing the Earth to Overheat. And They All Get Money from ExxonMobil." *Mother Jones* (May/June 2005). https://www.motherjones.com/environment/2005/05/some-it-hot/.

National Snow and Ice Center. n.d. "SOTC: Overview." http://nsidc.org/sotc.

NOAA. 2021. "Despite Pandemic Shutdowns, Carbon Dioxide and Methane Surged in 2020." NOAA Research News, April 7, 2021. https://research.noaa.gov/article//ArtMID/587/ArticleID/2742/.

Oreskes, Naomi. 2004. "The Scientific Consensus on Climate Change." *Science* 306, no. 5702 (December 3, 2004): 1686. American Association for the Advancement of Science.

Pelto, Mauri S. 2006. "The Current Disequilibrium of North Cascades Glaciers." *Hydrological Processes* 20, no. 4: 769–79.

Pierrehumbert, Raymond. 2005. "Tropical Glacier Retreat." www.realclimate.org/index.php/archives/2005/05/tropical-glacier-retreat/.

Public Employees for Environmental Responsibility. n.d. https://www.peer.org.

RealClimate. n.d. www.realclimate.org.

Rendall, Steven, Jim Naureckas, and Jeff Cohen. 1995. *The Way Things Aren't: Rush Limbaugh's Reign of Error.* FAIR (Fairness & Accuracy in Reporting), New York: The New Press.

Revkin, Andrew C., and Matthew L. Wald. 2007. "Material Shows Weakening of Climate Reports." *New York Times,* March 20, 2007.

Ruddiman, William R. 2003. "The Anthropogenic Greenhouse Era Began Thousands of Years Ago." *Climate Change* 61: 261–93. Kluwer Academic Publishers.

Sullivan, Charles. 2007. "Uncommon Grace: Biology and Economic Theory." Information Clearing House. .https://www.countercurrents.org/sullivan231007.htm.

Thompson, L. G., H. H. Brecher, E. Mosley-Thompson, D. R. Hardy, and B. G. Mark. 2009. "Glacier Loss on Kilimanjaro Continues Unabated." *Proceedings of the National Academy of Sciences* 106, no. 47 (November 24, 2009): 19773.

US Government Accountability Office. 2009. "Alaska Native Villages: Limited Progress Has Been Made on Relocating Villages Threatened by Flooding and Erosion." Report to Congressional Requesters. GAO-09-551. Washington, DC.

Warrick, J. 1997. The warming planet: what science knows. *The Washington Post*, November 11, p. A1. Washington, D. C.

World View of Global Warming. n.d. www.worldviewofglobalwarming.org.

World Wildlife Fund. 2005. "An Overview of Glaciers, Glacier Retreat, and Subsequent Impacts in Nepal, India and China." March 2005. http://assets.panda.org/downloads/glacierssummary.pdf.

Credits

Fig. 1.1: Source: https://pixabay.com/illustrations/photomontage-faces-photo-album-577022/.

Fig. 1.2: Source: https://unsplash.com/photos/2Qf2_k0Q5T0.

Fig. 1.3: Source: https://www.slideshare.net/JeckaCortez/lec-1-socio.

Fig. 1.4: Copyright © The Jane Goodall Institute/Dereck Bryceson.

Fig. 2.1: Copyright © Lacambalam (CC BY-SA 4.0) at https://commons.wikimedia.org/wiki/File:Hero_Twins.JPG.

Fig. 2.2: Source: https://commons.wikimedia.org/wiki/File:Cranach_the_Elder_Adam_and_Eve.jpg.

Source: https://www.pamd.uscourts.gov/sites/pamd/files/opinions/04v2688d.pdf.

Fig. 4.1: Copyright © 2017 Depositphotos/Ian Redding.

Fig. 4.2: Source: https://commons.wikimedia.org/wiki/File:Independent_assortment_%26_segregation.svg.

Fig. 4.3: Copyright © Community College Consortium for Bioscience Credentials (CC by 3.0) at
https://commons.wikimedia.org/wiki/File:Mitosis_vs._meiosis.png.

Fig. 4.4: Copyright © Madeleine Price Ball (CC BY-SA 3.0) at
https://commons.wikimedia.org/wiki/File:DNA_replication_split_horizontal.svg.

Fig. 4.5: Copyright © Dark Tichondrias (CC BY-SA 3.0) at
https://commons.wikimedia.org/wiki/File:Unlabeled_Renatto_Luschan_Skin_color_map.png.

Fig. 5.1a: Source: https://commons.wikimedia.org/wiki/File:Michelle_Obama_official_portrait_headshot.jpg.

Fig. 5.1b: Copyright © Cyrus Saatsaz (CC BY-SA 4.0) at
https://commons.wikimedia.org/wiki/File:Stephen_Curry_Shooting_(cropped).jpg.

Fig. 5.1c: Copyright © Paul Rudman (CC BY-SA 3.0) at https://commons.wikimedia.org/wiki/File:DenzelWashingtonMay05.jpg.

Fig. 5.1d: Source: https://commons.wikimedia.org/wiki/File:Michael_Jordan_in_2014.jpg.

Fig. 5.1e: Copyright © Craig (CC BY-SA 2.0) at https://commons.wikimedia.org/wiki/File:Shaquille_O%27Neal_in_2011_(cropped).jpg.

Fig. 5.1f: Copyright © Stephanie Moreno (CC BY-SA 2.0) at https://commons.wikimedia.org/wiki/File:Rashida_Jones_May_2017.jpg.

Fig. 5.1g: Copyright © Gage Skidmore (CC BY-SA 3.0) at
https://commons.wikimedia.org/wiki/File:Will_Smith_by_Gage_Skidmore_2.jpg.

Fig. 5.1h: Copyright © www.GlynLowe.com (CC by 2.0) at
https://commons.wikimedia.org/wiki/File:Kerry_Washington,_Deliver_Commencement_Address_GWU_(8755052944)_(cropped)_(cropped).jpg.

Fig. 5.1i: Copyright © Fernando Frazao/Agencia Brasil (CC by 3.0) at https://commons.wikimedia.org/wiki/File:AllysonFelixRio2016.jpg.

Fig. 5.1j: Source: https://commons.wikimedia.org/wiki/File:Tiger_Woods_in_May_2019.jpg.

Fig. 5.1k: Copyright © MingleMediaTVNetwork (CC BY-SA 2.0) at https://commons.wikimedia.org/wiki/File:Maya_Rudolph.jpg.

Fig. 5.1l: Source: https://commons.wikimedia.org/wiki/File:Halle_Berry_-_USS_Kearsarge_a.jpg.

Fig. 5.1m: Copyright © Tuomas Vitikainen (CC BY-SA 3.0) at https://commons.wikimedia.org/wiki/File:Common_-_Ilosaarirock_2008.jpg.

Fig. 5.1n: Copyright © Red Carpet report on Mingle Media TV (CC BY-SA 2.0) at
https://commons.wikimedia.org/wiki/File:Viola_Davis_(cropped).jpg.

Fig. 5.1o: Source: https://commons.wikimedia.org/wiki/File:President_Barack_Obama.jpg.

Fig. 5.1p: Copyright © WBLS (CC by 3.0) at https://commons.wikimedia.org/wiki/File:Mariah_Carey_WBLS_2018_Interview_4.jpg.

Fig. 5.1q: Copyright © Keith Allison (CC BY-SA 2.0) at https://commons.wikimedia.org/wiki/File:Derek_Jeter_2007_in_Baltimore.jpg.

Fig. 5.1r: Copyright © North Ireland Office (CC by 2.0) at https://commons.wikimedia.org/wiki/File:Meghan_Markle_-_2018_(cropped).jpg.

Fig. 5.1s: Copyright © PancakeMistake (CC BY-SA 2.0) at https://commons.wikimedia.org/wiki/File:Ciara_March_2007.jpg.

Fig. 5.1t: Copyright © Fernando Frazao/Agencia Brasil (CC by 3.0) at https://commons.wikimedia.org/wiki/File:ToriRio2016.png.

Fig. 5.2: Source: https://commons.wikimedia.org/wiki/File:Malaria_versus_sickle-cell_trait_distributions.png.

Fig. 6.2: Source: https://commons.wikimedia.org/wiki/File:Range_of_Non-human_Primates.png.

Fig. 6.3: Source: https://en.wikipedia.org/wiki/File:PrimateTree2.jpg.

Fig. 6.4: Source: https://pxhere.com/en/photo/158354.

Fig. 6.6: Copyright © http://www.birdphotos.com (CC by 3.0) at https://commons.wikimedia.org/wiki/File:Common_Marmoset_1280.jpg.

Fig. 6.10: Copyright © Charles J. Sharp (CC BY-SA 4.0) at
https://commons.wikimedia.org/wiki/File:Proboscis_monkey_(Nasalis_larvatus)_male_Labuk_Bay_2.jpg.

Fig. 6.11: Source: https://pxhere.com/en/photo/1417139.

Fig. 6.13: Source: https://pxhere.com/en/photo/1324428.

Fig. 6.14: Copyright © Roustam (CC BY-SA 3.0) at https://commons.wikimedia.org/wiki/File:Tupaia_javanica.jpg.

Fig. 6.16: Source: https://pxhere.com/en/photo/596919.

Fig. 6.17: Source: https://pxhere.com/en/photo/946634.

Fig. 6.18: Source: https://pxhere.com/en/photo/699483.

Fig. 6.19: Copyright © D. Gordon E. Robertson (CC BY-SA 3.0) at
https://commons.wikimedia.org/wiki/File:Purus_Red_Howler_Monkey.jpg.